THE HISTORY OF WIRELESS

HOW CREATIVE MINDS PRODUCED TECHNOLOGY FOR THE MASSES

IRA S. BRODSKY

TELESCOPE books
ST. LOUIS, MISSOURI
WWW.TELESCOPEBOOKS.COM

Printed in the USA

Cover design: Triune Communications
Back cover image courtesy of John D. Jenkins, SparkMuseum

ISBN: 978-0-9800383-0-9

Telescope Books
St. Louis, Missouri USA
www.telescopebooks.com

Sales inquiries: sales@telescopebooks.com

For Maureen, Sarah, Joseph, and Isaac

Contents

Introduction
Science or Magic?

How did the human race develop palm-sized devices that enable people to converse and exchange text messages worldwide, snap and upload pictures, download music and videos, and determine their precise locations?

I've been interested in the history of technology for a long time, having worked in the high-tech industry for 30 years; I specifically wanted to know more about the evolution of wireless, and I was surprised that I couldn't find a comprehensive history. There are many books on key figures and time periods in the history of wireless, but none that explain how we got to where we are today. So I decided to write such a book.

The following pages trace the entire journey—from the discovery of fundamental scientific effects to the development of next-generation wireless standards.

Arthur C. Clarke said that a sufficiently advanced technology is indistinguishable from magic. But most magic is just sleight of hand. Drawing back the curtain reveals the true sources of advanced wireless technology: brilliant science, ingenious products, and innovative business models.

Science rarely progresses in a straight line. Nor is there a single correct way of doing science. The history of wireless technology shows that the clash of opposing philosophies of science can be a catalyst and even a necessary ingredient for progress.

The history of wireless technology cannot be separated from the history of wireless business. Technology harnesses science to create valuable products and services. Business delivers those products and services to customers. Before a technology comes to life, someone has to determine who needs it and what they're going to do with it. It's also business's job to figure out how best to package and distribute technology—how to get it in the hands of as many people as possible in a form they can use.

The story of wireless is fascinating and inspiring, and the technology should be celebrated. Great technology is every bit as creative as great art. While we can often perceive the creativity in a work of art directly, we usually need to know the story behind a technology to fully appreciate the creativity that went into its development.

No one has figured out how to bottle and sell creativity, but the history of wireless provides important clues about its sources. There are lessons about persistence; luck and preparedness; synthesizing ideas; challenging common assumptions; and more.

The first decision for anyone writing history is deciding where to begin. A history of wireless communications could begin with the first person to commercialize the technology, Guglielmo Marconi. Or it could start with Heinrich Hertz, the first scientist to create and detect radio waves. Why not go back further? After all, Hertz was only verifying James Clerk Maxwell's theory of the electromagnetic field. The dilemma is that there would not have been a Marconi without a Hertz, nor a Hertz without a Maxwell, nor a Maxwell without a Faraday.

I chose to start with the debate between Luigi Galvani and Alessandro Volta that led to the invention of the battery. (Galvani actually witnessed wireless communications but did not understand its significance.) Once investigators were armed with a source of continuous current, the discovery of electromagnetism became almost inevitable.

The narrative proceeds to Michael Faraday, the great experimentalist who added more to our knowledge of magnetism and electricity than anyone before or since. Faraday laid the foundation for James Clerk Maxwell, who translated Faraday's observed facts into the symbolic language of equations and assembled them into a comprehensive theory of electromagnetism—an achievement that, ironically, might have been disowned by the strict empiricist Faraday.

A note about terminology: most early scientists were known as "natural philosophers." That term is used here, as well, because that's what investigators such as Michael Faraday wanted to be called. Faraday detested the word "physicist." I've also kept the jargon to a minimum; however, some of it is unavoidable. Most concepts are explained in place and reviewed in the Glossary.

Faraday did science in the laboratory; Maxwell did science in his head. Heinrich Hertz proved that Maxwell's fertile imagination produced something concrete. There really are electromagnetic waves that propagate through free space.

Next the journey takes us on an important detour. Wireless communications is technology for conveying human intelligence. There would be no wireless telegraph without Samuel F.B. Morse's wired telegraph and there would be no wireless telephone without Alexander Graham Bell's wired telephone. The stories behind these two great inventions are essential to the history of wireless.

The idea seems obvious today but taking wireless out of the laboratory, fashioning it to serve specific applications, and offering it for sale initially faced tremendous resistance. With the telegraph going great guns, Guglielmo Marconi struggled to build the first wireless business. He built it around a technology—spark transmission—that would prove a dead end. (At least, temporarily; more than a century later a technology called ultra wideband is emerging that uses spark-like signals.)

That brings us to several lesser known names: the people who put wireless on the right technological footing. Reginald Fessenden and Edwin H. Armstrong led the way. Fessenden understood that wireless needed to be based on continuous waves rather than sparks. Armstrong took the vacuum tubes invented by John Ambrose Fleming (the valve) and Lee de Forest (the Audion) and built vastly superior transmitters and receivers. Amateur radio operators—Armstrong was one of them—contributed numerous refinements.

David Sarnoff thought about becoming an engineer, but he ended up becoming the prototype for today's high-tech business leaders. He was a hands-on executive who understood that success requires the right technology, the right products, and the right marketing. He was also one of the first business leaders to successfully navigate the hazardous waters of intellectual property, government policy and regulation, and unscrupulous competition. During this era the word "radio" gradually replaced the word "wireless."

Wireless underwent a dramatic transformation in the years leading up to World War II. The wireless market, once the exclusive domain of entrepreneurs and small businesses, became a playground for big corporations. New technology was developed by teams. It becomes harder to identify individual inventors, but they are still there.

The aftermath of World War II saw the commercialization of frequency modulation, mobile radio, television, and mobile telephone. Less well known, it was also the gestation period for the wideband radio technology that later (after being declassified by the U.S. government) enabled unlicensed wireless LANs, the Global Positioning System (GPS), and third generation (3G) cellular systems.

We finally arrive at the modern era of wireless. It would be difficult if not impossible to recount this part of the story without research at the frontlines of development. Fortunately, several leading actors—including Andrew Viterbi, Martin Cooper, and Donald Cox—contributed to my research.

It would be hard to exaggerate the impact of cellular telephone on culture and the global economy. Ironically, its development was largely hidden from view—and its commercialization was significantly delayed. Perhaps that explains why it has grown way beyond the most optimistic forecasts. There are well over two billion mobile phone subscribers today and the number could reach three billion by 2010.

The historic role of industry standards must also be acknowledged. A degree of conformity is required so that products from different manufacturers can talk to each other. But it would be remiss to deny the impetus of proprietary technologies and business contrarians. The evolution of wireless continues to be driven by the clash of opposing ideas.

By no means has the era of individual discoverers and inventors come to an end. The current industry is obsessed with planning, and much is already decided about the next generation of wireless technology. Or so the experts think. Even the best planning cannot prevent unexpected twists and turns in the road ahead.

The book concludes by identifying some key lessons. How did the science behind wireless technology evolve? Why did some technologies succeed and others fail? And what can scientists, inventors, and entrepreneurs learn from the history of wireless about creativity? The history of wireless provides a treasure trove of lessons about how to avoid pitfalls—and how to succeed in science and business.

PART I

Chapter One
Luigi's Dancing Frogs

On January 26, 1781 an Italian obstetrician and physiologist stumbled on a most curious phenomenon. Luigi Galvani placed a dissected frog on a glass plate at one end of his laboratory table. At the other end of the table sat a hand-cranked static electricity generator. When one of his assistants lightly touched a scalpel to the frog's inner crural nerves, the animal's legs convulsed violently. Another assistant noticed that the contractions occurred at precisely the moment Galvani's wife Lucia drew a spark from the static-making machine.

It was the first recorded example of wireless communication. The static electricity generator was the transmitter; the frog's nerves and muscles were the receiver.

Galvani is not remembered as a wireless pioneer. He did not even realize he was witnessing wireless communications. The foundation of knowledge needed to conceive of such a thing did not yet exist. Instead, he viewed the incident through the prism of 18th century science—an era dominated by Isaac Newton's theory of gravity based on unfathomable action-at-a-distance. In Galvani's eyes, sparks act on a frog several feet away just as the earth exerts its pull on an apple falling from a tree. He could easily observe the effects on the frog; understanding how the spark projected its force—and what happened in the intervening space—was beyond comprehension.

More intriguing to Galvani was the spark's ability to excite the "highly subtle fluid that exists in the nerves." He hoped the newly discovered contractions-at-a-distance would help him isolate and illuminate the operation of nerves and muscles.

Encouraged by these novel effects, Galvani performed innumerable experiments over the next several years, trying every conceivable variation. He found, for example, that atmospheric electricity from an approaching storm can trigger frog leg contractions. Then in September of 1786 he made another serendipitous discovery. Tinkering on a clear day with his atmospheric setup, consisting of a dissected frog draped over a terrace railing with an iron hook piercing its spinal chord, he observed that merely pressing the iron hook against the railing was sufficient to make the frog's legs jump. Galvani believed this corroborated his theory that the contractions were due not to external forces but innate "animal electricity," the delicate equilibrium of which is easily upset by nearby sparks, an approaching thunderstorm, or a suddenly completed circuit.

Galvani's animal electricity experiments were carefully studied by Alessandro Volta, professor of physics at the University of Pavia. At first enthusiastic about Galvani's research, Volta soon changed his mind, suspecting that in his eagerness to prove the animal electricity theory Galvani overlooked an alternative explanation: contact between dissimilar metals produces electricity.

Volta's criticism initiated one of the most famous debates in the history of science. Did animal electricity or contact electricity cause the frog muscle contractions? The debate showed that even the most honest and meticulous scientists, when guided by divergent worldviews, may disagree about the causes of plainly observable effects. The desire for vindication drove both to further discoveries—and led one to an invention that would prove a watershed in the study and application of electricity.

Egged on by their respective supporters, each scientist sought a crucial experiment to prove his theory. Galvani struck first. He showed that contractions could be produced with a homogeneous metal arc and even with no metal whatsoever—flatly contradicting Volta's "dissimilar metals" claim.

It was a setback for Volta and he knew it, but he refused to abandon his theory that an external source of electricity caused the contractions. Pressing on with his experiments, Volta built a columnar apparatus consisting of alternating pieces of silver and zinc separated by moistened disks. On March 20, 1800 (more than a year after Galvani's death) Volta wrote a letter to Sir Joseph Banks, Secretary of the Royal Society in London that for all intents and purposes brought the debate to a close. He announced that by arranging specific materials in the proper order—known by posterity as the "voltaic pile"—he created a source of continuous current. Volta invented the battery.

In retrospect, neither scientist was entirely right. Galvani was correct in believing that the animal nervous system generates and uses electricity; Volta was right that different materials can be arranged to produce electricity. But Volta had tactical advantages: he outlived Galvani, excelled at self-promotion, and closed his argument by creating something other scientists could use. With the scientific community in receipt of Volta's wonderful gift, Galvani slipped into an obscurity from which he did not reemerge for 30 years.

Volta crossed the electric Rubicon. Up to that time, knowledge of electricity was confined to static discharges—equally a subject of scientific inquiry, parlor entertainment, and dubious medical treatment. By creating a scalable source of continuous current, Volta established the first beachhead in electronics. Easily replicated by others, the voltaic pile quickly enabled a series of discoveries in electrochemistry and electromagnetism. While the wireless incident in Galvani's laboratory is just an historical footnote, Volta's battery cleared a path to the telegraph, the telephone, and wireless.

* * *

Prior to Volta the growth of knowledge about electricity was excruciatingly slow. Thales of Miletus (a Greek city in what is now Turkey) wrote about static electricity in the sixth century B.C., observing that amber ("elektron" in ancient Greek) rubbed with dry materials attracts straw and feather. Anyone who encountered static cling or shock knew almost as much as Thales.

As meager as that knowledge was, two thousand years passed before it was augmented. The English physician and natural philosopher William Gilbert performed the first rigorous survey of electricity and magnetism, recounted in his seminal book "On the Magnet" published in 1600. Gilbert coined the term "electricity" and described how it differed from magnetism. For example, he explained that electrified materials attract unlike materials, while "a loadstone attracts only magnetic bodies."

Further study of electricity required a means of producing static charges on demand. The German inventor Otto von Guericke rose to the challenge, constructing the first static electricity generating machine in 1663. The machine consisted of a ball of sulphur inside a glass globe rotated with a crank against a pad; the globe became electrically charged and could be removed to conduct experiments. Like other natural philosophers of his day, Guericke studied diverse areas of science, and is best known for his dramatic demonstration of atmospheric pressure. (Guericke brought together a pair of hemispheric copper bowls to form a sphere, evacuated the air within the sphere using the pump he invented, and showed that even two teams of horses could not pull the bowls apart.)

Knowledge about electricity experienced a growth spurt in the 1720s. The English chemist Stephen Gray showed that electric charges can travel 150 meters over a wet hemp line and even further over metal wire. Gray also noticed that some materials are better conductors than others, and that the earth acts as a giant receptacle for electric charges. In 1733 the versatile French scientist Charles du Fay, whose interests ranged from botany to optics, concluded that there are two kinds of electric fluid, vitreous and resinous. He demonstrated that all bodies can be electrified to some extent. Gray and du Fay staged dramatic public demonstrations to promote scientific inquiry, electrifying everything from tea kettles to human volunteers.

Benjamin Franklin, another jack-of-all-trades scientist, showed that there is just one electric fluid and it comes in two flavors, positive and negative. He demonstrated this in 1747 by electrifying two individuals with opposite charges. Franklin's famous kite experiment established that lightning is an atmospheric form of electricity.

In 1745 Pieter van Musschenbroek of Leyden, Holland invented a device for storing electric charges. The Leyden jar, a glass bottle with inner and outer conductors, could be charged to capacity using von Guericke's friction machine, providing both natural philosophers and the public with a portable source of electricity. Du Fay pupil Abbé Nollet employed this primitive capacitor to shock more than 600 monks holding hands to form a circle, watching them jump, robes flying in the air. Shocking chains of humans became an 18th century craze.

The shock didn't always propagate all the way around the circle. Observers wondered if some individuals are poor conductors of electricity. Others speculated that the inability to conduct electricity might be symptomatic of more embarrassing deficiencies. Joseph-Aignan Sigaud de la Fond performed the experiment that solved the mystery. When the last person to feel the shock was moved to another place in the circle, the shock continued to stop in the original spot, which turned out to be a wet patch of ground.

Working near Paris, the French botanist Louis-Guillaume Le Monnier ran a long metal wire to convey electric shocks at a distance. William Watson, an English botanist, did the same across the Thames in London, using the river as one leg of his circuit. Both investigators understood that if they could measure the time it took for electricity to travel down the wire, they could calculate its velocity. Both failed.

The first mathematically rigorous characterization of the forces exerted by electric charges was presented by the French engineer Charles-Augustin de Coulomb in 1785. Coulomb's invention, the torsion balance, enabled him to make very fine measurements of attraction and repulsion. He confirmed that the force between two electrically charged bodies is inversely proportional to the square of the distance separating them.

John Wesley, cofounder of the Methodist Church, believed electricity could be used to treat more than two dozen medical conditions. Wesley published *The Desideratum, or Electricity Made Plain and Useful by a Lover of Mankind and of Common Sense* in 1760. It's tempting to dismiss Wesley as a charlatan, but he could just as easily be declared prescient. While using electric shock to treat mental disorders is controversial, electricity is widely used to regulate heart rhythm and is increasingly used to restore hearing.

Therapeutic uses of electricity took Europe by storm. There were two schools of thought: one believed that health requires a proper balance of electricity; the other concluded that some illnesses are caused by obstructions to electric fluid flow. Luigi Galvani was cautiously optimistic that electricity would prove useful in the treatment of paralysis.

As little was known about electricity prior to 1700, even less was known about nerve function. Natural philosophers agreed that nerves convey information and feed into the spinal chord which, in turn, is attached to the brain. How the information is conveyed remained an enigma.

By the close of the 17th century, there were three competing theories of nerve function. One, supported by the French philosopher and mathematician Rene Descartes, speculated that nerves house tiny canals for transporting a subtle (rarified) fluid. The second theory asserted that nerves secrete droplets. The third, advocated by the great scientist (and alchemist) Isaac Newton, said that nerves communicate via mechanical vibrations.

All three theories were seriously flawed. The Dutch microscopy pioneer Anton Van Leeuwenhoek could not find any hollow channels in nerves and scientist Jan Swammerdam was unable to detect evidence of fluid flow. The secretion theory couldn't account for the speed and force of nerve-muscle action. Albrecht von Haller pointed out that the structure and composition of nerves is unsuitable for transmitting mechanical vibrations.

A new theory was needed. The English physiologist Stephen Hales (born 1677) was first to suggest that electricity could be the "fluid" that runs through nerves. University of Bologna professor Leopoldo Caldani observed in 1756 that frog muscles contract in response to electric stimuli. Natural philosophers began studying electric fish in the 1770s. Oddly, no one managed to put all of these facts together.

* * *

The relationship between animals and electricity fascinated Luigi Galvani. Born in 1737, Galvani followed in the footsteps of his father and became a physician. He was appointed Professor of Anatomy by the University of Bologna in 1768, replacing Caldani, who left to take a position in Padua. A skilled surgeon, Galvani was also appointed Chair of Obstetrics.

Founded in 1088, the University of Bologna was the Western world's first university. Famous alumni include the writer Dante Alighieri, astronomer Nicolaus Copernicus, and artist Albrecht Dürer. During the 16th century, in defiance of traditional philosophy and theology, the University firmly embraced experimental science. The field of medicine prospered at the University thanks to pioneering use of the microscope in anatomical research and Gaspare Tagliacozzi's work in plastic surgery.

Galvani acquired equipment for studying the relationship between electricity and biology and set up a laboratory in his home. He conducted experiments using static electricity generators, Leyden jars, and related equipment, with frogs, sheep and humans as subjects. Galvani married Lucia Galeazzi, daughter of physics professor Domenico Gusmano Galeazzi, and she worked at his side in their home laboratory.

Galvani believed there are three types of electricity: natural, artificial, and animal. Lightning is natural electricity. Machine-generated sparks exemplify artificial electricity. Shocks produced by torpedo fish illustrate animal electricity.

Galvani began to study animal electricity in his early forties. The electrical fluid theory of nerve function was then in favor; only electricity exhibited the transmission speed and force consistent with nerve-muscle action. Electric shocks, it was known, caused animals and humans to jump. And the electrical properties of gymnotus and torpedo fish were firmly established by John Walsh, John Hunter, and Henry Cavendish. (Also known as electric rays, torpedo fish can generate up to 220 volts to stun or kill prey.)

Galvani must have been tempted to identify electricity as life's vital force. After all, Caldani demonstrated that electricity could sometimes reanimate dead creatures. However, Galvani was a committed vitalist; he firmly believed that sciences such as chemistry and physics can never fully explain life.

Benjamin Franklin's "one fluid" theory had a profound influence on Galvani. He was particularly impressed with Franklin's explanation of how a Leyden jar stores electric charges. Franklin contended that opposite charges accumulate on the inner and outer conductors. Galvani wondered if animals store electricity in a similar manner.

Galvani understood that there are two types of nerves: those that convey sensations to the brain and the kind that produce muscle action. He decided to limit his investigation to the latter because its effects could be clearly observed. He also considered it essential to prepare each animal specimen by isolating the nerves and muscles from the rest of its body.

His first finding was fundamental to neurophysiology: a constant flow of electricity doesn't cause muscle contractions. Only electrical impulses cause muscle contractions. Galvani also discovered that there does not have to be a direct connection between the source of electricity and the nerve—as long as the electrical impulse possesses sufficient force to overcome the resistance.

After several years of research, Galvani presented the results of his experiments in the Proceedings of the Bologna Academy of Science in 1791 under the title, "Commentary on the Effects of Electricity on Muscular Motion" ("De Viribus Electricitatis in Motu Musculari Commentarius"). He concluded that sparks and lightning stimulate a frog to produce animal electricity. The scalpels, railings, and hooks, he surmised, merely serve to complete the circuit.

Uncharacteristically, Galvani ignored a key anomaly in his experiments. Galvani believed that the animal's brain was the source of electric fluid. However, his experiments showed that the muscle contractions are stronger when a bimetallic arc is used. That suggested intensity, at least, was a function of some external factor.

Though usually described as an unassuming person, Galvani was not shy about publicizing his animal electricity research. He printed and distributed extra copies of his paper at his own expense, sending one to Alessandro Volta.

Volta was born in Como in 1745[1]. He attended the Jesuit's School of Rhetoric, enjoyed reading Tasso and Virgil, and wrote Latin verses. Upon completing grammar school, he became interested in electrical phenomena and read books by the subject's leading lights: Cesare Beccaria, Musschenbroek, and Nollet. He published his first work on the topic at the age of 24, "De vi Attractiva ignis Electrici ac Phaenomenis inde Pendentibus." Five years later, he was nominated superintendent of schools in Como.

Volta invented a static-generating machine that was a major improvement over Otto von Guericke's because it did not require continuous rubbing. He called it the "perpetual electrophorus" and it was soon embraced throughout Europe. He discovered he could re-electrify a pie-shaped resin (such as amber) and flat metal shield (with insulated handle) merely by

---

[1] Biographical information for Alessandro Volta was obtained from the University of Pavia's website at: http://ppp.unipv.it/volta/Pages/ePage0.html

placing the shield on top of the resin, discharging the pair, and removing the shield. The invention garnered Volta the Copley Medal and a fellowship in the Royal Society of Britain in 1794.

The electrophorus must have colored Volta's subsequent interpretation of electric phenomena. Volta discovered early in his career that electric charges can be created by contact and separation—and was widely acclaimed for it. Here's how it worked: The resin was rubbed with animal fur to give it an initial charge. The shield was placed on top of the resin and the combination was discharged (by touching both) to create an overall balance of positive and negative charges. However, the charges remained unequally distributed; removing the shield from the resin left the shield with a net positive charge and the resin with a net negative charge. Conveniently, the process of discharging and separating the resin and shield to create opposite charges could be repeated many times before the resin required a fresh rubbing.

Volta was appointed by Count Firmian as head of experimental physics at the state grammar school. While on holiday at Lake Maggiore the following summer (1776), he noticed bubbles floating to the surface in shallow water. He immediately recognized the bubbles were evidence of a chemical reaction. (This is important, because years later he would miss or ignore bubbles in a different context.) He collected the gas, which we now know was methane, and found it was highly combustible. He constructed a device—later dubbed "Volta's Pistol"—to measure its explosive force.

By 1778 Count Firmian realized that Volta was an extraordinarily talented natural philosopher, and appointed him Professor of Physics at the University of Pavia. Volta immediately turned his attention to condensers and developed a very sensitive instrument for measuring weak electrical charges, the condensing electroscope. Volta discovered the relationship between the quantity of charge, the condenser's capacity, and the electrical tension.

In 1792 Volta repeated Galvani's animal electricity experiments. The effort seemed to confirm Galvani's findings. However, Volta must have had lingering doubts because he decided to conduct a second round of experiments making more careful measurements. He became convinced that the contractions were caused not by electricity stored in the dead frog, but by currents generated due to contact between dissimilar metals. Volta found that when he applied a bimetallic arc to his own tongue it produced a tingling sensation and surmised that it acted likewise on the frog's nerves. "It's the dissimilarity of metals that causes it," Volta wrote.

Volta did not refute animal electricity. He acknowledged the hypothesis that electricity flows through nerves and acts on muscles is both "plausible and seductive." Volta only disagreed with Galvani about specific experiments. Namely, he felt that Galvani favored a highly speculative explanation over one that was relatively obvious. He called on Galvani to withdraw his animal electricity hypothesis.

While Galvani perceived the frog as a type of Leyden jar, Volta saw it as a very sensitive electroscope. He measured the quantity of charge required to trigger a contraction and found it to be very small—5/100ths of a degree on his thin-straw electroscope. The knowledge that tiny charges could trigger contractions only reinforced Volta's suspicion that external sources of electricity rather than innate "animal electricity" caused the contractions observed by Galvani.

Volta believed electric charges flow between the three materials in the same manner that charges migrate between the resin and shield of the electrophorus. (Two centuries later, Marcello Pera, Professor of Philosophy at the University of Catania in Italy, dubbed Volta's initial rebuttal of Galvani's explanation the "special theory of contact electricity." The theory states that an electromotive force is generated whenever two dissimilar metals and a moist body are placed in contact.)

Volta designed a colorful experiment to test his theory. Four people formed a chain; the first held his finger on the second's tongue, the second placed his finger directly on the eyeball of the third, and the third and fourth held a skinned and gutted frog between their wet hands. The first and last individuals held, respectively, a sheet of zinc and sheet of silver in their wet, free hands. Putting the metal sheets in contact with each other completed the circuit, causing a sensation on the second person's tongue, a flash of light in the third person's eye, and a convulsion in the frog's legs. Though the experiment bordered on bizarre, it attracted many to Volta's side in the debate with Galvani.

Galvani responded with a frontal assault. He showed that touching the nerve directly to the outer covering of the muscle stimulated contractions. It was a devastating experiment. It seemed to prove Galvani's contention that the animal was the source of electricity and that external stimuli served only to activate it. (It was not known at the time that injured tissue can generate electricity.)

The tide turned once again in Galvani's favor. He considered several hypotheses to account for the muscle contractions. He systematically examined the role of metal arcs in his previous experiments: homogeneous one-piece arcs, homogeneous multiple-piece arcs, dissimilar one-piece arcs, and dissimilar multiple-piece arcs. The evidence demolished Volta's hypothesis that dissimilar metals were the source of electricity. However, Galvani made a crucial mistake: he attempted to prove animal electricity by eliminating all other hypotheses. That was an invitation for Volta to introduce a new hypothesis that couldn't be as readily dismissed.

And that's exactly what Volta did. He now presented what Pera christened the "general theory of contact electricity." It states that all conductors of different kinds generate an electromotive force upon contact. It was a small change, but it made a big difference. In this case, it meant that even saliva or blood could supply the requisite dissimilarity.

Galvani's supporters protested that Volta introduced subtlety for the sole purpose of salvaging his theory. Volta essentially argued that any differences—even imperceptible ones—could cause an electromotive force. His "general theory of contact electricity" was so vague it could not be disproved.

There's no doubt that Galvani and Volta were both careful and skeptical inquirers. Each considered all credible hypotheses. Each conceived and performed repeatable and verifiable experiments. And each recognized that his position had limitations. Both understood that their differences were largely a matter of emphasis. However, each attracted an enthusiastic following; as the debate progressed, compromise became increasingly difficult.

Both men flirted with compromise—though at different times. Galvani wondered if they were both right; perhaps some of the experiments demonstrated animal electricity and others demonstrated artificial electricity. He quickly abandoned any thought of compromise, however, when he produced contractions without any metal. According to Giovacchino Carradori, an avid follower of the debate, at that point "All scientists predicted imminent defeat for Volta and total triumph for Galvani."

Volta admitted that certain fish generate electricity and accepted the possibility that the human brain produces electricity. Volta proposed a compromise but presented it in arrogant fashion, threatening to withdraw it if Galvani did not agree to his exact terms. Like Galvani, Volta was willing to admit that his adversary identified a genuine source of electromotive force, but he could never agree that it caused the muscle contractions in Galvani's experiments.

Unfortunately for Galvani, his fortunes were in decline from the debate's onset. He never recovered emotionally from the death of his wife in 1791.

With the arrival of Napoleon, Bologna became capital of the Cispadane Republic. Galvani, who held his university chair for 33 years, was dismissed in 1797 when he refused to take an oath of allegiance to Napoleon. Consequently, Galvani lost his home and savings, was forced to move to his brother's house, and died there on December 4, 1798.

Galvani's nephew Giovanni Aldini, Professor of Physics in Bologna, carried on the fight. He organized a pro-Galvani society in Bologna to oppose the pro-Volta society at the University of Pavia. Aldini traveled across Europe, publicly electrifying humans and animals in what was at best extraordinary theater and at worst grotesque. He treated an apparently schizophrenic patient with electric shocks to the head, reporting steady improvement and ultimately a complete cure.

Animal electricity was alluring to both scientists and the public. Aldini's work inspired Mary Shelley's novel about Dr. Victor Frankenstein and his monster—a creature pieced together from cadaver parts and brought to life with lightning discharges.

Two additional crucial experiments were performed in support of the animal electricity theory. Aldini showed he could obtain contractions using liquid mercury—an indisputably homogeneous conductor. Eusebio Valli, one of Galvani's most loyal supporters, put what looked like the last nail in the coffin by using his own hand to stimulate muscle contractions.

Volta, however, conceived a crucial experiment of his own. He arranged two bowls of salt water with a bimetallic arc dipped in each. One end of the arc was copper, the other zinc. Volta understood that this arrangement created a potential (now called "voltage") that could be increased by connecting identical setups in series—or decreased by adding reverse polarity setups (in which the zinc and copper switch sides) in series.

With this knowledge in hand, Volta arranged three sets of 20 bowls in series with the middle set configured for reverse polarity. He found that by dipping one finger in the first bowl he could use a finger on his free hand to detect and roughly gauge shocks as he moved it from one bowl to the next. He detected a barely perceptible shock at the fourth or fifth bowl; from there, the strength of the shock increased up to the 20th bowl. As he moved through the reverse polarity bowls, he observed that the shocks diminished.

Next, Volta created a columnar apparatus consisting of alternating copper and zinc disks with circular pieces of felt, paper, or leather soaked in a salt or dilute acid solution sandwiched between each set. Similarly, he found that the force of the electricity could be increased by building taller, same-polarity stacks.

Volta traveled a long road to this point. He started by suspecting there was a problem with Galvani's theory. He borrowed a concept from his electrophorus to create an alternative theory. (Namely, that making and breaking contact can generate electricity.) Finally, he conceived a simple experiment that demonstrated his theory quite convincingly.

The "voltaic pile" was an instant success. And to Volta went all of the spoils. Napoleon presented him with a gold medal and conferred on him the title of Count (1810). Volta spent his remaining years enjoying fame and fortune. In 1819, he retired to his country home in Camnago where he died on 3rd March, 1827.

* * *

One point about Volta's work mystifies science historians. Despite being a competent chemist, Volta failed to notice evidence (gas bubbles) of a chemical reaction in his voltaic pile. Some wonder if, like Galvani, he was too eager to prove his theory. However, Volta had no reason to look for a chemical reaction. His electrophorus taught him that electric charges can be accumulated by contact and separation. He believed his own propaganda and described his columnar apparatus as an inexhaustible source of electricity. Ironically, another Italian natural philosopher (Giovanni Fabroni) suggested a chemical cause shortly after Galvani published his first paper but was almost entirely ignored by the scientific community.

Volta's fame only grew as others found ways to improve his apparatus. Voltaic batteries weighing several tons were constructed. Humphry Davy, Michael Faraday's mentor, established the field of electrochemistry and built the first electric arc light using the Royal Society's 2000-plate voltaic battery in 1810. William Cruikshank developed batteries capable of mass production.

The first battery-operated telegraph was demonstrated in 1809 by Professor S. T. Soemmering, a German physician. The device used 27 wires—the 26 letters of the alphabet plus one return. Each wire terminated in a gold point at the bottom of a glass vessel filled with acidulated water. Gas bubbles were generated in the appropriate vessel to signal the desired letter over a distance of more than 600 meters, but the system was too slow and expensive for practical purposes.

Galvani and Volta joined the ranks of science's immortal figures. Though Galvani lost the debate, his ideas eventually resurfaced. He is now rightly celebrated as the founder of neurophysiology. In 1831, Carlo

Matteucci, professor of physics at Pisa, proved an element of Galvani's animal electricity theory. Using a very sensitive galvanometer (a device for measuring current named after Galvani), he demonstrated that an injured muscle emits a small electric current. Building on the work of Matteucci, German physiologist Emil du Bois-Reymond detected and measured the tiny electrical currents generated by the nervous system. His friend Hermann von Helmholtz measured, indirectly, the speed of nerve conduction.

Volta's invention led to one advance after another. Armed with a source of continuous current, natural philosophers could easily and quickly perform a wide range of experiments. It was only a matter of time before they discovered electromagnetism—upon which not only wireless communication but all electronics are based. The fundamental unit for measuring electromotive force, the volt, is named after Volta.

The significance of the Galvani-Volta debate was due to the process as much as the issues. The debate drove each investigator to change his research agenda in a way that was focused and purposeful. Galvani tried to defend his animal electricity theory by showing that causes not anticipated by Volta could elicit muscle contractions. Volta sought to extend the principles upon which his electrophorus was based to explain Galvani's fascinating results. By competing for validation of their respective ideas, Luigi Galvani and Alessandro Volta were driven to make further discoveries and an invention that changed the course of history.

Chapter Two
Faraday's Force Fields

Michael Faraday was the greatest experimentalist in the history of science. He single-handedly discovered and charted electric and magnetic fields. His method of visualizing magnetic lines of force—sprinkling iron filings on a card held over a magnet—has become a ritual for generations of students. And Faraday's revelation that a changing magnetic field creates an electric field provided the raw material for James Clerk Maxwell's epochal theory predicting radio waves.

Yet it would be hard to imagine a more unlikely candidate for such momentous achievements. Faraday was a blacksmith's son in an era when few Englishmen were allowed to rise above their station. His schooling consisted only, as he put it, of the "rudiments of reading, writing, and arithmetic." Even as a working scientist, he avoided the higher mathematics and theoretical excursions considered essential by his peers. He was never fully accepted by the European Continental science establishment.

The power of Faraday's intellect, however, overcame all obstacles. His fervent belief in the primacy of experimental facts not only guided his career—it inspired future inventors such as Guglielmo Marconi and Edwin H. Armstrong. His skill at conceiving, executing, and recording laboratory experiments remains unmatched. His research papers are so clear, precise, and perspicacious they are included in Encyclopedia Britannica's *Great Books of the Western World.*

Still, such praise does not do full justice to Faraday's achievement. Hired as a laboratory assistant, Faraday ultimately changed the way natural philosophers viewed the world. His experiments with electric and magnetic fields opened the door to an entirely new dimension of the universe.

By the early 19th century, most natural philosophers believed that Isaac Newton had perfected human understanding of the material universe. Newton's laws of motion and universal gravitation showed that all phenomena are the result of direct and instantaneous interaction between physical bodies. And Newton not only did the math (calculus) to prove it, he invented it.[2]

Based on Newton's beautiful theory, Enlightenment era natural philosophers concluded that the natural world consists solely of matter and motion. Newton supplied the immutable laws and mathematical tools; the only remaining task was filling in the details. Taking that as his cue, the French mathematician Pierre-Simon Laplace reasoned that if he could know the precise location and momentum of every atom in the universe, then using Newton's laws he could calculate the entire course of cosmic events, past and future.

But was that true—could Newton's system explain electricity and magnetism? Specifically, if the world consists only of matter and motion, then how can a magnet exert attraction or repulsion through a plate of glass? Natural philosophers confronted this challenge by devising the "effluvial theory" which says that the magnet emits an invisible vapor that passes through the plate's pores. The effluvial theory preserved Newton's system, but it was purely speculative.

If there was one thing Faraday could not tolerate, it was pure speculation. Faraday demanded empirical evidence. Newton surveyed empirical evidence from the macrocosm and demonstrated mathematically that heavenly bodies could be treated as point sources of gravity acting instantaneously over vast stretches of emptiness. Fair enough. But when Faraday probed the microcosm more than a century later, he discovered something quite different—a realm teeming with continuously varying electric and magnetic forces.

The contrast between Newton's macrocosm and Faraday's microcosm was profound. In Newton's system, the difference in gravitational force between nearby locations is negligible. For example, the weight of this book does not change if you move it a short distance in any direction. However, when you hold the opposite poles of two small magnets close together you feel a distinct pull; hold them an arm's length apart and you feel no pull at all.

Faraday was not trying to knock Newton off his pedestal. It just happened. In Newton's macrocosm, gravity is the direct result of its physical sources. In Faraday's microcosm, sources of electricity and magnetism produce force fields that take on a life of their own.

---

[2] So did Gottfried Leibniz, which led to a bitter priority dispute, but that's a story for another book.

* * *

Michael Faraday was born in 1791 just outside London. His father, James Faraday, moved from northern England to the London area in search of employment. James was frequently ill and, consequently, did not earn a steady income. The four children had barely enough to eat. Michael Faraday remembered being given a loaf of bread that had to last him the entire week.

The Faradays belonged to the tiny Sandemanian church. It was founded in Scotland around 1730 by John Glas and promoted by his son-in-law Robert Sandeman. Faraday himself described it as "a very small and despised sect of Christians." Sandeman believed that true faith is free from human reasoning, willing, and desiring. The Sandemanians advocated a purely spiritual religion—a religion devoid of both theology and clergy. A lifelong Sandemanian, Faraday believed that by studying nature he became closer to God.

Michael Faraday was apprenticed to George Riebau, a bookbinder, at the age of fourteen. During a seven-year apprenticeship, Faraday read voraciously with Riebau's encouragement. An article on electricity in the *Encyclopedia Britannica* piqued Faraday's interest. He built a crude electrostatic generator using bottles and lumber, and a weak voltaic pile, and began performing simple experiments. He was also greatly impressed by Jane Marcet's *Conversations on Chemistry*.

Science lectures were a very popular form of entertainment in early 19th century London. A free ticket to Sir Humphry Davy's lecture series at the Royal Institution changed Michael Faraday's life. Davy was the greatest chemist of his time. Making the most of his bookbinding craft, Faraday sent Davy a bound copy of the notes he took during Davy's lectures along with a letter seeking employment at the Royal Institution. Though Davy had no job openings at the time, he kept Faraday in mind, and when forced to dismiss a laboratory assistant for fighting he offered the position to Faraday. It was Michael Faraday's big break.

Following in the footsteps of the great French chemist Antoine Lavoisier, Sir Humphry Davy studied the basic substances and principles of chemistry. He learned that the properties of compounds are primarily due to their form rather than constituent elements. Davy investigated the physiological effects of nitrous oxide—also known as laughing gas—becoming addicted to it in the process. He showed that Volta's theory that electricity is generated by mere contact between dissimilar metals is wrong; a chemical reaction takes place. He built a large voltaic pile and used electricity to drive chemical reactions, separating out barium, calcium, magnesium, potassium, sodium, and strontium in 1807-1808.

Davy's greatest discovery, however, was Michael Faraday.

Faraday's first task as Davy's research assistant was to accompany Davy and his new wife, Jane Apreece, on a tour of the European continent from 1813-1815. Faraday was asked to serve temporarily as Davy's valet—but only until he found a replacement. He never did. Apreece, a wealthy socialite whose first husband was the son of a baronet, treated Faraday with extreme condescension; she insisted he ride on top of the coach and eat with the servants. Still, in the company of the illustrious Humphry Davy, he was privileged to visit many of Europe's greatest scientists.

With Faraday's help, Davy made several important discoveries during the trip. Despite the fact England and France were at war, and thanks to the personal invitation of Napoleon, their tour began in France. In Paris, Louis Gay-Lussac asked Davy to identify a mysterious substance isolated by Bernard Courtois. Noting its similarity to chlorine, Davy determined that it was an element—what we now know as iodine. The travelers also met Nicolas-Louis Vauquelin, the discoverer of chromium, and André-Marie Ampère, a pioneer in electromagnetism, and visited the Louvre and Paris' celebrated public library. In Florence, Italy Davy used the sun's rays to ignite a diamond and prove that it is composed of the element carbon. In Milan, the pair met the aging inventor of the voltaic pile, Alessandro Volta.

Upon returning to England, Faraday collaborated with Davy on the coal-mining safety lamp. When his stint as Davy's Chemical Assistant ended in 1820, Faraday was an accomplished chemist and experimenter in his own right. With Davy's support, he was hired directly by the Royal Institution as Superintendent of the House in 1821. That same year, Faraday officially joined the Sandemanian church, married Sarah Barnard (also a Sandemanian), and the couple took up residency at the Royal Institution.

Faraday's first independent accomplishments were in chemistry. He liquefied chlorine and produced the first compounds using "substitution reactions" in which chlorine replaced hydrogen. He isolated benzene, invented oxidation numbers (charges assigned to ions), prepared the first clathrate hydrate, and discovered the laws of electrolysis. Faraday studied steel alloys and is recognized as a pioneer in metallurgy. He improved the quality of optical glass for telescopes by increasing its refractive index— work that paid dividends 20 years later with discovery of the link between magnetism and light. Faraday's chemistry experiments also benefited his electricity research: he studied conductors, insulators, and battery components.

Both Davy and Faraday were influenced by 18th century Croatian professor Rudjer Josip Boscovich's atomic theory. Boscovich believed matter is composed of point sources of attraction and repulsion that combine to create complex force fields. Though Boscovich started from a Newtonian perspective, his theory led to belief in force fields exhibiting properties of their own, such as chemical bonds.

Most biographies of Boscovich suggest he influenced Faraday; some go further, insisting Faraday stole his force field concept. Actually, Faraday did not subscribe to any theories, though he admitted they sometimes suggest interesting and worthwhile experiments. Boscovich's ideas may have inspired Faraday, but Faraday's experiments stand on their own merit.

* * *

On the other side of the Atlantic, another young man prepared to leave his mark on the history of electromagnetism. Joseph Henry's pioneering work both rivaled and complemented Faraday's. The greatest American scientist since Benjamin Franklin, he showed that America could participate in the development of science despite being far from the hub of activity in Europe. Joseph Henry is remembered particularly for his work with inductors and as the first secretary of the Smithsonian Institution.

Henry's early life paralleled Faraday's in many ways. Henry was born to Scottish immigrants in 1797. His family was also poor due to the father's illness. Henry received a basic education in school, but developed a passion for reading on his own—the legend being that he stumbled on the local, one-room library while chasing a rabbit under the church housing the library. Henry's interest in science was fired by the book *Popular Lectures on Experimental Philosophy*. He was apprenticed as a watchmaker and silversmith at the age of 13.

In other ways, Joseph Henry was quite unlike Michael Faraday. The young Henry was torn between his interest in the theater and fascination with science. He spent most of his career as a teacher and administrator—neglecting laboratory research and the writing of scientific papers.

Henry entered the Albany Academy in 1819 as a student and soon found himself teaching. His first big break came when the Academy's principal, T. Romeyn Beck, a pioneer in forensic medicine, secured a tutoring position for him with the influential Van Rensselaer and James (ancestors of William and

Henry) families. These connections opened doors for him, and in 1824 he became a founding member of the Albany Institute. His presentation "On the Chemical and Mechanical Effects of Steam" at the age of 26 was well received and he was appointed curator of the Institute's Department of Natural History. Two years later, Henry was appointed professor of mathematics and natural history at the Albany Academy.

* * *

A discovery by the Danish natural philosopher Hans Christian Oersted in 1820 fired the imaginations of Faraday, Henry, and many other natural philosophers. Oersted reported that a compass needle is deflected when an electric current is switched on in a nearby wire. Though Oersted was famous for extracting aluminum from ore, he could not provide a satisfactory explanation for the compass needle phenomenon.

It was the first major dividend of Volta's battery beyond electrochemistry. William Gilbert described how electricity and magnetism are different. Now there was evidence that electricity and magnetism are not only related but convertible. If switching on an electric current in a nearby wire causes a compass needle to deflect, it could only mean that the current generated magnetism. At a minimum, that suggested opportunities for further experiments—and possibly an impending breakthrough.

With his intuitive grasp of conservation of energy, Faraday saw the writing on the wall: "Nowhere is there a pure creation or production of power without a corresponding exhaustion of something to supply it." If electricity can produce magnetism, he reasoned, magnetism should be able to generate electricity.

Faraday and Henry were both immediately attracted to André-Marie Ampère's theory that magnetism is caused by circular electric currents. Ampère demonstrated the concept by showing that a current-carrying wire wrapped around a bar-shaped metallic core behaved much like a bar magnet. Based on Ampère's theory, they also expected magnets to produce steady currents in nearby wires. They do not. That did not stop Faraday, however, from searching for evidence that magnetism can generate electricity.

Science often progresses in very small steps. Ampère showed that a current-carrying wire produces a cylindrical magnetic field. Armed with that knowledge, Faraday conjectured that an isolated magnetic pole would move in a circle around such a wire and he devised an experiment to verify the hypothesis. Unfortunately, the episode raised questions about Faraday's integrity.

William Hyde Wollaston was apparently first to suggest that a magnetic pole would rotate around a current-carrying wire. He conveyed his theory to Humphry Davy and together they performed experiments at the Royal Institution. Wollaston succeeded in showing that attraction and repulsion move in opposite directions around a current-carrying wire, but he never demonstrated rotation of a magnetic pole. Michael Faraday wandered into the laboratory while Davy and Wollaston were at work and subsequently devised an experiment of his own. He extended a wire into a pool of mercury containing a magnet. When he applied current to the wire, it rotated around the magnet.

Faraday published his findings in the October 1821 issue of the *Quarterly Journal of Science*, but did not mention Wollaston. A rumor, some think started by Davy, suggested that Faraday overheard Wollaston and Davy talking in the laboratory. Faraday responded by inviting Wollaston to examine his experiments; Wollaston came away satisfied that Faraday's results were obtained independently.

When Michael Faraday was elected Fellow of the Royal Society in 1824, the majority supported him—including Wollaston. Faraday's mentor Humphry Davy was among the minority that opposed him. A year later, Davy assigned Faraday to work on optical glass, an effort that yielded few results. It's clear that Davy was not trying to derail Faraday, but he may have been trying to reassert his authority over the rising star. Nevertheless, when the ailing Davy was forced to resign as director of the Royal Institution's laboratory that same year, he supported Faraday's promotion to the post. Upon Davy's death in 1829, Faraday ceased the largely fruitless optics experiments. (Years later, Faraday used one of the heavy glasses he developed during that period to demonstrate the relationship between magnetism and light.)

Faraday experimented with magnets and iron filings. He showed that magnetism is a force that acts on the filings—and not a fluid. He did this by sprinkling filings on a card and holding the card over a magnet. The experiment showed quite plainly that the filings orient themselves along discernable lines—the magnetic lines of force.

Faraday likewise doubted the popular theory that electricity is a fluid that travels through wires much as water flows through pipes. He suspected, instead, that electricity is a force that propagates through conductors. He knew that electricity can generate magnetism, and that could only mean that electricity could produce lines of force, too.

Davy was not the only person who was uneasy with Faraday's meteoric ascent. Many natural philosophers were skeptical about Faraday's lines of force. Some may have found it difficult to accept discoveries made by a blacksmith's son with little knowledge of higher mathematics. Others supported the effluvial theory or alternative explanations consistent with Newtonian mechanics.

Meanwhile, Joseph Henry made progress studying magnets and electromagnets. He discovered he could produce powerful horseshoe magnets by combining multiple magnetized elements, each the width of a saw blade. He found that a coil of wire multiplies the power of an electromagnet; while others used a few turns of wire on shellacked iron, Henry used tightly wound coils of insulated wire.

Henry experimented with different coil configurations, lengths of wire leads, and types of batteries. He used batteries with multiple plates to increase the "projectile force" of the current. By methodically testing such variations, Henry unknowingly matched the battery's internal resistance to its load for maximum power transfer—a principle described mathematically a few years later by Georg Simon Ohm.

Faraday and Henry both discovered induction—the ability of a "primary" coil to induce a current in a nearby "secondary" coil—around 1832. The principle of operation is simple: when a current is switched on in the primary coil it creates a changing magnetic field that, in turn, induces a current in the secondary coil. Later, induction would be applied to operate motors and electric transformers, generate electricity, and even communicate. For now, it was purely the subject of scientific investigation.

Henry used a "strong quantity" (current) electromagnet while Faraday used a "strong intensity" (voltage) electromagnet. Faraday wrapped the primary and secondary coils around the same iron ring; Henry wrapped the secondary around an iron armature attached to a horseshoe magnet, connected a galvanometer to it, and positioned the galvanometer and himself about 40 feet away.

Henry saw the needle swing when the primary electromagnet was activated and again when the primary circuit was opened. He wasn't looking for a transient effect, but that's what he observed. Henry later noted that primary and secondary coils could be used to transform high-intensity, low-quantity current to low-intensity, high-quantity current. Likewise, a modern transformer may convert 110 volt electricity from a common wall outlet to the 12 volt electricity required to operate a specific device.

In Faraday's eyes, this was evidence that magnetism can create electricity. Continuing to experiment, he substituted a permanent magnet for the primary coil. He found that when a permanent magnet is moved in and out of a coil it induces a current.

It all began to make sense. Faraday already knew that the field surrounding a magnet consists of lines of force which could easily be made evident by sprinkling iron filings on a card placed above the magnet. Now he understood that the amount of current induced is proportional to the number of lines of force cutting the conductor per unit of time.

Faraday's next experiment illustrates his genius. He took the concept a step further. He speculated that if moving a magnet causes magnetic lines of force to cut through a fixed conductor and induce an electric current, then moving the conductor in the magnetic field of a fixed magnet should also induce a current. To test his idea, he rotated a copper disk with leads attached to its center and rim between the poles of a strong magnet. Since most of the area of a circle is near the circumference, the rim of the disk should cut more magnetic lines of force than the center, creating a continuous direct current between the center and rim. Faraday invented the dynamo, which later took the Industrial Revolution to the next level by enabling the switch from steam power to electric power.

Faraday suspected that the relationship between electricity and magnetism also applied to light. That, in turn, suggested a relationship between electricity, magnetism, and wave phenomena. Thomas Young's double-slit experiment in 1801 demonstrated that light can produce interference patterns and is, therefore, a wave phenomenon.

Young's experiment was simple: light is shined on a plate or card with two narrow slits cut in it. A flat screen is placed on the other side of the plate. When the single wave front from the light source strikes the plate, it is split into two wave fronts by the two slits. When the two wave fronts hit the screen, they interfere with each other, creating a characteristic pattern of alternating light and dark bands.

In 1831, Faraday collaborated with scientist and inventor Charles Wheatstone to learn more about waves. Sometimes science intersects with art in interesting and useful ways. A German pioneer of acoustics, Ernst Chladni, found that by dusting iron plates with sand and drawing a violin bow up and down the plates' rims to produce musical tones he created distinct patterns in the sand. These beautiful outlines, which came to be known as Chladni figures, illustrate sound vibrations much as iron filings illustrate magnetic lines of force, and showed that a dynamic cause can produce a static effect. Faraday also observed that the patterns could be induced in a plate by bowing a nearby plate. No doubt, Faraday continued to ponder his hunch that electricity and magnetism are related to light, a known wave phenomenon.

When Faraday performed his induction experiments later that year, he noticed that the galvanometer needle deflected in one direction when the circuit was closed and the opposite direction when the circuit was opened. He attributed this to a change in the "electrotonic" state of the particles in the wire. That is, a current is induced whenever the tension between the particles is created or destroyed—but not while it is in a steady state.

The following year, 1832, Faraday sent a letter to the Royal Society describing magnetism and electricity as flowing in waves. He not only showed that a changing magnetic field creates an electric field; he produced a mathematical model that was ultimately employed by Maxwell. By 1839, he combined his tension and wave concepts, describing the flow of electricity in conductors as a cyclical buildup and breakdown of tension; an insulator was simply a material that could withstand a greater buildup before reaching breakdown.

Joseph Henry made another important discovery about coils: self-induction. He noticed a spark when the current was removed from a coil. Such a violent reaction to the cessation of current was unexpected. Faraday noticed the same effect around the same time, explaining that opening the circuit caused the magnetic field around the coil to collapse, which in turn caused a transient current in the opposite direction. Henry tried to show that his work preceded Faraday's, but freely admitted that Faraday's analysis was superior. As British scientist John Herschel remarked, "He who proves, discovers."

Oersted's announcement that an electric current deflected a compass needle inspired more than just experiments. Since the middle of the 18th century, natural philosophers wondered if electricity and wires could be used to communicate. However, schemes that relied on sparks, pith balls, and bubbles were slow, weak, and clumsy. Could electricity's ability to create magnetism be the breakthrough they were looking for?

The British researcher Peter Barlow threw cold water on the idea, insisting that the practical limit for electromagnetic communications is roughly 200 feet. Undeterred, Joseph Henry devised a circuit that could receive signals over more than 1,000 feet of wire. He placed a bar magnet on a pivot with its north pole between the poles of an electromagnet. When he activated the electromagnet over the wire, the bar magnet swung, causing its other end to strike a bell. Henry increased the length to one and one-half miles and was still able to ring the bell. Ironically, though Henry debunked Barlow's dismal analysis, he saw little practical value in the invention.

Though Faraday conceived and articulated the notion that electricity and magnetism propagate as waves, it was Henry who first attempted wireless communications. He decided to see how far he could separate two coils and still induce a current; he reached nearly 200 feet.

This was not wireless communications in the modern sense; it used a magnetic field rather than electromagnetic waves at radio frequencies. Nor was Henry the last person to pursue wireless communications via induction; the idea even survived for a short time after the discovery of radio waves. Only when scientists showed that signals conveyed via induction attenuate with distance much more rapidly than signals sent via radio waves was the idea of induction-based wireless cast aside.

During this period Faraday made an important career decision. Up to this time, natural philosophers routinely shifted from one area of science to another. Faraday concluded that a foundation of scientific knowledge had been laid and that building on it would require greater specialization. Deciding to focus on electricity, he wrote 45 articles on "Experimental Researches in Electricity" from 1831 to 1855.

Drawing on the knowledge of electrochemistry and electromagnetism he acquired through his experiments, Faraday put the final nail in the coffin of Volta's contact electricity theory. Natural philosophers wondered whether different sources of electricity (namely torpedo fish, voltaic piles, static electricity generators, lightning, and now electromagnetic generators) produced essentially the same thing. Faraday resolved in 1832 to show that they do.

Faraday posited two laws of electrochemistry. The first states that the amount of a substance deposited on each electrode of an electrolytic cell is directly proportional to the quantity of electricity passed through the cell. The second asserts that the quantities of different elements deposited by a given amount of electricity are in the ratio of their chemical equivalent weights. Faraday had no trouble demonstrating that voltaic piles and electric dynamos produce the same electrochemical effects.

Static electricity, however, was more problematic. Faraday came up with a novel solution. Since there is a relationship between the amount of electricity and the quantity of material deposited on the electrodes of an electrolytic cell, there should likewise be a relationship between the quantity of static charge engendered in a nonconductor and the non-conductor's composition. In proving his hypothesis, Faraday discovered capacitance. (Though a Leyden jar functions as a capacitor, early investigators failed to elucidate its principle of operation.)

Faraday conceived an experiment using two spheres—a larger outer sphere and smaller inner sphere. He measured the specific inductive capacity of different materials by placing them in the hollow space between the spheres.

A related experiment proved that the electric force acts from molecule to molecule and not instantaneously at-a-distance. Faraday demonstrated that he could charge a sphere from behind a screen, despite the fact that the sphere was completely shaded by the screen. This could only mean one thing: the electric lines of force were curved. However, instantaneous action-at-a-distance can only take place along the shortest path, which is always a straight line.

Though Faraday was a great experimenter, partial to facts and wary of abstract theories, he was not an extreme skeptic. He understood that facts are often related and that conclusions can be drawn based on those relationships. Such conclusions, in turn, could lead to novel predictions. After all, Faraday's belief in the unity of electricity, magnetism, and light began as nothing more solid than intuition. Joseph Henry was more extreme; he believed science should be based exclusively on sensory data and common sense, and even rejected intuition.

Though Faraday emphasized the primacy of facts, he did not limit facts to physical objects. He believed that force fields are real entities, seeing them as neither pure matter nor pure energy. Instead, he thought of force fields as mechanical tension in the elastic medium permeating all space, the ether.

Faraday's force fields violated Newtonian mechanics based on instantaneous action at-a-distance between point sources. In Newton's gravitational universe, differences in the quantity and direction of force between nearby locations are vanishingly small. With Faraday's force fields, in contrast, the quantity and direction of force is the result of complex interactions and can vary significantly between nearby locations. The punch line is that force fields are an aggregate effect; it would be futile to focus on the interaction between individual iron filings and individual electrons racing through an adjacent coil of wire.

Years of intense research took a heavy toll on Michael Faraday. He suffered from fatigue and vertigo, complained of poor memory, and finally succumbed to a nervous breakdown shortly before his 50th birthday in 1840. He was forced to cease his researches for four years.

Happily, when Faraday resumed his research, he finally discovered the long-suspected link between light and electromagnetism. The young William Thomson (later Lord Kelvin) suggested that he employ a strong magnetic rather than electric field. The influence of a magnetic field on the plane of polarization of light passing through a transparent dielectric is now known as the Faraday Effect; the property of materials that enables this effect was dubbed "diamagnetism" by Faraday.

Faraday observed a related, unexpected phenomenon. When he reversed the direction of the light ray, he found that the rotation continued in the same direction, suggesting that the magnetic lines of force rather than glass molecules were subjected to strain. This confirmed that force fields, though immaterial, truly exist.

It's no accident that Michael Faraday left an extensive and detailed written record of his work. His motto was "Work. Finish. Publish." Faraday was not only a great writer but a wonderful lecturer. His Friday Evening Discourses for lay audiences were quite popular, as was his famous Christmas lecture for children, The Chemical History of a Candle. The lecture series he founded continues to this day in Britain.

Faraday had many admirers. The poet Samuel Taylor Coleridge described Faraday as a man who took boyish delight in research. But he was also disciplined. As Faraday's successor as director of the Royal Institution John Tyndall observed, "Underneath his sweetness and gentleness was the heat of a volcano."

Faraday had his own ideas about his role, which he once described as "reading the book of nature... written with the finger of God." He never pursued practical applications, nor did he seek patents. When asked about the practical value of his research, Faraday responded with a question of his own: "What is the use of a newborn baby?" When Prime Minister Robert Peel asked Faraday what the uses of his electric dynamo might be, Faraday quipped, "I know not, but I wager that one day your government will tax it."

Faraday's legacy was perhaps best summarized by John Tyndall: "Taking him for all and all, I think it will be conceded that Michael Faraday was the greatest experimental philosopher the world has ever seen; and I will add the opinion, that the progress of future research will tend, not to dim or to diminish, but to enhance and glorify the labors of this mighty investigator."

In fact, Faraday's research was so original he was driven to create a new lexicon. For example, in collaboration with the versatile William Whewell he coined terms widely used in electrochemistry including "electrode," "anode," "cathode," "electrolyte," "ion," "anion," and "cation." Faraday also invented the monikers "magnetic field," "dielectric," and "diamagnetism."

Michael Faraday and Joseph Henry also had foibles. They both displayed pettiness towards Samuel F.B. Morse, inventor of the telegraph. Faraday would not respond to a letter from Morse because he saw him as a mere merchant rather than a true scientist, an ironic bit of snobbery, given his own treatment at the hands of Lady Davy. Henry was annoyed by Alfred Vail's book tracing the history of the telegraph because it mentioned him only in connection with electromagnets. Vail, with Morse's agreement, offered to correct a future edition of *The American Electro Magnetic Telegraph*, but Henry did not bother to respond. Instead, he began advising Morse's competitors.

Two electrical units of measure are named after Michael Faraday. The farad (F) is the unit of electrical capacitance. The faraday (Fd) is the unit of electric charge consumed by electrolysis. The unit of inductance, the henry, is named after Joseph Henry. The unit of current, the ampere, honors André-Marie Ampère. And the unit of resistance, the ohm, is a reminder of Georg Simon Ohm.

Michael Faraday retired from research in 1855 but continued lecturing until 1861. He died in his home at Hampton Court, the use of which was granted to him by Queen Victoria, on August 25, 1867 and was buried in Highgate Cemetery, London. Joseph Henry died in 1878 at his Smithsonian Institution living quarters from nephritis, a kidney disorder.

The life of Michael Faraday is an inspiration to everyone who performs laboratory research. His experiments were often ingeniously designed. He was a keen observer and articulate raconteur. Faraday was one of the first scientists to discover deeper truths by seeking unity in nature. When his intuition told him something was true, he would not give up until it was either proved or disproved.

With contributions by Joseph Henry, Faraday's study of capacitance and inductance paved the way to modern electronics. But most of all, Michael Faraday explored the invisible world of force fields, showing the fabric of the universe is richer than previously assumed, and laying the foundation for James Clerk Maxwell's theory predicting radio waves.

Chapter Three
James Clerk Maxwell: Mind over Matter

Maxwell's equations are among the most famous in theoretical science. They are universally praised for their elegance, beauty, and conciseness. They describe the relationship between electric fields, magnetic fields, electric charges, and electric currents. From these equations, Maxwell derived his electromagnetic wave equation predicting radio waves—though the waves would not be discovered for another twenty years. Ironically, the equations presented as Maxwell's in most modern physics textbooks are not the equations as Maxwell wrote them.

If Michael Faraday was the greatest experimentalist, James Clerk Maxwell was surely the finest theoretician of the 19th century. Though Maxwell greatly admired Faraday, the way Maxwell did science was a radical departure from the empiricism of Michael Faraday. Faraday performed experiments in the laboratory in the quest for facts; Maxwell performed experiments in his head in the quest for relationships and order.

In his relatively short life, Maxwell tackled problems ranging from color perception to the behavior of gases to Saturn's rings—repeatedly coming up with brilliant solutions. But he is most remembered for his work on electromagnetism. Maxwell gave precise mathematical expression to Faraday's observations regarding electric and magnetic fields; combined the discoveries of Faraday, Ampère and the German mathematician Carl Friedrich Gauss (whose law describes how to compute an electric field) to create a powerful new theory predicting the propagation of electromagnetic waves in space; and established that light is a form of electromagnetism.

The way that Maxwell developed his electromagnetic field theory flew in the face of what children are taught is the "scientific method." The conventional approach is to propose a hypothesis, design and perform an experiment, observe and record what happens, and analyze the results. Instead, Maxwell started with a few simple relationships based on empirical data, constructed an imaginary mechanical model brimming with spinning cells and idle wheels representing those relationships, and derived new equations. One of the greatest discoveries in the history of science—the equation describing electromagnetic waves—sprang from Maxwell's mechanical fantasy.

What happened after that is something of an enigma. There is no record that Maxwell ever attempted to create and detect electromagnetic waves, nor is there evidence he ever discussed the possibility with others. In fact, the theory Maxwell left behind was obscure, imperfect (as German physicist Gustav Kirchhoff said, "He is a genius, but one has to check his calculations"), and unproven. The task of refining, promoting, and verifying Maxwell's theory was left to a small group of self-styled followers—G.F. FitzGerald, Oliver Heaviside, and Oliver Lodge—who became known as the "Maxwellians." When the German scientist Heinrich Hertz stumbled upon an amazingly simple method of creating and detecting electromagnetic waves in free space, narrowly beating them to the finish line, the Maxwellians cheered.

* * *

James Clerk (pronounced "Clarke") Maxwell was born in Edinburgh, Scotland in 1831. He was the only surviving child of lawyer John Clerk and Frances Cay. His love for theory was not his only contrast with Faraday. James came from a distinguished, land-owning family. His ancestors included baronets and were well represented in the Royal Society. His family assumed the Maxwell name because the estate inherited by his father (Glenlair house at Middlebie near Dumfries) was located in the home district of the Maxwell clan.

James' parents married late; his mother was 40 years old when James was born. They provided a loving home marred only by his mother's early death. James was just eight years old when his mother died after surgery for stomach cancer—surgery performed without the aid of modern anesthetic.

As a child, James was always inquiring into how things worked. "What is the go o' that?" was his favorite question and he would not settle for vague answers. He was fascinated by locks and keys, bell wires, and indoor reflections of sunlight. James' father hired a local tutor but after one year sent James to live with his aunt so he could attend the Edinburgh Academy. There, James received a rough welcome due to his homemade shoes, was nicknamed "Dafty," but slowly won the other boys' respect and even admiration. He was shy and spent much of his time reading, drawing strange diagrams, and making primitive models. Only after a few years did he blossom as a student, winning prizes for his knowledge of mathematics and English verse.

At the age of 14, James wrote a paper on the use of pins, string, and pencil to draw and characterize ovals. It was the first hint of his unusual ability to solve problems using mechanical analogies. Others tackled geometry problems with axioms and proofs; James wanted to see and feel what made an oval an oval. The paper—an extraordinary achievement for a teenager—was read to the Royal Society of Edinburgh.

Three years later, James enrolled at the University of Edinburgh. He studied natural philosophy, mathematics, and logic. He was an outstanding student and wrote two more papers at the age of 18: *The Theory of Rolling Curves* and *The Equilibrium of Elastic Solids*.

Maxwell departed Edinburgh for Peterhouse, the most ancient of the colleges comprising Cambridge University, in 1850. He switched to Trinity College upon realizing it offered better chances of obtaining a fellowship. He was elected to the secretive Cambridge Apostles, an elite debating club boasting many famous alumni.

Maxwell completed considerable work on his electromagnetic equations during his undergraduate years at Trinity. He was encouraged by William Thomson (later Lord Kelvin) to read papers by Faraday and others. Maxwell met Thomson through his father. There were close ties between the two Scottish families; William attended Cambridge about a decade earlier and John Clerk sought his advice about the school.

Thomson was the first scientist to apply rigorous mathematical analysis to Faraday's work and Maxwell read his papers, too. He was particularly intrigued by Thomson's use of mechanical analogies. For example, Thomson showed that equations for static electricity were similar to equations for heat flow.

Maxwell graduated from Trinity in 1853 as "second wrangler" in mathematics (i.e. he scored second best on the examination) and shared the top spot for the coveted Smith's prize. (The "senior wrangler" was Edward John Routh, who later helped develop control theory.) He obtained a fellowship two years later and read his paper *On the Transformation of Surfaces by Bending* to the Cambridge Philosophical Society, following that with a paper entitled *On Faraday's Lines of Force*. These two papers exhibited his profound intellectual powers; he was appointed to the Chair of Natural Philosophy at Marischal College, Aberdeen in northeast Scotland in 1856.

The next episode in Maxwell's career reveals an extraordinary ability to think in mechanical terms. While at Marischal in 1859, Maxwell won the University of Cambridge's Adams prize for his original essay, *On the Stability of Saturn's Rings*. There was very little empirical data to go on. A ring encompassing Saturn was first observed about two centuries earlier; the ring was discovered to be composed of several smaller rings about twenty years later. Maxwell showed that the rings could neither be completely solid nor fluid. He demonstrated that only rings consisting of many small particles could achieve stability—a solid ring rotating about the planet would eventually break up. Maxwell's theory was confirmed more than 100 years later by interplanetary space probes.

Maxwell married Katherine Mary Dewar in 1858. With his wife's assistance, Maxwell investigated color perception and color blindness, acquiring hands-on experience with light, which he later demonstrated is a form of electromagnetism. He devised simple instruments to aid his investigations (though the German scientist Hermann von Helmholtz beat him to the punch by inventing the ophthalmoscope). Maxwell used spinning discs containing various proportions of three primary colors (Red-Green-Blue, or "RGB") which could then be compared to sample colors. This research revealed that all other colors are mixtures of the primary colors. He discovered that mixing pigments is a subtractive process (because pigments reflect light) for which the primary colors are Red-Yellow-Blue (RYB). Maxwell's research also verified Thomas Young's theory that color blindness is the result of missing or non-functioning color receptors on the retina.

Maxwell probed the electromagnetic spectrum even before he knew that light is a type of electromagnetism. He developed the color triangle for describing any color based on four parameters: hue, intensity, brightness, and tint. He is credited with taking the first (though not very practical) color photograph—created out of separate exposures with red, green, and blue filters. Maxwell received the Rumford medal from the Royal Society in 1860 for his work on colors.

Maxwell lost his professorship in 1860 when Marischal College was merged with King's College in Aberdeen. He soon landed a professorship at King's College in London—a modern university with courses on topics such as physics. In 1861, he was elected to the Royal Society. He resigned from King's College in 1865 to spend time at his estate at Glenlair, though he visited London and Cambridge frequently.

Maxwell paved the way to information theory—essential to today's digital radio technology—when he became the first scientist to employ statistics in describing a physical process. Until then, researchers only used statistics to analyze measurement errors. Maxwell's 1866 investigation of the kinetic theory of gases built on the work of Daniel Bernoulli (who described gases as composed of particles moving rapidly in all directions), James Joule (who showed that heat is equivalent to mechanical work), and Rudolf Clausius (who formulated the second law of thermodynamics). Maxwell's innovation was treating the movement of the particles (and the heat associated with it) as statistical phenomena.

The second law of thermodynamics says that the temperature difference between two systems in physical contact will decrease over time. However, Maxwell pointed out that under certain circumstances the second law could be violated. He illustrated this with his now-famous demon paradox: imagine a small creature that can see individual molecules and open and close a door, permitting heat to flow from a cold body to a hot body. Maxwell's point was that the second law of thermodynamics is true in terms of the statistical behavior of a large number of particles, but it is not necessarily true for each individual particle (unlike other scientific "laws" that must be obeyed in each and every instance.) The theory was further developed by Ludwig Boltzmann and is now known as the Maxwell-Boltzmann kinetic theory of gases.

Maxwell's demon was obviously himself. He gained insights about nature's hidden mechanism by visualizing himself inside the machine. In 1859, he imagined what it would be like to orbit the planet Saturn. In 1866, he fantasized about inhabiting the molecular-scale world of gases. Once he could see the particles moving in all directions up close, it became clear to him that the behavior of gases on a macro level can only be explained in statistical terms.

It would be hard to overstate the significance of Maxwell's statistical approach. Normal science assumes nature operates according to immutable laws; Maxwell's suggestion that nature is sometimes ruled by chance was heresy. It led to a huge controversy when it was applied to the behavior of subatomic particles; Albert Einstein responded with words to the effect of "God does not play dice with the universe."

It makes perfect sense, however, to think about the transmission of information over a radio channel in statistical terms. What are the chances that a message sent over an imperfect channel will arrive intact? And what can be done to improve those chances? Information theory deals with such questions daily.

In 1871, Maxwell returned to academia, accepting the Chair of Experimental Physics at Cambridge. Thanks to the financial support of the Duke of Devonshire, he was able to build a well-equipped laboratory. Over the next few years, Maxwell put the final touches on the theory of electromagnetism he had been developing since the 1850s.

* * *

In 1845, William Thomson developed a mathematical representation of Faraday's discovery that induction occurs through a medium rather than as a result of action-at-a-distance. Maxwell aimed even higher, setting himself the lofty goal of describing electricity generally in the simplest and most precise manner possible. Inspired by Thomson's analysis based on heat flow, Maxwell made his first attempt at reducing nature to matter and motion. In his 1855 paper *On Faraday's Lines of Force*, he represented Faraday's lines of force as tubes containing an incompressible fluid.

Maxwell was not suggesting that electric and magnetic lines of force are caused by incompressible fluids. He was suggesting that a mechanical analogy might help us better understand how lines of force behave. He knew it was highly speculative. But he also knew that all theories are speculative—and that some of them work.

Maxwell took an even bigger step in 1861 with his paper *On Physical Lines of Force*, introducing the idea that electric and magnetic lines of force are caused by imaginary machinery built out of common components (spinning cells and idle wheels). This physical analogy not only enabled Maxwell to keep his theory grounded in matter and motion, it guided him in the development of precise mathematical equations. To wit, Maxwell based his equations describing electric and magnetic lines of force on the motions of spinning cells and idle wheels comprising his fanciful model.

Though Maxwell's mechanical model was fictitious, a great deal of thought went into its composition and structure. The model had to accurately represent the forces between electric charges; the forces between magnetic poles; the creation of a magnetic field by a current; and the creation of a current by a changing magnetic field. The model also had to reflect Maxwell's belief that electric and magnetic fields are properties of the medium rather than just effects of the objects.

To create the model, Maxwell borrowed from William John Macquorn Rankine's molecular vortex theory. Rankine's theory was that elastic solids and liquids are composed of circulating vortices that adapt to their environment. Though his vortex theory was highly speculative, Rankine succeeded at discovering the relationships between temperature, pressure, and density in gases.

First, Maxwell filled space with vortices (spinning cells) representing magnetic energy as rotational energy. However, he quickly realized that in a chain of gears, each member transmits counter motion to its immediate neighbors. In order for his model to work, all of the vortices had to spin in the same direction. Maxwell solved the problem by inserting idle wheels between the vortices. The idle wheels represented electric current and also served as flywheels, resisting changes in current and helping to explain the difference between conductors and insulators. This allowed Maxwell to incorporate electromagnetism and induction in his model. Maxwell accounted for electrostatics by attributing elasticity—the ability to store energy like a wound spring—to the vortices and idle wheels.

Maxwell never believed that his mechanical model accurately depicted nature's hidden mechanism. "The conception of a particle having its motion connected with that of a vortex by perfect rolling contact may appear somewhat awkward. I do not bring it forward as a mode of connexion existing in nature, or even as that which I would willingly assent to as an electrical hypothesis. It is, however, a mode of connexion which is mechanically conceivable, and easily investigated, and it serves to bring out the actual mechanical connexions between the known electromagnetic phenomena: so that I venture to say that any one who understands the provisional and temporary nature of this hypothesis, will find himself rather helped than hindered by it in his search after the true interpretation of the phenomena." As Maxwell explained on another occasion, he found mechanical models useful in "reducing to order" the facts.

That brings us to one of the most momentous discoveries—or was it an invention?—in the history of science. In the 1861 paper based on his mechanical model, Maxwell introduced the "displacement current" as a correction to Ampère's circuital law. Ampère's law relates the current density in a wire to the magnetic field it produces. Maxwell realized that, in a changing electric field, atoms in a dielectric (or the ether) are stretched and that this motion constitutes an additional current contributing to the magnetic field.

The displacement current was a breakthrough in solving the electromagnetic riddle. Faraday's law says that a changing magnetic field produces an electric field. Maxwell's corrected version of Ampère's law says that a changing electric field creates a magnetic field. Taken together, the two laws predict the propagation of electromagnetic waves in free space. It was the link that no one even knew was missing.

The displacement current is most readily illustrated by a capacitor. A capacitor is an electric component consisting of two conducting surfaces separated by a dielectric (i.e. non-conducting) material. When a source of direct current is connected across a capacitor, there is no current flow through the capacitor, but the resulting electric field stretches the atoms of the dielectric, with positive and negative charges leaning in opposite directions. Maxwell believed this reorientation of charges represented a type of current, which he dubbed the "displacement current," and that like a current in a wire loop it generates a magnetic field.

Maxwell assumed that something similar happens in the ether he and others believed permeates space. Therefore, even in seemingly empty space a changing magnetic field creates an electric field, which displaces charged particles, which in turn creates a magnetic field, and the process repeats ad infinitum, resulting in the propagation of electromagnetic waves. Maxwell also noticed that the calculated propagation speed for such electromagnetic waves is the same as the observed speed of light. Therefore, he concluded, light must be an electromagnetic wave phenomenon.

There is just one problem. Experiments conducted years later to prove that the ether exists failed to detect any of its anticipated effects. The most famous was the Michelson-Morley experiment which found no evidence of an "ether wind" caused by the motion of the earth around the sun (at about 108,000 km/hour). Though a counter theory was proposed to explain this anomaly—namely that an object as massive as the earth drags the ether along with it—other experiments failed to discover evidence of an "ether drag."

However, if there is no ether, then how can there be a displacement current in otherwise empty space? Today, most physicists accept Maxwell's displacement current as a necessary component of the equations describing the propagation of electromagnetic waves in free space, even though there is no movement of charged particles in a vacuum. What's important is not whether nature's underlying structure includes vortices and idle wheels or the luminiferous ether, but whether the theory makes accurate predictions.

The evolution of science from Newton to Faraday to Maxwell brings us full circle. Newton's law of universal gravitation assumed action-at-a-distance, a necessary but imponderable force. Faraday was repulsed by ideas such as action-at-a-distance because they defy empirical investigation. Maxwell built his theory on facts uncovered by Faraday and others, adding his displacement current as a necessary correction. Given that the ether does not exist, however, Maxwell's displacement current turns out to be no more comprehensible than action-at-a-distance.

How did Maxwell come to propose the displacement current? There are competing explanations. One theory is that he simply generalized Ampère's circuital law to account for conditions not anticipated by Ampère, such as open circuits. Another theory is that he noticed a lack of symmetry between Faraday's law, which said that a changing magnetic field creates an electric field (or current) and Ampère's uncorrected circuital law describing how an electric current in a loop of wire creates a magnetic field. The existing laws did not show how a changing electric field produces a magnetic field.

Historians Daniel M. Siegel and Bruce J. Hunt believe that while Maxwell may have wanted to generalize Ampère's law and was (later) pleased by the symmetry in his equations, it was his mechanical model that drove him to propose the displacement current. When Maxwell attributed elasticity to his vortices in order to depict electrostatic polarization, he realized any distortion of the vortices also represented a sort of current. Maxwell's imaginary mechanical model led to an imaginary current; together, they led to a theory that has proved exceptionally useful and accurate.

In 1864, Maxwell presented his famous equations in a paper entitled *On a Dynamical Theory of the Electromagnetic Field*. He elaborated on his theory in 1873 with the publication of his 400+ page textbook *A Treatise on Electricity and Magnetism*.

Though Maxwell admired Michael Faraday, he subscribed to a very different philosophy. Maxwell believed our knowledge of the physical world is fundamentally knowledge of relationships between objects. Observations and measurements can only provide clues regarding underlying processes. Theories, requiring both analysis and imagination, are needed to illuminate experimental results.

A better sense of Maxwell's philosophy can be gleaned from an excerpt from his 1860 inaugural lecture at King's College: "Last of all we have the Electrical and Magnetic sciences, which treat as certain phenomena of attraction, heat, light, and chemical action, depending on the conditions of matter, of which we have as yet only a partial and provisional knowledge. An immense mass of facts has been collected and these have been reduced to order, and expressed as the results of a number of experimental laws, but the form under which these laws are ultimately to appear as deduced from central principles is as yet uncertain. The present generation has no right to complain of the great discoveries already made, as if they left no room for

Beginning in 1860, however, Maxwell went into full retreat. He concluded that the underlying mechanical universe is unknowable. However, he may have deceived himself. According to French scientist and philosopher Pierre Duhem, by the time Maxwell wrote his *Treatise on Electricity and Magnetism* he had traded-in his mechanical model for a new model—a model comprised of mathematical symbols.

Maxwell started with laws obtained by other investigators (Faraday, Ampère, and Gauss). Then he constructed and enhanced an imaginary mechanical model to illustrate those laws. Using mathematics, he derived an equation describing how electromagnetic waves propagate through space, and presented compelling evidence that light consists of electromagnetic waves.

There was just one problem. He never proved it.

Fortunately, a trio of admirers championed his theory of the electromagnetic field after he died. Oliver Heaviside consolidated Maxwell's twenty equations into four equations and recast them in modern vector form. In fact, what textbooks now call "Maxwell's equations" are actually Heaviside's renditions. The reclusive Heaviside also helped develop transmission line theory (applicable to antenna feed lines), predicted the existence of an ionized layer of the atmosphere (eventually exploited for long-distance radio communications), and invented a number of important mathematical techniques. His only problem was that he was afraid to leave the house; he corresponded with other scientists and wrote many technical papers, but refused to attend scientific gatherings.

George Francis FitzGerald was an Irish professor who extended and enhanced Maxwell's theory. His friend Oliver Lodge generated and detected electromagnetic waves over wires.

But it was Heinrich Hertz, breaking with the action-at-a-distance paradigm still dominant in Continental Europe, who first generated radio waves in free space in 1888, confirming the theory of the dynamical electromagnetic field and inducting Maxwell into the pantheon of history's greatest scientific thinkers.

James Clerk Maxwell died from stomach cancer, the same disease that claimed his mother, in 1879 at the age of 48. His theory predicting radio waves assures him an exalted place in the history of wireless. Yet he accomplished something even more important. He showed how ideas borrowed from other disciplines, doubtful assumptions (such as the luminiferous ether), and even weird thought experiments can lead to great discoveries. In doing so, he taught us that scientists must remain free to explore all ideas—even those that are unpopular, crazy sounding, or discredited.

Chapter Four

The Wave Makers

Two scientists working independently in different countries simultaneously produced experimental proof of Maxwell's electromagnetic field theory. One earned history's equivalent of an honorable mention. The other became an international celebrity practically overnight.

Responding to a competition sponsored by the Berlin Academy of Science, the young German physicist Heinrich Hertz set out only to prove obscure effects associated with Maxwell's electromagnetic field theory. Thanks to a combination of ambition, a sharp eye, and serendipity he accomplished much more. Hertz discovered radio waves in late 1887—nine years after the death of Maxwell.

Hertz was not the first person to create radio waves. Anyone who produced an electric spark did that. Nor was he first to detect radio waves. Luigi Galvani did that in 1781—though without realizing it. Hertz, however, was first to discover that sparks can be used to generate and detect electromagnetic waves traveling through the air or a vacuum—what we now call "free space." Working at radio frequencies, he demonstrated wave properties including wavelength, reflection, interference, and refraction.

That was just the start. By creating and detecting radio waves, Hertz discovered the scientific equivalent of a new continent. More precisely, he landed on the coast of a vast scientific wilderness: the electromagnetic spectrum.

Think of the electromagnetic spectrum as a very long ruler with two scales. One of the scales, frequency, increases to the right. It measures the number of complete waves or cycles per second. The other scale, wavelength, increases to the left. It measures the length of a complete sinusoidal wave with its characteristic peak (crest) and trough.

The electromagnetic spectrum extends infinitely in both directions. Practically, we are only familiar with a finite stretch—though it's still fairly long. We start at the low end of the frequency scale (the high end of the wavelength scale) with radio waves. This region includes AM radio, FM radio, and broadcast television. Above the radio portion (in frequency) are microwaves. A microwave oven uses frequencies in this range. Surprisingly, cellular telephone and wireless LANs are also technically in the microwave region.

Microwave frequencies span a long stretch of spectrum. Somewhere along the line they morph into infrared light waves. Continuing up the spectrum, we come to visible light, which occupies a rather narrow patch. Above that are ultraviolet light waves. Even higher in frequency are x-rays. The highest frequency electromagnetic waves are gamma waves.

While any conceivable wavelength can be located within the electromagnetic spectrum, not all waves are electromagnetic. For example, sound waves produced by the human larynx are mechanical vibrations. However, electrical signals can be produced at audio frequencies and converted to sound waves by a loudspeaker.

Hertz' discovery of the electromagnetic spectrum was immediately hailed by scientists outside his native Germany. But Hertz was less excited about it than we would expect. He believed radio waves were important only because they corroborated Maxwell's theory. Most of his peers could see no practical applications. Hertz himself remarked "It's of no use whatsoever …this is just an experiment that proves Maestro Maxwell was right - we just have these mysterious electromagnetic waves that we cannot see with the naked eye. But they are there." The scientific community's blind spot—or was it animosity towards anyone who dared to commercialize science?—created opportunities for entrepreneurs such as Guglielmo Marconi.

The British physicist and Maxwellian Oliver Lodge produced and observed electromagnetic waves at the same time, but his experiments attracted little attention. Lodge's setup was unlikely to captivate anyone: he created and detected electromagnetic waves traveling along wires, which was like showing waves in water compared to Hertz' magnificent demonstration of invisible electromagnetic waves traveling through the air. Like Hertz, Lodge had confirmed Maxwell's theory, yet instead of ensuring his place in history by dashing off a paper he promptly left on vacation—oblivious to the risk of losing priority.

Lodge still could have made a convincing case that he deserved equal credit with Hertz. When Lodge was asked a few years earlier to deliver lectures on lightning rods, he began experimenting with sparks from Leyden jars, and soon found evidence of "electric waves." Ironically, his friend and fellow Maxwellian G.F. FitzGerald was first to draw the world's attention to Hertz' experiments, which produced similar evidence. Oliver Heaviside declared that the two sets of experiments were essentially equivalent. But deep inside, Lodge knew he didn't have a chance: Hertz published first and his experiments were more appealing to the imagination.

* * *

Though Oliver Lodge came from a prosperous family, his journey to become a physics professor followed an unconventional path. He grew up in the township of Penkhull in the Staffordshire pottery district, where his father built a thriving business supplying materials to potteries such as Royal Doulton, Wedgwood and Spode. It was Oliver Sr.'s fond hope that one day Oliver Jr. would take the reigns particularly since, in Oliver Sr.'s estimation, there was little prospect of making a living as a scientist. He wasn't entirely wrong; science in Lodge's youth was somewhat like poetry-writing is today. Oliver Sr. gave his son a basic education, but like many English boys Oliver Jr. found the experience at Newport Grammar School in Shropshire and subsequently the rectory in Combs abusive; students were routinely caned for failing to memorize their lessons.

Lodge experienced his first break at age 15 when he visited his Aunt Anne in London and attended lectures by Michael Faraday's successor, John Tyndall. Upon returning home, Lodge took classes at the Wedgwood Institute, and did exceptionally well on some exams, particularly in physics. Thanks to a lucky sequence of events, Lodge was admitted to an educational program for teachers in London, despite the fact that he was not a teacher. There Lodge worked under (but had little contact with) the fierce evolutionist Thomas Huxley. He was offered 200 pounds to teach physics and chemistry at a school in St. Heliers, Jersey but was forced to decline in favor of his father's more lucrative business. Even though the offer was too small, it was an eye-opener for his father, who didn't think there was any money to be made in science.

At age 20, Lodge and his younger brother Alfred took advantage of a program enabling students to earn bachelor's degrees just by passing the requisite exams. After failing botany and zoology on the first try, Lodge earned his B.Sc. in 1873 at age 22.

In rebellion against his father, Oliver enrolled at University College, London in 1874. Unsure of how he would defray his living expenses, he was offered 50 pounds per year as a laboratory assistant, and also wrote papers for Philosophical Magazine. He earned his D.Sc. in 1877.

In 1876 at a British Association for the Advancement of Science meeting in Glasgow, Lodge's paper on stress in a dielectric medium followed by another on thermo-electric phenomena elicited a long and humorous letter from James Clerk Maxwell that, unfortunately, has not survived. In 1878 at the British Association meeting in Dublin, Lodge met G.F. FitzGerald, who became a life long friend and collaborator.

In fact, it was FitzGerald who sparked Lodge's interest in electromagnetic waves. In 1880, FitzGerald wrote a paper originally titled "On the Impossibility of Originating Wave Disturbances in the Ether by Electromagnetic Forces." The title was quickly revised to "On the Possibility..." when FitzGerald realized he had been too pessimistic. FitzGerald's two 1883 papers, "The Energy Lost by Radiation from Alternating Electric Currents" and "A Method of Producing Electromagnetic Disturbances of Comparatively Short Wave-Lengths," were important contributions to the fledgling science of wireless. FitzGerald theorized that electromagnetic waves could be generated by discharging condensers through low-resistance circuits. In other words, he thought that relatively violent electrical action was needed to catapult electromagnetic waves into the ether.

After failing to win the chair in applied mathematics at Owens College at Manchester, Lodge applied for the newly established physics chair in Liverpool. On the strength of testimonials, Lodge won the chair without an interview in 1881. According to Lodge, one of the college's governors later joked that never again would he make such an appointment without first seeing the candidate.

It wasn't the ideal chair for Oliver Lodge, but at least it was a chair. University College, Liverpool was primarily a medical school. The new physics lab was to be housed in a former lunatic asylum. Encouraged to equip his laboratory as he judged best, Lodge requested funds to tour European labs. He visited Berlin, Leipzig, Chemnitz, Dresden, Prague, Vienna, Wurzburg, Heidelberg, Bonn, and Paris. He hoped to meet the great Helmholtz, but was shuffled off to a young and unknown demonstrator, Heinrich Hertz, with whom he soon became friends.

In Lodge's day, only a short distance separated academic research from applied technology. (There weren't many corporate research and development labs standing in the way back then.) For example, Lodge first witnessed a demonstration of the telephone when Lord Kelvin brought one back from the United States. Shortly thereafter, Alexander Graham Bell crossed the Atlantic to speak about his invention; Lodge was particularly impressed by his "beautiful enunciation." After laying hands on one of

Edison's new phonographs—an extremely primitive device—Lodge gave a public demonstration.

Most of Lodge's early papers dealt with electricity. He became very interested in self-induction and showed how it could be applied to motorcar ignition, lightning protection, and the tuning of electric waves. His moving coil design for loudspeakers was a significant improvement and is still used today. Nevertheless, Lodge clearly perceived himself as a theorist rather than an experimenter or inventor.

Lodge's research concerning the efficacy of lightning rods was particularly first rate and led to his discovery of electromagnetic waves traveling over wires. Contrary to the popular belief that lightning seeks the path of lowest resistance to earth, Lodge determined through his experiments with Leyden jars that oscillatory discharges seek the path of least reactance (opposition to the flow of alternating current). In other words, lightning is not necessarily attracted to a metal rod on top of a building even when it is connected via a heavy wire to earth.

(Lodge believed that lightning, like Leyden jar discharges, is oscillatory. That isn't quite true: lightning bolts consist of pulsating direct current, as Lodge realized later, but still seeks the path of least reactance.)

Lodge concluded that the only reliable way to protect a building or any other object from lightning would be to place it in a solid metal or fine wire frame enclosure with a ceiling, four walls, and a floor. This was an important and disturbing finding considering that the British Post Office, alone, deployed an estimated half-million lightning rods.

How did Lodge reach the conclusion that lightning rods don't necessarily work? He did an experiment in which the Leyden jar was offered two alternative discharge paths. He observed that the current often chose a small air gap (causing a spark) over a wire loop. In other words, the discharge actually preferred what would normally be considered the high resistance path over the low resistance path. He also noticed that sparks sometimes appeared at the lip of the Leyden jar—sparks he believed were caused by reflected energy. (Just as light waves are reflected by a mirror, he suspected that electric waves are reflected by certain wire arrangements.)

Experimenting further, Lodge found that he could maximize the intensity of the spark across the air gap by positioning the gap in specific locations on the wire loop. That suggested electric waves were involved for a couple of reasons.

Thomas Young's double slit experiment showed that two wave fronts of light interfere with each other to produce a series of light and dark bands.

The light bands are places where the two waves combine constructively—where one wave's peak combines with the other wave's peak. The dark bands are places where they combine destructively—where one wave's peak is cancelled out by the other wave's trough. The variations in spark intensity suggested something similar was going on with the Leyden jar discharges.

Lodge also knew that the Leyden jar provides capacitance and the wire loop provides inductance. He soon realized that a circuit may behave like a tuning fork. Namely, it will vibrate naturally at a certain frequency—a frequency determined by the amount of capacitance and inductance in the circuit. When he positioned the air gap to obtain the maximum intensity sparks, it meant the air gap circuit was resonant (or as he liked to say, was in "syntony") with the Leyden jar discharges.

William Thomson was first to observe that Leyden jar discharges oscillate. However, Thomson was skeptical of Maxwell's theory. As a fan of Maxwell's theory, Lodge speculated that Leyden jars might produce "ether waves." Lodge studied discharges through long wires and soon discovered evidence of such waves. For example, in a darkened room a glow could be observed in certain parts of a long wire loop but not others—a phenomenon Lodge attributed to "standing waves" caused by the collision between direct waves and their reflections.

Lodge immediately saw an analogy with sound waves. He measured wavelengths and recognized that wavelength multiplied by frequency equals the speed of propagation. He suspected (as had Maxwell) that his invisible electromagnetic waves and light were different forms of the same thing.

Lodge sent an article about his experiments to Philosophical Magazine in the summer of 1888. The article was titled "Lightning Conductors" but clearly identified and discussed electric waves. However, news of Hertz' experiments demonstrating electromagnetic waves dominated the fall British Association meeting. Hertz found the same kind of evidence as Lodge—nodes and loops caused by interference between direct and reflected waves—but without employing wires.

Unfortunately, Lodge had a knack for eluding fame and fortune. For example, Lodge discovered that high frequency sparks do not trigger frog leg contractions. (High frequency currents tend to flow along the surface of a conductor.) But it was the showman Nikola Tesla who became famous for demonstrating that high frequency sparks are harmless. Lodge also demonstrated wireless signaling prior to Marconi, but he neglected to use the Morse code to drive the point home to his audience.

Lodge's reticent personality is illustrated by an incident at a public meeting. The British physicist J.J. Thomson was demonstrating Leyden jar-driven vacuum tube discharges. However, Thomson couldn't get his jars to spark. Lodge knew from experience that it was easier to create a spark between two oppositely charged jars than from a single jar. He told one of Thomson's assistants what to do during a break—instead of offering advice in front of the audience. Thomson later wrote a paper on the phenomenon.

There was another, even more self-defeating side to Lodge's personality. Though a careful and honest experimenter, Lodge had a tendency to believe in highly speculative forces. For example, Lodge conjectured that electricity stimulates growth. He and his friend George Newman tried to sell farmers a system for surrounding chickens and crops with current-carrying wires. He was also a staunch supporter of the ether hypothesis—though in that regard he was in much better company (FitzGerald had an almost mystical belief in ether). However, his interest in psychical phenomenon hurt his credibility. Today, he is remembered in some circles for promising to communicate from beyond the grave.

Perhaps we should allow Lodge some slack. He was the first to admit he was not a strict empiricist. He searched for hidden causes and sometimes found them. For example, he found evidence of electromagnetic waves outside the visible light spectrum. He suggested the use of cryogenics to reduce electrical resistance. And he was a pioneer of radio astronomy. Besides, Britain's Society for Psychical Research had several distinguished members in Lodge's day including Arthur Balfour (later prime minister), American psychologist William James, and physicist Sir William Crookes.

To his credit, Lodge accepted the consequences when experiments failed to support favorite hypotheses. For example, Maxwell's theory appeared to depend on the existence of the ether. Lodge understood that the results of the Michelson-Morley experiment (showing that the speed of light is the same in all directions) could not be explained unless the ether was somehow dragged along with the earth. He devised an experiment to detect "ether drag."

He constructed a machine with twin one-meter steel disks spinning at 4000 revolutions per minute. Then he projected two beams of light between the disks and observed the interference pattern. If the velocity of either light beam changed, the interference pattern would change. Nothing he did—such as changing the direction of rotation of one of the disks—affected the interference pattern. Though he hoped to find evidence of ether drag, he freely admitted there was none.

Unintentionally, Oliver Lodge helped end the dominance of mechanistic theories. Until the early 20th century, it was assumed that all waves—including electromagnetic waves—must travel through a medium. But if there is no ether, then light from the stars propagates through empty space. It was a revelation that demanded a whole new way of looking at the universe—a perspective more open to highly abstract theories such as quantum physics.

Lodge's ether drag experiments also laid the foundation for the theory of relativity. The Michelson-Morley experiment showed that the earth does not move with respect to the ether. Lodge showed that the ether is not dragged along by large masses. Was there any way to salvage the ether hypothesis? FitzGerald and Hendrik Lorentz suggested, independently of each other, a conspiracy of natural forces to conceal the effects of the motion of the ether; namely, objects contract just enough to offset changes in the velocity of light. Einstein saw this as a purely ad hoc explanation; his hypothesis that the speed of light is constant engendered a much more elegant theory.

When Hertz was widely acclaimed for demonstrating the propagation of electromagnetic waves in free space, Lodge took it in stride. He never complained that he deserved equal or even partial credit. When he received the Rumford medal in 1898 (as did Faraday and Maxwell before him) for "researches on radiation and on the relations between matter and ether," the president noted in his address that Lodge would have discovered electromagnetic waves in free space had not Hertz done so first. Years earlier, Lodge pointed out that electromagnetic waves are "ridiculously easy to produce" but not as easy to detect. And Lodge observed that Leyden jar waves also travel in free space; the wires serve only to guide them.

Lodge may have been first to prove Maxwell's theory, but Hertz was first to demonstrate the magical propagation of electromagnetic waves through the ether. Oliver Lodge did not always finish second, however. While Hertz died young, Lodge lived a long life. And there is one achievement no one can ever take away from him—an achievement for which he eventually asserted his rights. Lodge realized that by setting transmitters and receivers to specific frequencies he could avoid interference and improve efficiency. He called it "syntony." We call it "tuning the dial" (radio) and "channel surfing" (television).

* * *

Heinrich Hertz was born in 1857 in Hamburg, Germany. He was the son of Gustav Ferdinand Hertz, a convert from Judaism to Christianity. Heinrich excelled in science, Arabic, and Sanskrit at the University of Hamburg. Initially, he planned on a career in engineering, but soon realized he was more interested in physics. He continued his studies in Dresden, Munich and Berlin. He studied under two of the great scientists of his day, Gustav R. Kirchhoff and Hermann von Helmholtz, and received his PhD in 1880.

Helmholtz is an extraordinary figure, claimed as founding father by both physicists and neuroscientists. However, Helmholtz may be remembered most for proposing conservation of energy and inventing the ophthalmoscope. Hertz was particularly influenced by Helmholtz's rejection of both fields (Maxwell) and particles (Weber) as abstractions; Helmholtz believed instead that there are only interactions between laboratory objects. In addition to Hertz, Helmholtz's protégés included Ludwig Boltzmann (famous for his work in statistical thermodynamics), Albert Michelson (who measured the speed of light), and Max Planck (a pioneer of quantum physics).

With Helmholtz' encouragement, the young Heinrich Hertz entered a competition sponsored by the Berlin Academy of Science's Philosophical Faculty. The question was to determine whether electric current possesses mass. It was a profound philosophical question disguised as a laboratory experiment. The contestants were being asked to determine whether an electric current involves matter flow. Weber's theory said it does; Helmholtz believed it does not.

Hertz quickly realized he was unlikely to prove that currents have zero mass. Instead, he planned to determine the upper limit of any mass, which in turn could be used to calculate more easily detected effects, the absence of which would at least cast doubt on the proposition that current possesses mass.

The Philosophical Faculty suggested experiments based on inductive coupling between two spiral wires carrying currents flowing in opposite directions. Hertz concluded the margin of error associated with such a setup was too great, and replaced the spirals with rectilinear circuits. He also designed an ingenious commutator (a rotating disk configured as a switch for rapidly and repeatedly reversing current direction) to help extract the desired effects from the background noise.

In 1879, Hertz won the prize for his paper "Kinetic Energy of Electricity in Motion." He did not come up with a decisive answer, but he demonstrated considerable skill in conceiving and modifying experiments and apparatuses, and his results tended to support Helmholtz's view. The experience played a subtle but important role in directing Hertz' future research efforts. It convinced him to concentrate more on obtaining novel results and less on experiments requiring precise measurements. Hertz was acutely aware—without knowing he would die young—that each of us has limited time to achieve anything of significance.

After obtaining his PhD (his dissertation was titled "Induction in Rotating Spheres") he worked for three years as assistant professor to Helmholtz in the physical laboratory of the Berlin Academy conducting research on the contact of elastic solids, hardness, evaporation, and electric discharge in gases.

In 1879, the Berlin Academy offered a prize to the experimenter who could provide "decisive experimental proof" of the relationship between electromagnetism and polarization in dielectric materials. The year before, the Academy offered a prize for determining if current has mass—an almost impossible goal given available knowledge and tools. Now the Academy was essentially asking contestants to prove Maxwell's theory (namely, demonstrate Maxwell's displacement current). At Helmholtz' urging, Hertz put together a proposal but decided not to proceed because he could not think of any experiments likely to succeed. At the time, Hertz possessed only meager knowledge of Maxwell's theory.

In 1883 Hertz went to Kiel University to become a privatdozent (a private tutor) where he began studying Maxwell's electromagnetic field theory in earnest. About two years later, frustrated by the lack of a well-equipped laboratory, he took a position at the Karlsruhe Technical High School. Now he began to develop some ideas about how to prove Maxwell's theory; namely, he identified the approximate wavelengths best suited to the task and possible methods of measuring their velocity. However, he suffered from depression for much of 1885—until he met Elizabeth Doll, who he married in the summer of the following year.

Hertz found a pair of Riess (also known as Knochenhauer) spirals in his new laboratory. They were made of heavy wire twisted to form a spiral and terminating in two metal balls brought together to form a spark gap. He decided to use them to demonstrate electromagnetic induction to his students. He would show that current in one spiral induced a current in the other (indicated by a spark across its spark gap). He was surprised to discover that even a small Leyden jar was sufficient to drive the primary spiral and induce a current in the secondary spiral. Though he didn't quite know it at the time, his setup consisted of an exciter of electromagnetic waves (the Leyden jar plus the primary spiral) and a receiver (the secondary spiral). Hertz knew that Leyden jars can produce oscillating discharges. That had been demonstrated by Joseph Henry in 1842. In 1853, William Thomson showed that these oscillations are caused by capacitance and inductance. Then in 1858 Berend Wilhelm Feddersen captured oscillating currents in the act with a spark gap, a rapidly revolving mirror, and a camera. What Hertz probably didn't know was that G.F. FitzGerald suggested electromagnetic waves could be produced by discharging a Leyden jar across a spark gap; Hertz did not begin corresponding with the Maxwellians until after publication of his paper confirming Maxwell's theory.

Hertz was puzzled by the fact that even a small Leyden jar driving the primary spiral produced sparks in the secondary spiral. The current seemed too weak for ordinary induction. He began to investigate by modifying the primary spiral. He unwound the heavy wire and broke it in the center, producing a straight wire with a spark gap in the middle. It was still able to induce sparks in the secondary spiral. That was even more suggestive that something other than induction was at work.

He began to probe the straight-wire spark gap using a Riess spark micrometer—a small, adjustable spark gap. The Riess micrometer was essentially a primitive voltmeter. By attaching the two legs of the Reiss micrometer circuit to points along the straight-wire spark gap, he could adjust the gap until it just began to spark. That would give him a relative measure of the voltage between the two points.

There was just one problem: no matter where he connected the Riess micrometer, he couldn't get the sparks to go away. So he tried detaching one leg of the micrometer circuit from the straight-wire spark gap, but even that did not eliminate the sparks. When he detached both legs, the sparks persisted.

At first he attributed the sparks to familiar causes: the electrostatic effect and electromagnetic induction. But when he moved the detached circuit about five feet away, he found that the sparks were just as strong. That ruled out the electrostatic effect because it diminishes very rapidly with distance.

It wasn't until months later that Hertz realized he was witnessing the propagation of electromagnetic waves. After a false start, he discovered in December, 1887 that whatever force was causing sparks in the detached circuit it traveled at a finite velocity. Hertz began to see the detached circuit, which he called the Nebenkreis, as a resonant circuit that oscillated in response to electric waves produced by the straight-wire spark gap, which he now perceived as a spark-switched oscillator.

The moment of discovery came on Christmas Eve 1887 when he reoriented the Nebenkreis to eliminate induction. He now understood he was witnessing the propagation of electromagnetic waves. He proceeded to demonstrate that the invisible waves behave very much like light.

Hertz' paper "On Very Rapid Electric Oscillations" describes his experiments. He replaced the straight-wire spark gap with two metal rods with spheres attached to their opposite ends. He replaced the Leyden jar with a Ruhmkorff coil—a powerful induction coil equipped with an automatic interrupter to produce a continuous train of large sparks. And he replaced the secondary spiral with a circular or rectangular heavy wire with a spark gap.

The Ruhmkorff coil feeding the metal rod spark gap was his electromagnetic wave generator. The wire ring spark gap was his electromagnetic wave detector. He quickly discovered he could detect radio waves—signified by a spark in the wire ring spark gap—from across the room. He studied how changes in the detector's size and configuration affected resonance. That is, he configured the detector to maximize the sparks.

As he continued to experiment, Hertz made yet another serendipitous discovery. To facilitate viewing small sparks, he sometimes placed his detector inside a darkened case. He found, however, that when he moved the detector inside the case the sparks became noticeably smaller. Successively removing parts of the case, he found the only part that affected spark size was the one that screened the spark gap from the exciter. He concluded, correctly, that ultraviolet light from the exciter made the detector's spark gap more conductive. Hertz discovered the photoelectric effect[3], but decided not to interrupt his current research to pursue it.

(Long before Hertz, natural philosophers used prisms to discover that the light spectrum extends above and below visible light. They knew that infrared light is situated below visible red and could be detected with a special prism and thermometer. And they knew that ultraviolet light blackened silver nitrate more rapidly than violet light.)

It was an ironic discovery because Hertz accepted the Maxwellian view that light is a wave phenomenon; the photoelectric effect demonstrates the particle-like properties of light. Today, it's simply accepted that light displays wave behavior in some situations and particle behavior in others.

---

[3] The photoelectric effect is used by light sensors, solar cells, and many other devices.

Hertz went on to study the propagation of electromagnetic waves through space as described in his 1888 paper "On the Action of a Rectilinear Electric Oscillation on a Neighbouring Circuit." Using detectors equipped with adjustable spark gaps, he was able to measure the maximum spark length, sometimes with the aid of a microscope, and used this information in turn to plot the relative radiation strength at different locations and with different orientations. He found that his electromagnetic waves obeyed the same power law that governs light. Namely, that the power per unit area is inversely proportional to the square of the distance.

Next, Hertz provided experimental evidence that the velocity of electromagnetic waves in air is the same as that of light in a paper titled "On the Velocity of Propagation of Electro-dynamic Actions." Hertz understood that he could obtain the velocity by multiplying the wavelength (which he could determine by doubling the measured crest-to-crest distance of standing waves) by the frequency (which he could calculate from the capacitance and inductance). He came up with a figure of 200,000 km per second; the actual number is closer to 300,000 km per second. Some attribute the difference to interference caused by reflections in his laboratory, while others suggest his capacitance measurements were erroneous. Since the equipment he used was not preserved, we may never be certain.

In his paper entitled "On Electro-dynamic Waves and their Reflection," Hertz described interference phenomena caused by reflections off a large zinc plate. More specifically, he explained that when direct waves meet reflected waves, they produce stationary waves (now called "standing waves") with nodes and loops. Standing waves could be demonstrated by moving the detector between the exciter and reflecting plate and observing that in certain locations the sparks disappear while in other spots they peak in intensity.

Through further experiments, Hertz found that electromagnetic waves also exhibit refraction and polarization. He observed that the waves vibrate at right angles to the direction of travel, propagate in cones, and travel right through certain types of materials. Actually, it was a wonder that he achieved so much using spark transmitters, which splatter their energy over a range of frequencies. It would have been much easier to observe wave effects using a single-frequency source of radio waves.

Hertz found the experiments exhilarating. There he was, working alone with nature, having discovered something unique, and not having to worry about competitors. But the most impressive feature of Hertz' experiments was their simplicity. He was producing and detecting electromagnetic waves using nothing more than electric sparks.

In the process of pursuing science, Hertz invented wireless technology. But he was quick to dismiss talk of practical applications. He, like Oliver Lodge, was an academic and not an inventor.

In hindsight, we know that Hertz confronted three extreme challenges. To calculate the frequency of his waves, he had to obtain accurate values for the inductance and capacitance. He could only guess what impact his immediate surroundings had on his measurements. And there was no way to tune his spark-driven exciter to a single frequency. A less careful and determined investigator could have easily been thrown off course.

Though Hertz's equipment was discarded, it's believed his first experiments were conducted in the very high frequency (VHF) and ultra high frequency (UHF) ranges. In other words, Hertz worked with wavelengths ranging from about one foot to several meters. Interestingly, when wireless was first put to practical use it was at much lower frequencies (low frequency and even very low frequency) using much longer wavelengths.

Hertz's research attracted considerable attention. The public could see the potential of wireless communications. However, there was no rush to put Hertzian waves to commercial use. The telegraph was near-ubiquitous and transatlantic cables had been in regular use since around the end of the U.S. Civil War. The telephone, invented in 1873, was still fairly new. Having achieved his goal of confirming Maxwell's theory, Hertz was ready to move on to other research.

In 1889, Hertz was appointed to succeed the late Rudolf Clausius as professor of physics at the University of Bonn. In his new post, Hertz investigated the effects of electrifying luminous, rarified gases contained in Geissler tubes. He believed the rays produced in the tubes were not electric currents but something more akin to electromagnetic waves. However, in 1892 Hertz found that the cathode rays penetrated very thin metal foil. That should have told him that the rays consist of small particles—particles much smaller than atoms. Later, Joseph John (J.J.) Thomson showed that cathode rays are indeed negatively charged subatomic particles; Thomson is credited with the discovery of electrons.

One of Hertz's students, Philipp Lenard, investigated further. Using a modified tube, he created rays that passed through a second evacuated chamber. He concluded they were electromagnetic waves at very short wavelengths. He was right on both counts, but failed to recognize that they were fundamentally different; Lenard observed x-rays but it was Wilhelm Röntgen who was credited with their discovery.

The rising star of German science, Heinrich Hertz, died at the tragically young age of 37 on Jan. 1, 1894 from blood poisoning caused by treatment for a jaw infection. He discovered electromagnetic waves and the photoelectric effect, and was only a few steps away from discovering electrons and x-rays at the time of his death. As Helmholtz wrote in Hertz's obituary, "He is a victim of the envy of the gods." But it was not the end of his family's contributions to science. Hertz's nephew Gustav Ludwig Hertz won a Nobel Prize for his research on electrons, helping to establish the Bohr model of the atom, and Gustav's son Carl Hellmuth Hertz is credited with inventing medical ultrasonography.

The Hertz (Hz) was established in 1930 by the International Electrotechnical Commission (IEC) as the unit of frequency—the measure of the number of times that a repeated event occurs per unit of time (also known as "cycles per second"). In 1969, East Germany cast the Heinrich Hertz memorial medal. The IEEE Heinrich Hertz Medal, established in 1987, is "for outstanding achievements in Hertzian waves [...] presented annually to an individual for achievements which are theoretical or experimental in nature." A crater located on the far side of the Moon, just behind the eastern limb, is also named in Hertz's honor.

Oliver Lodge delivered a lecture on Hertz' achievement and subsequent advances five months after Hertz passed away. Perhaps the most important of these advances was Edouard Branly's coherer detector. The coherer consisted of a tube filled with powdered metal between two metal contacts. In the presence of Hertzian waves, the particles "cohered," causing the resistance between the contacts to drop sharply. It was no longer necessary to see sparks in order to detect Hertzian waves. A circuit consisting of a battery, a coherer, and an electromagnet-actuated bell signaled reception with a ring.

The coherer had one major problem: upon receiving a Hertzian wave it assumed a low resistance state and remained there. Oliver Lodge developed a simple solution. A small hammer, which Lodge called the "tapper," could be actuated by the same circuit to immediately restore the coherer to its high-resistance state by knocking the "cohered" particles loose. Like Hertz, neither Branly nor Lodge saw practical applications for their discoveries.

Marconi was astonished that Hertz, Lodge, and others could not see the potential utility of wireless communication for several years after Hertz's discovery, but Lodge freely admitted much later that that had been the case. While Oliver Lodge was skeptical about using Hertzian waves to signal across the Atlantic, he was optimistic about communicating with the dead. During the Victorian era, people could imagine communicating with the world beyond through séances, but wires seemed to have the corner on earthly communications.

Oliver Lodge was more interested in pursuing scientific knowledge than fame and fortune. He sought recognition only belatedly. He was a creative thinker, an honest if sometimes naive investigator, and a pleasant individual. While he never quite made it to the top of his field, he was always right up there with the leading lights.

Heinrich Hertz was more driven. He knew early on that he wanted to accomplish something great. Always on the lookout for novel effects, he was not one to let anything unusual pass. Luck played a big role in his discovery of electromagnetic waves and the photoelectric effect. But it is more to the point to say that Heinrich Hertz made his own luck.

PART II

Chapter Five

The Wired Foundation: Morse and Bell

The telegraph and telephone, though conceived and developed for wires, form an integral part of wireless history. It was easier to convey intelligence over wires first; doing so without wires required further advances. Think of the "wireless telegraph" as the "horseless carriage" of telecommunications.

Morse's telegraph and Bell's telephone also provide a grand introduction to the trials and tribulations of inventors. Few great inventions go undisputed. The winners are usually the persons deemed first to conceive, develop, and publicize an invention. The losers invariably complain that their ideas were stolen, suppressed, or ignored. Determining priority can be a miserable and thankless affair.

History is less ambiguous; the greatest credit usually goes to the individuals who translate scientific effects into technology and apply it to serve human needs. Samuel F.B. Morse was not the first person to use electricity and wires to convey intelligence. However, along with his partners he did more than anyone else to bring the electromagnetic telegraph into common use. Likewise, though others claimed they invented the telephone, none came close to matching Alexander Graham Bell's record for commercializing and promoting it.

* * *

Prior to the telegraph, information traveled only as fast as humans could carry it. It took days for news to travel by land and weeks to cross oceans. People accepted the fact that they learned about distant events only days later because that's how it always had been.

From the time (1729) Stephen Gray discovered electricity could be transmitted over conducting threads, natural philosophers dreamed of using electricity to transmit information. They understood that a wire could be used to signal by prior arrangement—much like a bonfire. Sending impromptu messages was another matter.

It wasn't long before natural philosophers hit on the idea of using separate wires for each letter in the alphabet. In 1746, Professor Johann Heinrich Winckler at the University of Leipzig signaled by generating sparks at the far end of wires. In 1774, the French mathematician and physicist Georges-Louis Lesage remotely actuated pith ball electroscopes. In 1809, German anatomist Samuel Thomas von Soemmering produced hydrogen bubbles on distant electrodes immersed in acid. All of these systems exhibited the same limitations: they required multiple electricity sources and wires, had very limited range, and were excruciatingly slow.

The limitations were conquered one by one. Sir Francis Ronalds built a single-wire telegraph using synchronized rotating disks and pith balls in 1823. The sender momentarily switched the current on when the send disk indicated the desired letter; as long as the disks remained synchronized the receive disk indicated the same letter. Harrison Gray Dyar's telegraph discolored litmus paper at the distant end of an eight-mile line in 1828. Dyar understood that letters could be indicated based on signal timing and spacing; a moving litmus paper tape was used to record the signals. Joseph Henry used electricity to ring a bell about one mile away in 1831. Other telegraphs were invented around this time by Baron Schilling (using multiple wires and compasses) and the team of Carl Friedrich Gauss and Wilhelm Eduard Weber (using a mirror galvanometer). These telegraphs exploited Hans Christian Oersted's discovery that an electric current deflects a compass needle.

The first practical telegraph was invented by Charles Wheatstone and (in partnership with William Fothergill Cooke) placed in regular service in 1839. It spanned the thirteen miles between two railway stations in London, but required five circuits to actuate five needles, two of which pointed to the desired letter on a diamond-shaped dial. The invention won public acclaim when it was used to help capture a fleeing murderer who hopped a London bound train. But it was too complex for everyday use.

* * *

Samuel Finley Breeze Morse (known as "Finley" to his family) was born April 27, 1791 in Charlestown, Massachusetts. His father, Jedediah Morse, was a pastor and became known as the "the Noah Webster of Geography" for his atlases, school geography texts, and travel guides. Jedediah and his wife, Elizabeth Finley, had six more children but only Richard and Sidney survived.

Morse was enrolled in Phillips Academy in Andover, Mass. in 1799. He demonstrated a flair for art at age 11. His father boasted of his talent, but warned him that art was only an "amusement." In 1805, Morse entered Yale College at age 14-1/2 years.

Morse became interested in science thanks to lectures on electricity given by chemist Benjamin Silliman and Jeremiah Day, who would serve as Yale's president for nearly three decades. However, upon graduating from Yale in 1810, he decided he wanted to be an artist and asked his parents' permission to study under Washington Allston, one of America's first great landscape painters. His father opposed the idea and apprenticed him to a book publisher. However, after three months at Farrand & Mallory's bookstore, Morse's parents relented and permitted him to accompany Allston to England.

Through Allston, Morse gained access to London's literary and intellectual circles. He found himself in an uneasy situation, however, when the U.S. Congress voted for war against England in 1812. Morse stayed on despite growing friction with his parents, who demanded evidence of artistic progress. He obtained portrait commissions and sent home his *Dying Hercules*, winning his parents' admiration for his talent if not their confidence in his ability to make a living as an artist. Their patience and largesse having run out, Morse was forced to return home in 1815.

Upon arrival in Boston, he set out to make money as an artist, renting a room to exhibit ten paintings including *Judgment of Jupiter*, *a Scene from Don Quixote*, and *Dying Hercules*. Morse toured New England as a portrait painter. He met and fell in love with Lucretia Pickering Walker in 1816.

Morse's interest in science was reawakened the next year. He and his brother Sidney invented a flexible leather piston, applied for patents, and sought investors. They concluded the most promising application was an improved fire engine. No less an authority than Eli Whitney (inventor of the cotton gin) agreed.

Morse visited his great uncle in Charleston, where there was demand for northern portrait painters. Morse's art career flourished. After several weeks, he completed 27 portraits and had commissions for another 40—earning $60-$70 each. Believing he could make $1,000 per month—a significant sum in those days—he lost interest in his leather piston. With more than $4,000 worth of portraits booked for the next season, he now had the means to marry Lucretia.

Morse's success as an artist appeared assured. He was commissioned to paint a portrait of President James Monroe for the princely sum of $750.

After two strong seasons the economy slowed, however, and the demand for portraits plummeted. Morse came up with the idea of doing a large painting of the new House of Representatives while in session. He exhibited it in Boston and did well the first day, but poorly over the remaining seven weeks.

Meanwhile, his brothers prospered. Richard studied theology, and Sidney became a lawyer. Together, his brothers published a religious newspaper, the *Observer*, in New York City. Morse was also drawn to New York. Between painting commissions and teaching art, he soon found himself doing well again. He landed a prestigious commission to paint the Marquis de Lafayette during his farewell tour.

Then tragedy struck: Morse's 25-year old wife died suddenly while recuperating after giving birth to their third child. Morse was traveling; there was no way to alert him to rush home. He would not learn of her death until she was already buried. Grief-stricken, Morse took his sons to live with his parents and brought his daughter Susan to live with him in New York City.

The next year, Morse co-founded the Drawing Association, which later became the National Academy of the Arts of Design, in a rebellion against the American Academy of the Fine Arts. The National Academy's future members included great American artists such as Winslow Homer, John Singer Sargent, and Frank Lloyd Wright.

The first hint of Morse's interest in electromagnetism surfaced in 1827. He met and became friends with Professor James Freeman Dana of Columbia College, who gave a series of lectures on electricity and electromagnetism at the New York Athenaeum, where Morse also gave lectures. Two years earlier, the British physicist William Sturgeon exhibited the first electromagnet and showed it could lift nine pounds.

In an effort to revive his spirits after his *Lafayette* was criticized, Morse embarked on a three-year trip to Paris and Rome, leaving his children behind. In Rome, he copied paintings by Poussin, Rubens, and others on commission. In Paris, he painted the Louvre's Salon Carré. This famous painting, brought to America from Paris, enabled Americans to view nearly three dozen great works of art without crossing the Atlantic.

Upon returning home in 1832, Morse was appointed Professor of Painting and Sculpture at the University of the City of New York (now called New York University). Under the pen name Brutus, he wrote against Catholicism and clannish immigrant groups and was nominated to run for Mayor of New York City as the Native American Democratic Association candidate. At the time, "native American" referred to people of European descent who were born in the United States; Morse believed the U.S. was the target of foreign conspiracies.

Morse also began work on another invention. In 1831, Joseph Henry developed a more powerful electromagnet using tightly-wound coils of insulated wire. Henry also showed how an electromagnet could be mounted on a pivot to serve as an automatic switch (also known as a "relay"). During Morse's return trip from Europe, he discussed advances in electromagnetism with the ship's captain and other passengers, and wrote down some ideas for a prototype electromagnetic recording telegraph in his sketchbook.

Morse worked quietly on the telegraph for the next three years. Little is known about the sequence of steps he took to develop his telegraph. What is clear, however, is that Morse was interested in a wide variety of subjects—not just painting--and he invariably became an active participant. In late 1835, he began demonstrating his recording telegraph to friends and acquaintances. The next year, he demonstrated it to Dr. Leonard D. Gale, a professor of science at New York University.

In 1837, Morse became alarmed when he heard that two Frenchmen were touring the U.S. demonstrating a telegraph. He was relieved to learn it was an "optical telegraph" using semaphores. Suddenly, he realized the importance of establishing priority for his invention. With the help of his brother Sidney, he publicized the invention and its history.

Morse's telegraph consisted of a port rule transmitter and a register receiver. It was not the first electric telegraph, but it was arguably the first practical design. It was easy to use and elegant in its simplicity, enabling automatic transmission and recorded reception.

The port rule transmitter was a grooved stick that could be loaded with metal blanks and passed (by use of a crank) beneath a tooth projecting from a lever. At the other end of the lever were copper prongs that completed a battery circuit when dipped into small cups of mercury by the lever's action. Each metal blank contained a series of from one to nine V-shaped notches that could be arranged to represent different numbers.

The receiver consisted of a pendulum with a pencil attached at its bottom to make marks on a ribbon of paper passing beneath it. The pendulum was controlled by an electromagnet that, in turn, was controlled by signals received from the transmitter.

Not long after publicizing the invention, Morse was shocked to hear that he was accused of stealing the idea by a man he met while sailing home from France. Morse never denied that he discussed electromagnetism and conceived and divulged the idea of using it for communication during the voyage. Dr. Charles T. Jackson, a geologist and physician, wrote that he was glad to see "our Electric Telegraph" mentioned in the press but was dismayed that he was not mentioned.

Morse contacted two passengers and the ship's captain, and all three confirmed he was the idea's originator. While the learned Jackson may have contributed suggestions or confirmed the idea's practicality, it is clear that the automatic transmitter and receiver were of Morse's own design. Though Jackson harassed Morse for years, Jackson's credibility steadily declined as he laid claim to other inventions and discoveries. For example, Jackson insisted that he and not William T.G. Morton was first to conceive the use of anesthesia in surgery.

With the help of a Yale classmate, Commissioner of Patents Henry L. Ellsworth, Morse obtained a patent caveat. (Though eventually discontinued, a patent caveat was a notice of intent to file for a patent that helped establish priority.) Morse also worked to improve his invention. On the advice of Professor Leonard Gale, Morse substituted a stronger battery and added windings to the electromagnet, increasing his telegraph's range from 40 ft. to 1,000 ft.

Around this time, the U.S. government began to express an interest in faster communications. Secretary of the Treasury Levi Woodbury issued an RFI (request for information) for an optical semaphore network. Morse submitted an alternative proposal, pointing out that semaphores are inaccurate, slow, and useless at night and in fog. Woodbury was impressed.

Morse knew that demonstrating his telegraph could connect cities was crucial to selling the idea, as many were skeptical it could be done. He quickly realized that Joseph Henry's relay could be used to regenerate the signals and conquer any distance. When a signal was sent, it activated an electromagnet at the distant end of the wire, switching on another circuit with its own battery. Morse envisioned long telegraph lines composed of multiple segments spanning up to 20 miles each.

However, it was not something Morse could afford to build on his own. Professor Gale enlisted the technical and financial assistance of a former student, Alfred Vail. Vail's family owned a machine shop and a foundry in Speedwell, New Jersey. Meanwhile, Morse developed a telegraph code in which each word was assigned a unique number that had to be looked up in a codebook.

Public demonstrations were conducted in Speedwell. The first attempt to transmit over ten miles of wire failed. But another attempt succeeded. Morse discovered he could communicate at faster rates using a dot-dash alphabet. One of the first messages sent was "Attention, the universe!"

Like modern digital communication systems, Morse's telegraph used discrete signals. The other end of the link could only receive a dot, a dash, or nothing. This type of code facilitated the exchange of messages over relatively primitive circuits. It was fairly easy to tell a dot from a dash—or either from the absence of a signal. The Morse code was made efficient by assigning the shortest symbols to the most common letters. For example, the letter "e" was represented by a single dot.

Then Morse forwarded his equipment by railroad (itself a new technology) to Philadelphia for a demonstration at the Franklin Institute. The Franklin Institute endorsed Morse's invention in a report to the Secretary of the Treasury in Washington, concluding it was superior to both optical and electrical telegraphs developed in Europe.

The Congressional Committee on Commerce recommended appropriating $30,000 for a 50-mile test line. However, Committee Chairman F.O.J. Smith audaciously suggested that Morse take him on as a partner and, while waiting for Congress to pass the appropriation bill, that they go to Europe to obtain patents. While Morse recognized the value of Smith's connections and legal experience, he was concerned about the appearance of impropriety. Smith offered to take a leave of absence and not stand for reelection. Morse agreed to those terms.

In England, Morse's patent application was denied. He waited in vain to demonstrate his telegraph to the last King of France, Louis-Philippe. Nor did he receive word of passage of the appropriation bill. However, the trip was not a total bust: He learned about competing designs, received the French equivalent of a patent, and visited Louis Jacques Mandé Daguerre, inventor of the Daguerreotype photographic process.

Feeling stymied, Morse put his telegraph aside to pursue "photographic paintings." He started a portrait studio in partnership with New York University Professor of Chemistry John William Draper, who pioneered the use of photography with artificial lighting, microscopes, and telescopes. When the New York City press praised Morse's Daguerreotypes, one of Daguerre's associates, Francois Gouraud, publicly complained of Morse's ingratitude.

Was there a pattern here—did Morse fail to acknowledge others who contributed to his success? Morse briefly took lessons from Gouraud, who tried to pass himself off as a professor at the Sorbonne, which he wasn't. If there was a pattern, it was that Morse was repeatedly a victim of knaves.

When Morse ran for Mayor of New York a second time, two newspapers published a letter purportedly from Morse announcing his withdrawal just prior to the election. The letter was a counterfeit.

Finally, Morse received US Patent 1647 for his electromagnetic telegraph on June 20, 1840. He partnered with lobbyist Isaac Coffin and reconnected with Smith, Vail, and Gale. In 1842, Morse launched a new campaign to sell his telegraph to Congress.

New York Congressman Charles Ferris asked Morse to explain his system in writing. This was Morse's big chance. He skillfully argued that a single line running from New York to New Orleans would more than pay for itself. Ferris proposed a $30,000 appropriation. Acutely aware of competing overseas designs, Congress now viewed Morse's invention in terms of the prestige it would confer upon the nation. On March 3, 1843, the $30,000 appropriation passed and was signed by President John Tyler.

Morse elected to run the trial line between Washington, DC and Baltimore—about 44 miles. Vail built the instruments, including the first hand-operated telegraph key. Gale supervised the laying of the wire-carrying conduit. Smith handled the legal issues. Morse hired James Fisher to oversee wire manufacturing.

Using a powerful Grove battery consisting of hundreds of nitric acid cells with platinum electrodes, Morse demonstrated he could signal across the entire 160 miles of spooled wire. He tested different lengths and wrote an article for Benjamin Silliman's *American Journal of Science*. Having experimented with signaling across water, Morse predicted telegraph links would eventually cross the Atlantic.

Then Morse hit a series of bumps. There were problems manufacturing and installing the pipe. Squabbles erupted with Fisher and Smith, and Smith joined Morse's enemies. In March of 1844, an exasperated Morse switched to overhead cables. He used 30-foot posts, planted 4 feet deep, spaced 200 feet apart, with two wires attached to cross arms.

A successful test was conducted at the seven-mile mark. The completed Washington-Baltimore line officially opened on May 24, 1844. Morse set up his instruments at the US Supreme Court. Annie Ellsworth, daughter of the Commissioner of Patents, selected the words for the first official message: "What hath God wrought!"

Morse scored a public relations bonanza when Vail telegraphed the raucous proceedings of the Democratic Convention in Baltimore to Washington. When anti-slavery Senator Silas Wright was nominated as

Polk's running mate, he telegraphed back to decline. Hundreds of onlookers cheered Morse.

Morse and his supporters thought of additional applications for the telegraph including synchronizing distant clocks and determining longitude with greater accuracy. In fact, Samuel Morse did more than anyone else in establishing universal time.

The telegraph made it possible for individuals in two locations observing a defined astronomical phenomenon to measure the difference in time. For example, each observer could signal via telegraph when the sun reached its zenith at their location. The difference in time could be used to calculate the difference in longitude between the two locations. If the longitude of one location was known with precision, the longitude of the other location could be calculated.

Reactions to the telegraph ran the gamut. Some marveled at what human innovation achieved; others saw supernatural forces at work; and still others dismissed the telegraph as unnecessary. The press was exuberant. Some predicted a dramatic decline in crime once felons realized there was no escaping the law.

Samuel F.B. Morse became a national hero. While he craved recognition for his achievement—the culmination of years of hard work and frustration—his religious upbringing taught him that reversal could be just around the corner. (After meeting Lucretia, Morse briefly flirted with the idea of becoming a minister.) At one point, Morse proposed to sell his nine-sixteenths ownership of the electromagnetic telegraph patent for $110,000 to the U.S. government if, in return, the government built a nationwide network and appointed him superintendent. Luckily for Morse and posterity, Smith refused to go along.

There was also friction with Vail, who felt underappreciated. Later, Vail's widow claimed that her husband rather than Morse invented the Morse code. But Vail himself wrote that Morse was the code's creator.

Morse focused on convincing Congress to fund extending the Washington-Baltimore line to New York City. He also continued to improve the technology, experimenting with power generators, lightning arrestors,[4] and methods of communicating across bodies of water.

The bill to extend the line to NYC was defeated. However, $8,000 was allocated to keep the existing line in service. Morse turned over financial

---

[4] A lightning arrestor is a surge protector installed just before wires enter a building. It shorts the current to earth when exposed to a high-voltage spike, protecting people and equipment.

management of the telegraph business to Amos Kendall, famous for fixing the corrupt and mismanaged U.S. Post Office. Kendall formed the Magnetic Telegraph Company and expanded telegraph service coverage by building new lines and licensing others to build lines.

Thanks to Kendall, Morse got to build that line between New York and Washington. There was, however, a key technical challenge: communicating across the Hudson River. Several solutions were considered. Initially, messages were shuttled across the river via steamboat. (Eventually, cables were routed across bridges and underwater when necessary.) By late 1846, lines were opened between New York and Boston and New York and Buffalo—the latter with intermediate stations at Troy, Albany, Utica, Syracuse, Auburn, and Rochester. As more cities were linked by telegraph, newspaper stories appeared with the header "By Magnetic Telegraph."

It was not long before Morse was once again under attack. Kendall entered a business agreement with Henry O'Reilly's Atlantic, Lake, and Mississippi Telegraph Company. However, Smith refused to recognize it; O'Reilly fought Smith in court and won. Justifiably angry, O'Reilly decided to construct his own lines and partnered with Royal House, inventor of a printing telegraph. Morse believed House's device infringed his patent. O'Reilly appealed to the public, calling his circuit using House's gear "The People's Line," and portraying Morse as a monopolist.

Morse brought legal action. In 1849, Judge Thomas B. Monroe ruled in favor of Morse, and ordered the U.S. marshal to seize O'Reilly's lines. O'Reilly vowed to take the case all the way to the U.S. Supreme Court if necessary.

Morse honed the description of his invention to better withstand legal challenges. Specifically, Morse claimed a system using the motive power of magnetism developed through the action of electric current to operate machinery to imprint signals on paper or produce sounds for the purpose of telegraphic communication at any distance. He also claimed specific transmitting and receiving instruments; a system for relaying signals between circuits as a means of overcoming the distance limitations of a single circuit; and the now famous dot-dash code.

O'Reilly also sought to strengthen his position. He bought the rights to a telegraph system claimed to be three times faster than Morse's and invented by the Englishman Alexander Bain. Bain's transmitter used perforated tape and its receiver used electrochemical action to mark a treated paper disk.

Morse was convinced that Bain's method was simply a more compli-cated version of his own method. Playing it safe, Morse quickly obtained a

U.S. patent for an electrochemical system. When Bain filed for a U.S. patent, he was refused. Leonard Gale, Morse's former colleague at New York University, was now an examiner at the Patent Office and refused to accept the date of Bain's British patent as proof of priority. Bain appealed Gale's decision in court. The judge ruled that Morse and Bain were both entitled to patents for their respective electrochemical telegraphs.

Meanwhile, competition heated up. O'Reilly was granted a release from the 1848 injunction forbidding him to build telegraph circuits. Smith became embroiled in a legal battle with another telegraph line developer, Hugh Downing. In *Smith vs. Downing*, the judge ruled that Morse was entitled to patents for his devices and code, but that did not give him the exclusive right to convey intelligence using electromagnetism.

O'Reilly finally succeeded in taking his dispute with Morse to the United States Supreme Court. The court cut right to the key issues: Was Morse the original inventor of the electromagnetic telegraph and was O'Reilly's method substantially different?

O'Reilly's counsel Senator Salmon P. Chase of Ohio argued that Morse's telegraph was based on the work of others, particularly Wheatstone and German physicist Carl August von Steinheil. In essence, he argued that Morse's invention was nothing more than the first practical electromagnetic marking telegraph.

In February 1854, the U.S. Supreme Court handed Morse victory by ruling he was the sole inventor of the electromagnetic telegraph. However, the Court also found that his patent was too broad and inhibited improvements. The ruling protected Morse while permitting competition. Morse was granted a seven-year patent extension in consideration of the fact that he did not receive just remuneration in the normal 14 years due to litigation costs.

By 1855, telegraph lines stretched an estimated 42,000 miles across the U.S., dramatically increasing the speed of information. The cultural and philosophical ramifications were enormous. The press referred to the telegraph as a "lightning line." The learned celebrated the conquest of space and time. Futurists contemplated the possibility of thought transference.

The word "telegram" became common. The telegraph proved synergistic with railroads, steamboats, and printing presses. Skilled operators often replaced paper marking machines for greater speed.[5] Fifty small telegraph

---

[5] It was a rare case in which the switch from an automated to a manual system was considered progress; a skilled operator could read messages in real-time.

companies were consolidated into a few regional companies. Prussia, Sweden, Australia, India, Russia and China deployed Morse telegraphs.

But the best was yet to come. New York businessman Cyrus W. Field asked Morse's opinion regarding the viability of transoceanic telegraph lines. A British company had already linked London and Paris in 1852 with a cable across the English Channel. Might the same approach work over a far greater distance?

Though Field made his fortune in paper manufacturing, he was just the person to build the first transoceanic telegraph line. Field possessed not only vision, but almost superhuman patience and persistence.

Field's strategy was to connect Ireland to Newfoundland via an undersea cable and run a landline from Newfoundland through Maine to New York. The idea was ridiculed by the newspapers. Morse felt otherwise; he invested $10,000, joined the board of directors of the Atlantic Telegraph Company, and was appointed honorary "Electrician." Charles Tilston Bright supervised cable laying in the British Isles. William Thomson (Lord Kelvin) wrote a letter to a popular magazine explaining how the cable's design affected data rate and, consequently, profitability; it was an impressive analysis and Thomson was also elected to the board of directors.

Morse had experimented with underwater telegraph links since 1842. He studied the challenges of a transatlantic cable and wrote Michael Faraday for advice. Faraday would not condescend to reply directly, but he told a mutual acquaintance that he saw no reason why it shouldn't work and suspected laying the cable was the biggest challenge.

Four years after Morse's triumphant Baltimore-Washington line opened, he married Sarah Elizabeth Griswold. His telegraph stock made him wealthy, and he built an estate he called Locust Grove on one hundred acres just outside Poughkeepsie, N.Y. Morse ran for Congress as a Democrat and lost, though this time he made a respectable showing.

Morse was annoyed by some of Field's business deals. Field moved to acquire east coast telegraph companies using Royal House's printing telegraph. He also bought the rights to David Hughes' synchronous, keyboard telegraph. He wasn't doing it to harm Morse, however. Field understood that he needed unencumbered access to multiple markets to ensure the success of his longer and much more expensive lines.

The transatlantic cable project moved forward. Morse traveled to London in 1856, working with Bright and Dr. Edward Whitehouse to test signaling over long cables. They succeeded in sending 8-10 words per minute over interconnected spools containing 2,000 miles of wire. The British government offered to supply cable laying ships and pay £14,000 per year for use of the cable. The U.S. government essentially matched the British offer.

Two ships were required to carry the enormous length of cable. The cable consisted of seven strands of thin copper wire sheathed in three layers of insulation. The entire assembly was coated with gutta-percha (an excellent and long-lasting, runner-like insulator) to 0.5-inch diameter and then wrapped in tarred yarn inside spiral iron wire.

According to the original plan, both ships would sail to mid-ocean, splice their cables together, and proceed with the cable-laying in opposite directions. This eliminated the need to meet at an exact location. However, an even simpler method was devised: The first ship would lay cable on the way to mid ocean.

The first attempt to lay the transatlantic cable failed when the cable snapped 40 miles from shore. During the second attempt, the cable snapped after just five miles, but was retrieved and spliced. Another break was suffered after 300 miles, but this time the cable could not be retrieved.

In response to these disappointments, Field made numerous changes and stripped Morse of direct involvement in the cable-laying. However, Morse received good news from France around the same time. A committee consisting of counts and ministers from ten European countries agreed to pay him 400,000 francs for the use of his patent.

The cable broke three times during the third cable-laying expedition in 1858. However, the line was completed and a message was successfully transmitted across the Atlantic. The first official message read: "Europe and America are united by telegraph. Glory to God in the highest, on earth peace, good will toward men."

Public celebrations followed and both Morse and Field were hailed as prophets. Unfortunately, after sending 732 messages over three months, the cable went silent. Ironically, the last word successfully transmitted was "forward."

Around this time, Morse endured yet another challenge to his credentials—a challenge that resulted in part from his having unintentionally offended Joseph Henry years earlier. Henry neither forgave nor forgot—though Morse offered to right the wrong when Henry first took offense. The Smithsonian Institution depicted Henry as the true inventor of the telegraph and Morse as an amateur. (During the public celebrations, Henry praised the event but not the people who brought it about. Later, Morse publicly thanked Henry for his contributions to the telegraph.)

But once again, the bad news was offset when Cyrus Field's North American Telegraph Association invited Morse's Magnetic Telegraph Company to join forces in 1859. After the Civil War, Field finally conquered the Atlantic with a new and better cable, and was even able to retrieve and repair the old cable, using it as a backup.

Samuel F.B. Morse spent his last years living in style. He died of pneumonia in New York City on April 2, 1872 at the age of 80.

Morse did more than anyone else to bring electronic communications into common use. As Tom Standage described in his book *The Victorian Internet*, the telegraph quickly evolved from individual communication links into a global network. The telegraph brought qualitative changes in the daily operations of business and government. Everything from local culture to foreign affairs was transformed. The whole became greater than the sum of its parts.

Ironically, the telegraph's ability to convey intelligence by the mere presence or absence of a signal was all that would be needed to one day transmit voices and even images. Such is the simplicity of digital binary communications—though no one imagined it at the time.

But how did an artist become a great inventor? If there is an answer, it is probably that Morse combined a number of seemingly contradictory personal qualities. He was extremely opinionated, yet remained open to a wide range of ideas. He was highly sensitive, yet resilient in the face of attacks against both his intellectual property and business ventures. He was a creative person who changed the world, yet he felt threatened by people and movements advocating social change.

By setting high standards for himself, maintaining diverse interests, and valuing action over talk, Morse had no choice but to create.

* * *

Natural philosophers pursued ways of conveying intelligence over long distances for decades before Morse came up with his simple and reliable telegraph. But there was never much doubt that codes representing words could be transmitted over wires; in the worst case, each letter could have its own wire. In contrast, there was rampant skepticism about whether it was possible to communicate the variations and nuances of the human voice via electromagnetism.

The first scheme for transmitting voices over telegraph lines bore little resemblance to what we now know as the telephone. German immigrant

Joseph Faber developed a mechanical speaking figure that he called "Euphonia" based on the human larynx, mouth, and lungs. He spent 17 years perfecting the machine, which consisted of bellows and an eerie, disembodied head. Euphonia was keyboard-driven and spoke in what was variously described as a "ghostly monotone" or "hoarse whisper." When Euphonia was demonstrated to Joseph Henry in Philadelphia, he suggested conversing by installing two such machines at the opposite ends of a telegraph link.

Using the telegraph to transmit one's own voice seemed preposterous at the time. No one even knew whether it was possible to convert speech into electromagnetic signals that could be sent over wires and converted back to speech. Remotely controlling the Euphonia, however, seemed quite plausible. The only requirement was a machine that could translate codes received via telegraph into the desired operations of the Euphonia's keyboard. (The idea bears an amazing resemblance to modern digital voice communications in which binary codes represent sounds.)

Ironically, the road to an invention that could transmit the human voice over telegraph lines started with a similar speaking machine on the other side of the Atlantic.

Alexander Bell, known in his youth as "Aleck," was born on March 3, 1847 in Edinburgh to Alexander Melville Bell and Eliza Grace Bell. Aleck's father wrote *The Art of Reading* for treatment of stammering and became a lecturer at the University of Edinburgh. His mother was deaf.

On Aleck's 11th birthday, he took "Graham" as his middle name. (Unlike his brother, he wasn't given a middle name at birth, and felt deprived.) He and a friend invented a wheat cleaning machine, but nothing came of it. At age 15, Aleck traveled to see his grandfather in London. Before returning home, Aleck and his father visited Charles Wheatstone and saw his improved version of Baron De Kempelen's speaking machine—a contraption capable of pronouncing a few simple words. Wheatstone amazed people with his acoustical inventions, which included a clever sounding box, a primitive microphone, and his kaleidophone for visualizing sounds. De Kempelen was something of a prankster, promoting a chess-playing automaton called "The Turk" with a concealed human operator, but his crude speaking machine was genuine.

Aleck's father asked him and his brother Melly to build their own speaking machine. (In those days, building a cutting edge machine was a tall order, but at least it didn't require custom integrated circuits.) They did—but not before sacrificing their pet cat to learn about the larynx. The boys' talking machine was a modest success, teaching Aleck about development through trial and error. When the boys made it say "mama" on the stairway, a tenant came down to see "what can be the matter with the baby."

Meanwhile, Aleck's father developed a universal phonetic alphabet. He taught the system to his sons and attracted the interest of Alexander J. Ellis, a well-known English philologist. Ellis told him about experiments performed by Hermann von Helmholtz using electromagnets and tuning forks to create vowel sounds—a device called the "rheotome." Aleck decided he needed to learn more about electricity.

Alexander Graham Bell found work teaching the deaf and stammerers. However, his father was determined to immigrate to America. Upon the death of his brother Melly from tuberculosis, he became his parents' only surviving son, and immigrated to Brantford, Ontario with them.

Bell didn't stay in Brantford for long, though. He moved to Boston and taught the deaf to great acclaim. In late 1872, he began attending science lectures and decided to try his luck at developing the "multiple telegraph," a system enabling multiple messages to be sent over a single telegraph line at the same time. Fellow Bostonian Joseph B. Stearns had already invented the "duplex telegraph" for sending and receiving at the same time, effectively doubling the capacity, and the multiple telegraph promised even greater message-handling capacity.

The young Bell was attracted to the idea of sending different telegraph messages at different frequencies and using tuned receivers at the far end to sort them out—an approach now known as frequency division multiplexing. He experimented with a variant of Helmholtz's "rheotome" apparatus. At the transmitter, he sounded one of several tuning forks, each of which was attached to a wire that barely touched the mercury in a cup. At the receiver, an electromagnet caused the corresponding tuning fork to vibrate. The wire transmitted a current that pulsated at the frequency of the source tuning fork, causing the appropriate tuning fork at the receiver to resonate.

Bell obtained financial backing for his multiple telegraph from Gardiner Hubbard and Thomas Sanders. He eventually married Hubbard's daughter Mabel, who was also one of his deaf pupils.

Bell modified his setup. At the sending end, he substituted a steel strip for the tuning fork, creating a tunable transmitter. Next, he tried using two steel reed transmitters connected in parallel and two electromagnet-actuated steel reed receivers connected in series. The idea was that the selected transmit reed would actuate the corresponding receive reed. It didn't quite work.

After rebuilding the circuit, Bell heard a compound sound. He was trying to keep the sounds separate—not combine them. Unexpectedly, Bell was confronted with evidence that complex tones could be transmitted over a telegraph line.

Bell realized over time that there are an infinite number of possible variations and that a theory was needed to guide his trial and error efforts. He began searching for an overall strategy. He tried inductively coupling each transmitter to the main line. He tried using the same reed as both transmitter and receiver.

He also realized that the mercury make-and-break system was problematic: it transmitted pulses rather than continuous tones. At this point, he tried an idea suggested in a book about electricity: instead of using the mercury make-and-break system, he allowed the steel reed to vibrate over two electromagnets. He didn't fully realize it yet, but this approach enabled him to reproduce amplitude as well as frequency.

Around the same time, Bell became interested in a couple of instruments he felt could help him teach the deaf to speak. The phonautograph recorded speech waveforms by tracing them on a piece of glass covered with lampblack. The manometric flame capsule reflected a flame modulated by the speaker's voice off rotating mirrors. With these devices, deaf students could be shown correct waveforms for specific sounds (using the phonautograph) and then practice making them (using the manometric flame capsule). This also provided Bell with further insights regarding the wave (or "undulatory" as he called it) nature of speech.

In addition to the multiple telegraph, Bell thought about developing a device that transformed sounds into vibrations that deaf people could feel. For example, using this method a deaf person might "hear" an approaching team of horses.

Next, Bell experimented with a transmitter consisting of a series of reeds tuned to slightly different frequencies to create a continuous fluctuating current that could be converted back to magnetic force to drive a similar array at the receiver. In other words, he thought he needed a series of reeds to transmit and receive complex sounds. However, he should have known from his work with the phonautograph that a series of tuned reeds was unnecessary; a single diaphragm can pick up a range of frequencies.

In 1875, Bell began working with Thomas A. Watson, who had worked for a maker of custom electric components, Charles Williams. He finally built a working multiple telegraph and applied for three patents: a harmonic telegraph using direct current; a harmonic telegraph using induced current; and an autograph telegraph with vibratory circuit breaker.

Bell continued to make incremental discoveries. For example, he found that plucking a transmit reed induced sufficient current in an electromagnet to sound the reed at the receiver. When he tried using diaphragms, he realized he had discovered (but not yet perfected) a means of transmitting human speech. In July 1875, Watson told him "I could hear your voice plainly." However, Hubbard was not impressed and insisted he continue to focus on the multiple telegraph.

Bell was by no means the only person closing in on a means of transmitting human speech over telegraph lines. In fact, the word "telephone" was coined by the German inventor Philipp Reis who developed a "make-and-break" device for transmitting simple tones in the early 1860s. Closer to home, Elisha Gray developed a device he thought could be used to transmit simple music. While Gray's receiver responded to any frequency, his transmitter was limited to single tones or chords.

Not only did others claim to invent the telephone—some claimed Bell stole their ideas. Allegedly, Antonio Meucci developed a telephone more than a decade earlier and stored some of his materials in the same building Bell used for his laboratory. Innocenzo Manzetti later claimed Bell visited him and examined his device.

But it's hard to deny Alexander Graham Bell's credentials. His family had a long and intimate interest in human speech and hearing. Bell was an exceptionally competent and creative individual, and he demonstrated it repeatedly throughout his life. His records and patents show he understood that inventing is a step-by-step process.

Ultimately, Elisha Gray mounted a serious legal challenge. Bell and his partners withdrew their request for a patent caveat since Gray had priority for at least one claim, but they recorded and dated all subsequent advances. Ultimately, Elisha Gray and Alexander Graham Bell became embroiled in a patent interference dispute. Bell won on the basis that he filed earlier on the same day, despite an initial ruling that the time-of-day was irrelevant.

Bell and his partners also feared that Western Union would try to defeat them by hiring Thomas Edison. Edison was not yet world famous—he had not yet invented the phonograph—but he was known in telegraph circles for developing a number of improvements. Fortunately, Patent Office examiners formally approved Bell's patent on his 29th birthday. On March 7, 1876, Bell was issued US Patent No. 174,465. The patent was ostensibly for the multiple telegraph and was titled "Improvement in Telegraphy" but it clearly established a method of transmitting and receiving undulations including "the telegraphic transmission of noises or sounds of any kind."

Specifically, Bell asserted that physical vibrations could be used to initiate and control undulating current, and that such vibrations could be set in motion by a musical instrument or the human voice. The patent also claimed the use of induction to convert physical vibrations into undulating current; a direct way of creating undulations in a continuous current (i.e. modulation); and the use of variable resistance to create undulations in a continuous current.

Bell finally made the telephone speak three days after receiving his patent by dipping a platinum needle in sulphuric acid solution. The words "Mr. Watson, come here, I want to see you" were uttered on March 10, 1876. Bell immediately recognized the implications—that this would lead to "telegraph wires" to the home. He continued to experiment. When Bell tried a magneto transmitter (an electromagnet next to a tin diaphragm), he obtained even better results, and realized he could eliminate the troublesome acid solution.

Hubbard arranged a demonstration for several professors from Harvard and MIT. They were impressed to hear a muffled version of Hamlet's soliloquy. Audiences at public demonstrations were astonished. Bell exhibited at the Centennial Exhibition in Philadelphia and met with Emperor Pedro II of Brazil and William Thomson (Lord Kelvin). He also had a friendly talk with Elisha Gray.

(The fact that Bell was able to have a friendly talk with Gray may seem odd. Bell and Gray spent many hours pursuing the same invention and must have felt a kinship. Today, it's not unusual for companies engaged in a legal dispute in one area to be collaborating in another area.)

Bell performed tests over long lines. First, he tested an eight-mile line from Brantford to Paris, Ontario. Then he tested a line from Cambridge to Boston. Bell also made systematic improvements to his telephone. And he adopted the idea suggested by John Ponton, editor of the Titusville, Pennsylvania *Morning Herald*, of using telephone exchanges rather than point-to-point links.

People interested in buying telephones began writing Bell. Bell's lectures, some of which paid quite handsomely, attracted notable figures such as Oliver Wendell Holmes and Cyrus W. Field. People speculated about telephone "broadcasting" of political campaign speeches, sermons, news, and music.

The world's first regular telephone line was placed in service April 4, 1877. It connected Charles Williams' Boston workshop and his home in Somerville. The Bell Telephone Company was founded July 9, 1877, jointly owned by Hubbard, Sanders, Bell, and Watson. Bell favored a leasing business model because he felt selling telephones would invite competition.

On Mabel's urging, Bell began calling himself Alexander Graham Bell. There were roughly 200 phones in use when the couple married on July 11, 1877. By Aug. 1, the number increased to 778. The first printed telephone directory was published Feb 21, 1878. It had 50 entries.

Alexander and Mabel Bell left for England on the steamship *Anchoria*. Their first child, a daughter, was born in London. Bell obtained patents and formed partnerships in several countries. William H. Preece, consulting engineer for the British Post Office and later its engineer-in-chief, predicted Bell would be accused of stealing the invention.

Meanwhile, Edison went to work for Western Union as feared. He made considerable progress on variable resistance transmitters, directing his staff to test 2,000 different chemicals. As a result, Edison invented the carbon microphone used in virtually all telephones for the next 100 years.

Though he was called "electrician," Bell became his era's equivalent of a chief technology officer (CTO). He introduced the use of twisted pair wires to self-cancel induced interference, for which he obtained a patent, but the idea had been anticipated by Faraday and others.

Perhaps Hubbard's biggest contribution to the business was hiring Theodore N. Vail as general manager. In 1878, investors in Massachusetts and Rhode Island founded the New England Telephone Company at Hubbard's request. (Hubbard apparently thought there was an advantage to forming separate companies.) During the same year, Western Union entered the telephone market, hoping to capitalize on patents obtained by Edison, Gray, and Amos Dolbear. However, Western Union's William Orton, who led the firm's push into the telephone business, died suddenly in April 1878. The threat of competition diminished, and New England Telephone merged with Bell Telephone.

Around this time, Bell Telephone Co. discovered that German-Jewish immigrant Emile Berliner had filed a variable-pressure transmitter caveat 13 days before Edison's first carbon transmitter patent application. The Company hired Berliner as protection.

Inevitably, other inventors' thinking evolved from "Why didn't I think of that?" to "I did think of that." In July 1877, Tufts College professor Amos Dolbear claimed he invented the telephone and demanded a share of the profits. When Hubbard declined he published, as threatened, a short treatise titled "The Telephone" making his claim but also admitting Bell was first to reduce the invention to practice. Dolbear complained that a mutual friend, Percival D. Richards, misinformed him regarding Bell's patents. When the Bell Telephone Co. persisted in refusing to make a deal, Dolbear signed an agreement with Western Union.

The legal battle with Western Union became known as the Dowd case. Bell Telephone Co. was led to victory by lawyer James J. Storrow. On Nov. 10, 1879, Western Union agreed to give up its telephone business and assign all related patents (including Edison's carbon microphone patent) to Bell Co. In exchange, they asked for and received 20% of telephone rental receipts for the next 17 years.

In the end, Bell's patents were tested in 600 separate cases. Most were actions brought against patent infringers. Some simply tried to get away with evading Bell Telephone Co.'s patents. Others honestly believed they had a right to do so.

One of the most prolific retroactive inventors was Daniel Drawbaugh. In 1880, he announced he invented the telephone sometime between 1866 and 1876. His rights were purchased by People's Telephone Company. Eight years of litigation were required to shake him loose. He resurfaced in 1903 claiming he, not Marconi, invented radio.

The "Government case" also deserves special mention. Dr. James W. Rogers, his son J. Harris Rogers, and his son's friend and former Congressman Casey Young hoped to shield infringers until Bell's patents expired or were annulled. Along the way, they bribed a number of influential people. The U.S. Supreme Court saw through the scheme and ruled in Bell's favor.

Amos Dolbear resurfaced and formed the Dolbear Electric Telephone Company. In 1881, the Bell Company enjoined Dolbear Electric and in 1886, the U.S. Supreme Court ruled for Bell.

Eighteen years of litigation solidified Bell's place as the inventor of the telephone.

Alexander Graham Bell went to work on other inventions. He tried communicating using a light beam of variable intensity impinging on selenium. He pursued flying machines, the phonograph, and a metal detector (used in a failed attempt to locate the bullet in President Garfield after he was shot). Bell also conceived sonar and a precursor to the iron lung.

Some people question Alexander Graham Bell's character. During the last decade of his life, he became involved with the eugenics movement.

Today, that movement is depicted as ignorant at best and racist at worst. However, eugenics was seen at the time as a natural offshoot of Darwin's theory of evolution, and its abuse by Nazi Germany was yet to come. If species evolve through genetic variability and natural selection many reasoned, then it may be possible to reduce the occurrence of harmful health conditions and improve the entire human race. Certainly, Bell never sought to create a "master race" or do away with those deemed genetically inferior. His involvement in eugenics was well-intentioned and harmless.

Alexander Graham Bell died August 2, 1922 at his estate Beinn Bhreagh on Cape Breton Island in Nova Scotia, Canada.

Bell showed that technical obstacles could be overcome through patience and hard work, and that in the process further dividends may be realized in the form of new discoveries. His work, as well as Thomas Edison's, remains a worthy model for modern research and development efforts. (Bell Telephone spawned Bell Laboratories, the birthplace of numerous inventions and theories, a model that didn't quite work after the Bell system was split up.) Together with Samuel F.B. Morse, Alexander Graham Bell laid the technological, commercial, and inspirational foundation for numerous wireless inventions.

Chapter Six
Marconi's Thunder

Scientists could observe Hertz's invisible electromagnetic waves for themselves; his experiments were simple and repeatable. They could also see that Maxwell's theory of the electromagnetic field correctly predicted the waves. But they still could not envision practical applications for Hertzian waves.

The young Italian Guglielmo Marconi was incredulous. Though a rank amateur with no academic credentials, he was certain there must be practical applications for Hertzian waves. So sure, in fact, he saw wireless communications as his ticket to fame and fortune.

It's easy to criticize the late 19th century science establishment for its lack of imagination. But the establishment had a point. The telegraph sprouted a worldwide network. For the first time in history, news raced around the globe in minutes. Heinrich Hertz only demonstrated that electromagnetic waves could traverse the length of his cramped laboratory. There was no evidence that wireless could link neighboring towns—let alone bridge the immense distances already spanned by undersea telegraph cables.

The newer telephone also argued for wire: No one had a clue how to send voice over wireless—if it was even possible.

Marconi's gift was his business acumen. He was the first person to take wireless out of the halls of academia and plant it firmly in the marketplace. He understood instinctively that pitting wireless against existing cable-based services would invite fierce opposition. He wisely pursued applications for which wires were useless or prohibitively expensive, such as communicating at sea or across rugged terrain.

Ironically, Marconi bet on a technology that ultimately proved a dead end. Knowing that everything hinged on communicating over long distances, he took Hertz's sparks and made them larger. They became so large, in fact, that they resembled lightning bolts—replete with thunder claps. What Marconi didn't know is that sparks are inefficient, defy tuning (to prevent interference), and are almost impossible to modulate (to carry speech). Marconi the technologist could not keep up with Marconi the business visionary.

Born in 1874, Guglielmo Marconi grew up at the Marconi family home built in 1600, Villa Griffone. His mother, Annie Jameson Marconi, was the daughter of Andrew Jameson of the venerable Jameson Irish Whiskey distillers. Annie met Guglielmo's father, Giuseppe, while visiting Italy and, despite her family's opposition, eloped with the older Italian. Once the deed was done Annie carefully mended relations with her family.

Annie Jameson figured prominently in Guglielmo's career. She had complete confidence in his abilities. Thanks to Annie, he became fluent in English, and it was through her Irish and British connections that Guglielmo found many of his customers, investors, and most talented engineers.

Guglielmo was primarily home schooled; his mother feared Italy's Catholic schools would turn him against her Protestant religion. He was fascinated by books about Michael Faraday and Benjamin Franklin he found in his father's small library. Around 1887, Guglielmo and a friend constructed a lightning detector. This device probably convinced him that it is possible to signal wirelessly over significant distances. The detector consisted of a coherer (an easy to make component) acting as the on/off switch in a bell ringing circuit.

In 1891, Marconi convinced his father to hire Professor Vincenzo Rosa to tutor him in physics. Rosa introduced him to experimental techniques. Marconi's mother arranged a meeting with Professor Augusto Righi at the University of Bologna; Righi assigned Marconi to be a lab assistant. Reading Righi's article on Hertz' experiments, Marconi became fascinated with wireless. Like Oliver Lodge, Righi was mainly interested in showing that high frequency Hertzian waves behave like light.

Marconi was never completely alone in believing there were applications for Hertzian waves. The English chemist and physicist William Crookes understood that radio waves could penetrate or go around obstacles opaque to light waves. In his article "Some Possibilities of Electricity" published in the February 1, 1892 issue of *Fortnightly Review*, Crookes wrote "Any two friends living within the radius of sensibility of their receiving instruments, having first decided on their special wave length and attuned their respective instruments to mutual receptivity, could thus communicate as long and as often as they pleased by timing the impulses to produce long and short intervals on the ordinary Morse code."

Oliver Lodge was intent on proving that Hertzian waves and light are different forms of the same phenomenon. That suggested at least one application: Lodge envisioned replacing lighthouses with "electric houses" beaming signals that could cut through heavy fog.

Ironically, one of the first persons to aggressively pursue practical applications of wireless was a man who knew nothing of Hertz. In 1884, the Welsh engineer William Preece noticed that telephone signals could be picked up by nearby wires. Though it was due to induction rather than radiation, Preece pursued the effect, and in 1892 he succeeded in signaling from Lavernock Point to Flat Holm Island in the Bristol Channel, a distance of 3.3 miles.

(Because induction is a magnetic field effect, it requires "antennas" roughly as long as the distance between the stations. Preece failed to communicate with Steep Holm Island just 5.3 miles away and never succeeded in establishing communications the nearly nine miles between opposite shores of the channel. Preece eventually became engineer-in-chief of the British General Post Office and wrote a paper in 1897 admitting Marconi's system was superior.)

Marconi began tinkering with Righi's spark gap Hertzian wave generator. He soon discovered he could improve the machine's performance by refining individual components. That was a critical lesson—a lesson Marconi would employ throughout his career. The only advantage Marconi's relationship with Professor Righi offered was access to a well-equipped laboratory; once Marconi developed an improved Hertzian wave generator, he built a private lab in the attic of his parents' home.

Marconi began experimenting in earnest at age 20. He built his own spark gap transmitter and receiver. Next, he added a Morse key to the transmitter and a Morse printer to the receiver, creating a wireless telegraph system. But there was one problem: Each time his detector encountered Hertzian waves it was switched on and remained in that state until reset.

In 1884, the Italian physicist Temistocle Calzecchi Onesti noticed that an approaching lightning storm causes a dramatic increase in the conductivity of loosely packed metal powder in an insulated tube. In 1890, the French physicist Edouard Branly showed the effect was due to Hertzian waves and referred to such tubes as "radio-conducteurs." Oliver Lodge speculated that tiny sparks between the filings caused adjacent particles to cohere and, consequently, dubbed the devices "coherers."

To receive Morse code, Marconi needed a coherer that could automatically receive a string of symbols, distinguishing dots from dashes. To communicate over appreciable distances, he also needed a coherer that was sensitive and reliable. He conquered these challenges in 1895.

The solution to the first problem was a small hammer (conceived and demonstrated by Oliver Lodge in 1894 as his "trembler") that tapped the particles loose. When electromagnetic waves were received, the coherer switched "on." The current immediately actuated a Morse printer and the hammer, and the coherer was ready to receive the next signal.

Distinguishing dots, dashes and spaces between characters was a bit tricky, however, because the Morse printer only recorded the leading edge of each signal. Consider the standard "S-O-S" message. In Morse code, an "S" is signified by three dots in succession; an "O" is signified by three dashes in succession. Upon receiving an "S-O-S" the Morse printer would record three closely-spaced marks, a long space, three widely-spaced marks, a long space, and another three closely-spaced marks.

Marconi solved the second problem by optimizing the coherer's performance. He methodically tested a variety of materials and configurations. He found a mixture of 95% nickel- and 5% silver-filings enclosed within a tube with silver plugs worked best. Later, he discovered that a vacuum increased the tube's sensitivity.

Marconi considered himself a self-taught scientist like Michael Faraday. He recreated Benjamin Franklin's kite experiment and later Hertz' electromagnetic wave experiments. He raced to prove there are practical applications for wireless before better-equipped university labs realized their mistake. He knew instinctively that success depended on range. The greater the distance he communicated with his wireless system, the more applications he could serve, and the higher the cost of the comparable wired infrastructure.

Marconi conquered distance one small step at a time. First, he successfully communicated between adjacent rooms. However, he needed funds to move ahead. His father was skeptical, but took notice when Marconi's always sensible cousin Daisy spoke enthusiastically about his experiments. Giuseppe asked him to explain why his experiments were a good investment. After all, that question would be asked by bankers. Marconi's response convinced his father to hand him 500 lira on the spot— not a fortune, but enough to buy additional materials.

Now he was ready to conduct experiments outdoors. Marconi's antenna proved a breakthrough. Inspired by Benjamin Franklin's kite experiment, he found the higher he raised his antenna the greater the distance he could communicate. Soon he was communicating hundreds of meters. He experimented with sheet, tube, and wire antennas. He discovered vertical aerials work best when one end is grounded (connected to earth). Obsessed with achieving ever greater range, he jumped far ahead of current theory.

Marconi conducted his first outdoor experiments in 1895 with the help of his 29-year old brother Alfonso and a young tenant farmer. He was soon transmitting Morse code signals further than his helpers, manning the receiver, could be seen or heard. They arranged to fire a rifle whenever they received the three dots representing the letter "s" in Morse code. Rifle shots rang out across the Bolognese countryside. Marconi even managed to reach the receiver with a hill blocking the path.

Now even Giuseppe was impressed. He invited the family physician and the parish priest to a demonstration and conference about how to proceed. Together, they composed a letter to the Italian Ministry of Posts and Telegraphs. After a long delay, they received a reply acknowledging the potential maritime applications, but offering only words of encouragement. The Marconis took the civil servant's words at face value and fixed their sights on Britain, the sea power in whose name more than half of the world's ships were registered. Annie wrote her British relatives.

After packing up his wireless apparatus, Marconi and his mother departed for England in February 1896. Conscious of the need to protect his intellectual property, Marconi installed the most important circuitry (particularly his improved coherer) in a black box. When they arrived in England his black box was disassembled by a suspicious British customs agent, causing considerable damage. Fortunately, his maternal cousin Henry Jameson Davis was a mechanical engineer and helped him repair the apparatus.

The Marconis' family physician wrote a letter of introduction to the Italian ambassador to England, who advised Marconi to immediately file for a patent. His patent application was accepted on March 19, 1896. Next, his cousin Henry introduced him to Alan Archibald Campbell-Swinton, who would become famous for describing an all-electronic television in 1908, and who wrote a letter of introduction dated March 30, 1896 to William Preece, engineer-in-chief of the General Post Office (GPO). Marconi met Preece in April.

Winning over Preece was essential. Marconi knew that to succeed in England he had to neutralize opposition stemming from the GPO's monopoly over telegraph service, established as part of the Telegraph Act of 1868. Preece could open other doors, as well.

Preece worked with Marconi in the GPO's workshop to improve his wireless apparatus. Within a few months, they were ready to demonstrate the invention at Salisbury Plain to high-ranking GPO officials. First, Marconi demonstrated that he could signal 300 yards. Then the distance was increased to one and one-quarter mile. Marconi's invention was also demonstrated to the British Army and Navy.

Why was William Preece so eager to assist Marconi? The British Association was composed of two major factions. There were theoreticians such as Oliver Lodge and Oliver Heaviside, and there were practical engineers such as William Preece. Preece had little patience for abstract concepts and, consequently, the Maxwellians. Heaviside looked down on Preece, once referring to him as "the eminent scienticulist." Preece was happy to ally himself with young Marconi who, like him, preferred practice over theory and whose black box outperformed anything the Maxwellians had produced.

Heaviside's fellow Maxwellian, Oliver Lodge, missed yet another golden opportunity.

Lodge demonstrated wireless signaling at the British Association meeting in Oxford on August 14, 1894 using a mirror galvanometer lent to him by Dr. Alexander Muirhead. Was this the first public demonstration of wireless telegraphy? By Lodge's own account, he used a Morse key and a Morse recorder, but didn't actually transmit Morse code.

Though some physicists believed the range of Hertzian waves was limited to the visible horizon, Lodge suspected otherwise. His friend G.F. FitzGerald theorized that there is a conductive layer of the atmosphere capable of reflecting Hertzian waves. Once again, Lodge proved his own worst enemy. Instead of investigating a scientific controversy he was eminently qualified to resolve, Lodge shifted his attention to Fabian socialism and psychical research.

At the British Association meeting in Liverpool in the fall of 1896, Preece announced that his Italian protégé successfully signaled over a distance of one mile at Salisbury Plain. Back in London, Marconi publicly exhibited his invention on Dec. 14, 1896 in Toynbee Hall. Marconi sent a signal that caused a bell to ring in a separate box with no wires attached; Preece carried the box around to show this was no parlor trick.

Next, in May of 1897 Preece arranged for Marconi to demonstrate signaling across the Bristol Channel in Wales—the same spot where Preece tried and failed to signal using induction. After attempting to signal from Lavernock Point to Flat Holm Island for two days without success, Marconi descended from a cliff to the seashore and achieved immediate results. This was witnessed by the German professor Adolphus Slaby who rushed back to Germany in order to replicate Marconi's invention. Later, when Marconi began to deploy his wireless systems outside Britain, Germany tried to undermine and block him.

In July of 1897, Marconi and Preece suddenly parted company. It was now obvious that Marconi's invention was of great value. The GPO offered to buy Marconi's patent and he declined, instead forming a company to pursue commercial opportunities. Preece immediately stopped supporting Marconi, but he had already served his purpose.

Marconi founded the Wireless Telegraph and Signal Company in July 1897; it was quickly subscribed to £100,000, a huge sum in those days, with Marconi's friends and relatives the main investors. Meanwhile, cable and telegraph stocks tumbled. At his father's suggestion, Marconi later (1900) changed the company's name to Marconi Wireless Telegraph Co. Ltd.

In November 1897, Marconi set up the first permanent wireless telegraph station at the Royal Needles Hotel on the Isle of Wight. By early 1898, Marconi was operating a wireless link from there to Madeira House at Bournemouth. When Lord Kelvin (William Thomson) and Tennyson visited, they insisted upon paying for the wireless telegrams they forwarded to Bournemouth. This was not just a friendly gesture; it added the weight of their names to Marconi's contention that his wireless service did not violate the Post Office's landline telegraph monopoly.

The episode was a personal triumph for Marconi for another reason. Lord Kelvin was initially among those who dismissed commercial applications of Hertzian waves, reportedly saying "Wireless is all very well, but I would rather send a message by a boy on a pony." That would have been quite a feat between the Isle of Wight and Bournemouth.

Another incident highlighted the value of wireless communications. Bournemouth attracted many notable visitors. Former Prime Minister William Gladstone happened to be in Bournemouth in early 1898 when he fell gravely ill. His near-death was a headline-maker, and reporters rushed to Bournemouth, but a snowstorm promptly knocked out the town's telegraph lines. Marconi's wireless station was able to relay stories via the Isle of Wight, where telegraph links to London were still operational. (Gladstone survived, but only for a few months, dying at his estate.)

Marconi landed his first commercial contract later that year. In May, Lloyds of London asked Marconi to test the feasibility of signaling the arrival of steamboats. The tests were successful and Lloyds became Marconi's first major customer. However, that success came at a human cost: One of Marconi's assistants, Edward Glanville, fell 300 feet from a cliff to his death while working on the tests.

In July 1898, Marconi was engaged by the Dublin *Daily Express* to cover the Kingstown Regatta sailboat race. For the first time, people on shore could follow the race's progress as it occurred. The distances also proved Marconi's system could communicate over-the-horizon and around or over hills. A new era of communications was inaugurated.

Queen Victoria and Edward, Prince of Wales were impressed by Marconi's Kingstown Regatta coverage and asked him to set up a wireless link between the Queen's residence at Osborne and the royal yacht in August 1898. Over one-hundred years before sending text messages swept the globe, Queen Victoria received regular wireless text messages from Prince Edward.

Marconi was next asked by the French government to establish the first cross channel wireless link, which he achieved on March 27, 1899 amid enthusiastic coverage in *McClure's* magazine. Marconi was now communicating wirelessly over distances in excess of 30 miles. Every major country was interested in this new communications medium.

Not everyone was happy for Marconi, though. Oliver Lodge glibly opined, "One of the students in Prof. A. Righi's class at Bologna being gifted, doubtless, with a sense of humour as well as with considerable energy and some spare time, proceeded to put a coherer into a sealed box and bring it to England as a new and secret plan adapted to electrical signaling at a distance without wires."

Lodge adopted a more defensive tone in a letter to *The Times*: "It appears that many persons suppose that the method of signaling across space by means of Hertz waves received by a Branly tube of iron filings is a new discovery made by Signor Marconi, who has recently been engaged in improving some of the details."

"It is well known to physicists, and perhaps the public may be willing to share the information, that I myself showed what was essentially the same plan of signaling in 1894. My apparatus acted very vigorously across the college quadrangle, a distance of 60 yards, and I estimated that there would be some response up to a limit of half a mile..."

Lodge finally decided to pursue commercial opportunities, developing his own technology and filing for patents. Unfortunately, he outsmarted himself, believing that induction has advantages over radiation, and confident he could improve on Preece's original induction system. For example, Lodge knew he could amplify induction signals merely by adding turns to the coils. (Lodge believed, incorrectly, that in contrast electromagnetic waves could not be amplified.) Most important, Lodge knew he could add tuning (he called it "syntony") to his induction system. His first patent application was titled "Improvements in Syntonised Telegraphy without Line Wires."

As Preece discovered to his chagrin, induction has a serious limitation. While the field strength of a radio signal is inversely proportional to the distance from the transmitter, the field strength of a signal due to induction is inversely proportional to the square of the distance. Double the distance of a radio link and the field strength drops by half; double the distance for an inductive link and the field strength drops by three-quarters.

Lodge could not make up his mind so he decided to pursue both the radiation (Hertzian waves) and induction (magnetic field) approaches simultaneously. He developed an improved coherer, having discovered that a single-point junction was more sensitive, and that decoherence could be reestablished electrically rather than mechanically—though the device proved extremely delicate.

In a lecture in 1898 in Liverpool, Lodge demonstrated wireless telegraphy using Leyden jar oscillators, tuned ("syntonic") circuits, and his improved coherer. Though he once favored the induction system, he finally admitted the electromagnetic wave (radio) system offered greater range. However, by now Marconi had jumped way ahead. Lodge's syntony patent was his only real asset.

James Gordon Bennett, publisher of the New York *Herald*, asked the 25-year old Marconi to cover the America's Cup race in October 1899 off Sandy Hook, New Jersey. Bennett paid Marconi handsomely: $5,000. Marconi traveled on the Cunard Line's *Aurania* and consequently developed a life-long love for transoceanic liners. The U.S. media portrayed Marconi as an inventor-hero, and he did his best to endear himself to Americans.

The U.S. Navy asked Marconi to demonstrate his wireless system. He set up wireless stations on the cruiser *New York* and battleship *Massachusetts*, and successfully exchanged messages at a distance of 35 miles. The Navy was impressed, and there was talk of equipping all of its ships with Marconi's wireless equipment. But that also presented a dilemma: with so many ships sharing the frequency band, how could interference be prevented?

Reportedly, Marconi said he had equipment in England that solved the problem, and he promised to bring it to the U.S. However, the patent chronology suggests that Marconi was pitching vaporware—he knew that to win big orders from big customers he needed wireless gear that could be tuned to different wavelengths to prevent interference, so he said what the Navy wanted to hear, and then made it happen. Shortly after returning to

Britain, he hired John Ambrose Fleming as a consultant to help develop and patent a tuning solution. Fleming, a former professor of physics and mathematics, lent credibility within the British science establishment to Marconi's organization, until then looked down upon as a purely mercantile enterprise.

In late 1900, Marconi filed a patent application for "Improvements in Apparatus for Wireless Telegraphy" describing his tuning solution and he received the now-famous "four-sevens" patent (British patent No. 7777) in June 1904. Marconi's solution entailed four tuned circuits per wireless link. There was one in the transmitter and one feeding the transmit antenna, plus one connected to the receive antenna and another connected to the detector. This differed from Lodge's solution (Lodge was indisputably first to patent tuning) which used only two tuned circuits per wireless link—both in the antenna circuits.

By now, wireless was practically Marconi's exclusive domain. Radios of all types were called "Marconi devices" and messages were dubbed "Marconigrams." Others could say they contributed to the development of wireless technology, but no one could claim to have done as much to commercialize and popularize wireless communications as Marconi.

Buoyed by his successes, Marconi decided on two strategic moves. In 1900, he created two subsidiaries of the Marconi Wireless Company: Marconi International Marine Company and American Marconi. The latter company would eventually become RCA Corp.

Marconi also resolved in 1900 to attempt wireless communications across the Atlantic, but kept his intentions secret for fear that failure would cause incalculable harm to his reputation. He re-hired John Ambrose Fleming, now Professor of Electrical Engineering at University College London (a position he would hold for 42 years) and a recognized expert in power engineering, as a consultant at £500 per year to lead the design and construction of a transmitter with unprecedented power.

It would be no easy feat: the furthest Marconi had communicated so far was 200 miles. Marconi estimated that sending signals across the Atlantic Ocean would require two inch sparks; Fleming believed that would require generating 100,000 volts.

The transmitting station was to be located at Poldhu in south Cornwall. Fleming devised a transmitter consisting of a 25-kilowatt alternator (driven by a 20 HP engine) producing 2,000 volts at 50 hertz; a huge capacity condenser; and transformers in place of the conventional inductor. Three transformers stepped up the voltage to 20,000 volts. Construction began in

October 1900 and the station was completed in January 1901. The antenna consisted of 20 wooden masts 60 meters high forming a circle 66 meters in diameter.

The last transformer was Marconi's innovative "jigger." It served to couple the transmitter's closed circuits with the open circuit of the antenna. It also converted the original 50-hertz oscillations to 800-900 kilohertz. Marconi put this part of the transmitter in a separate building, perhaps as a way of demarcating where Fleming's authority ended.

Despite its many refinements, the Poldhu station relied on brute force. The goal was simple: generate a signal sufficiently powerful to be detected on the other side of the Atlantic. Local residents reported that the transmitter produced what sounded like thunderclaps.

In March 1901, Marconi set off for America with engineer Richard Vyvyan. Initially, Marconi selected an isolated promontory near Cape Cod, Massachusetts for the receive station. Vyvyan feared the aerials at both ends were unsound and might be damaged by high winds. It turned out he was right. When the Poldhu aerial collapsed, Marconi decided to abandon Cape Cod. He picked St. John's, Newfoundland as the new receive station location because Newfoundland was the closest part of North America to Poldhu— 1,800 miles distant.

Marconi and assistants George Kemp and Percy Paget sailed for Canada on November 26, 1901. He led reporters to believe he and his men were listening for ocean-going traffic and that is exactly what the *Halifax Herald* printed. After wrestling unsuccessfully with hydrogen-filled balloons on December 10 and 11, Kemp and Paget requisitioned large, sturdy, Levitor kites to keep the aerial aloft. Developed for the British Army, these kites were designed to lift a man for observational purposes.

Marconi finally heard the Morse code "S-S-S" signals at 12:30, 1:10, and 2:20 pm on December 12, 1901. Marconi's critics suggested he heard static; after all, there were no independent witnesses. And Marconi had no shortage of critics—degreed engineers looked down on Marconi just as Edison looked down on degreed engineers. Many engineers felt the press gave Marconi too much credit and ignored the many scientists whose work benefited Marconi. Some engineers doubted anyone could signal wirelessly across the Atlantic.

Even Edison hesitated to believe that Marconi had heard signals from the other side of the Atlantic. He reasoned that it was a clever publicity stunt on the part of a man building a maritime communications business. But the newspapers believed Marconi, as did key officials in the Canadian government, and apparently the undersea cable operator Anglo-American Cable

Company did, too; the company warned Marconi that it would sue if he continued experiments violating the company's transatlantic communications monopoly.

When the American Institute of Electrical Engineers invited Marconi to appear at its annual dinner at the Waldorf-Astoria Hotel on January 13, 1902 the floodgates opened. Marconi and Kemp were mobbed. A telegram from Edison was read congratulating Marconi. He received effusive praise in Britain from Preece, Kelvin, and Silvanus Thompson (who is remembered as the author of *Calculus Made Easy*).

Oliver Lodge remained skeptical. Lodge believed it is possible to communicate with the dead, but he did not believe it was possible to communicate wirelessly between Cornwall and Newfoundland. Marconi had a hunch that somehow—exactly how he did not know—wireless signals would follow the earth's curvature. The public's perception of wireless bordered on superstitious; this was illustrated when a reporter asked Marconi: "Are big storms caused by too much high-power radio in the sky?" Marconi laughingly replied: "No. There were bad storms in prehistoric days."[6]

Oliver Heaviside and Arthur Edwin Kennelly suggested, simultaneously but independently, that an ionized layer of the upper atmosphere was responsible for long-range transmission. This became known as "the Heaviside layer" and more popularly as "the ionosphere." The existence of the ionosphere was ultimately proved by Edward V. Appleton in 1927.

In hindsight, Marconi's use of low frequencies made signaling across the Atlantic much harder than it needed to be. Marconi's experiments suggested that lower frequencies enable greater distances. And that is partly true. But low frequencies require large antennas, and there was not yet an accurate method for measuring wavelengths. Fleming solved that problem in 1904 when he invented the first frequency measuring instrument, the "cymometer."

What Marconi didn't know is that under certain conditions the ionos-phere enables worldwide communications at high frequencies. We now know that the ionosphere's ability to reflect signals back to earth varies by frequency, time of day, time of year, and period in the roughly 11-year sunspot cycle. When the U.S. Congress passed the Radio Act of 1912, it banished amateur radio operators to frequencies above 1.5 megahertz (MHz). The "Hams" quickly discovered it is possible to communicate great distances

---

[6] "Master of Micro-Waves," *Time Magazine*, October 9, 1933.

with relatively low-power transmitters in the 3-30 megahertz (MHz) range. This high frequency (HF) region of the radio spectrum became known as the "shortwave" band.

Marconi's successful transatlantic test ignited wireless mania. However, excitement had been growing for some time. About six months earlier, physicist and writer William Ayrton described a future in which people are always in contact with others, regardless of location, via wireless communications. In Ayrton's fantasy world, if you try to reach someone and they don't respond, it can only mean they are dead. Ayrton envisioned the world we now take for granted.

While Marconi's triumphs sparked Ayrton's imagination they also awakened pecuniary interests. Though Oliver Lodge once referred to patents as an "...inappropriate and repulsive form of registering a claim to an attempt at monopoly," he founded the Lodge-Muirhead Syndicate in 1901 with Alexander Muirhead.

The Lodge-Muirhead Syndicate mainly developed custom wireless equipment—specializing in low-power, tunable systems. Ironically, the Lodge-Muirhead Syndicate was denied access to the coastal areas where its equipment made most sense on the basis that it might interfere with existing Marconi gear. Marconi had the further advantage that he provided a turnkey service based on a growing network while the Lodge-Muirhead Syndicate sold equipment outright.

As time passed, it became clear the Lodge-Muirhead Syndicate's most valuable asset was the syntony patent. Marconi would need a tuning solution if only to prevent self-interference within his growing wireless network. Lodge finally began to demand recognition and compensation. There was sympathy for him within the British judiciary; he secured an extension to his patent, which was approaching expiration.

In 1908, Godfrey Isaacs was appointed Managing Director of the Marconi Company. As a hired manager, he was able to look at patent disputes dispassionately. Ironically, it was William Preece who brought Lodge and Isaacs together in 1911 to discuss an out-of-court settlement.

With 19 patents for his black box, Marconi was in a reasonably strong position. But he now had an international business to protect. An agreement was reached under which Marconi bought Lodge's patent for an undisclosed sum (according to one report, £20,000) and paid Lodge £1,000 per year for the remaining life of the patent. In return, Lodge and Muirhead agreed to dissolve their company. From that point on, Lodge restricted his wireless endeavors to writing for publications including *Popular Wireless*, *Wireless Review*, and *Harmsworth's Wireless Encyclopedia*.

Spark technology reached its zenith with Marconi's commercial service between Glace Bay, Nova Scotia and Clifden, Ireland. At Glace Bay, Richard Vyvyan used a steam-powered 50-kilowatt generator feeding an upside down, double cone antenna.

Built in 1905, the Clifton station was immense, occupying a site of nearly 2.5 square kilometers. It transmitted at 45-kHz (6.7 km wavelength) and required a giant condenser consisting of 1,800 galvanized iron plates. It employed a directional transmit antenna almost 1 km long consisting of eight wooden masts (later steel), each 64 meters high, and fed by a rotary spark gap transmitter. The earth ground was provided by a copper mesh 180 meters long and 1.2 meters wide buried directly beneath the antenna wires. The receiving antenna consisted of four parallel wires situated above the transmit wires. The steam-driven generator produced 300 kilowatts. At its peak, the Clifton station had 150 employees.

John Ambrose Fleming, the consultant Marconi hired to develop tuning, and Guglielmo Marconi parted ways when Fleming botched a public demonstration of Marconi's tuned wireless system in June 1903 at the Royal Institution. Marconi touted his tuned system as enabling private conversations. The magician Nevil Maskelyne clandestinely injected messages designed to embarrass Marconi.[7] Maskelyne had obtained a few wireless patents, but instead of developing his own wireless business he set himself up as one of Marconi's most vocal critics. While the partially deaf Fleming lectured, Morse code rolled in, including the rhyme "There was a young fellow of Italy, who diddled the public prettily." Marconi promptly fired Fleming.

Maskelyne simply used a nearby, untuned spark transmitter. Fleming accused him of trying to wreck the exhibition; Maskelyne countered that he was only trying to ascertain whether Marconi's claims were accurate. And he had a point: Tuning minimizes interference provided that all wireless stations use it, but it does not guarantee privacy. (Maskelyne is not remembered fondly, however—he is credited with inventing the pay toilet.)

Fleming subsequently invented a device that served as the foundation for the next 50 years of progress. The "valve" was a simple diode and the first vacuum tube. Fleming was probably motivated, in part, by the desire to prove

---

[7] The incident is remembered as "the Maskelyne affair."

Marconi erred in dismissing him. Ultimately, Marconi was forced to adopt Fleming's valve as a more sensitive detector.

In 1909, Marconi shared the Nobel Prize with Germany's Karl Braun, inventor of the crystal diode rectifier. The crystal diode, also known as the cat's whisker diode, is a key component in crystal radio kits that have amused children for decades.

In 1912, the *Titanic* tragedy demonstrated the value and even necessity of wireless communications at sea. Thanks to wireless, more than 700 lives were saved; without it, no one would have noticed the ship was lost until days later. Consequently, the U.S. Congress passed the Radio Act of 1912 requiring all seafaring vessels to maintain around-the-clock wireless communications and the licensing of amateur radio operators to prevent interference.

Despite having the foresight to launch a communications revolution, Marconi clung to spark technology for too long. Vacuum tubes enabled continuous waves and soon rendered spark technology obsolete. While Marconi achieved considerable fame and some fortune, the big payoff came after he retired.

Marconi became an Italian marquis and senator—but also an ardent fascist and Mussolini supporter. Over the last two decades of his life, he experienced several angina pectoris attacks, recovering each time until his worst attack on July 19, 1937. Guglielmo Marconi passed away the following day, July 20, 1937.

Was Marconi "the father of radio"? A common complaint is that Marconi merely exploited others' discoveries and inventions without acknowledging them. But that misses the point.

Nikola Tesla demonstrated wireless communications in 1893, and the U.S. courts eventually ruled that his patents invalidated Marconi's. But Tesla never pursued wireless communications. David E. Hughes probably stumbled upon radio waves before Hertz, but thought he was observing induction. The Russian physicist Alexander Popov demonstrated a wireless lightning detector in 1895, but did not apply for a patent. In India, Jagadis Chandra Bose employed microwaves and an innovative coherer in 1895 to remotely ignite gunpowder, but also did not apply for a patent.

Despite conflicting claims, wireless communications was never more than the subject of scientific research to experimenters such as Popov and Bose (who many justifiably consider the "father of wireless science"). Only Marconi believed there were practical applications requiring immediate attention. Only Marconi perceived the role of the technology entrepreneur—

bringing wireless to market—as worthwhile and noble. And only Marconi saw the importance of communicating wirelessly over long distances.

Oliver Lodge again deserves an honorable mention. Though he was a physicist more than a businessman, Lodge enjoyed working at the intersection of science and technology and made several important contributions, particularly his pioneering work with coherers and tuning. He lived a long and productive life, passing away in 1940 at the age of 89. Just before he died, Lodge vowed to prove the existence of an afterlife by communicating from the other side. He has not been heard from since—but neither will he be forgotten.

Perhaps it would be more accurate to call Marconi "the father of the wireless industry." Guglielmo Marconi did more than anyone else to show that there is a need for wireless technology. That seems obvious today, but it was far from obvious at the time, and successfully bringing a new technology to market is both more challenging and important than it might at first appear.

Chapter Seven
Continuous Waves

Reginald Aubrey Fessenden, though not a name familiar to Americans, was a prolific inventor. His creations ran the gamut from microphotography to sonar to the turbo-electric drive for battleships. His wireless inventions, however, were staggering in both number and farsightedness. In Canada, the centenary of the first audio broadcast was celebrated with a postage stamp honoring Fessenden.

When Fessenden learned of Marconi's spark technology he immediately recognized its limitations. Sparks are inefficient, prone to giving and receiving interference, and an unlikely candidate for carrying speech or music. Fessenden knew exactly what the problem was, and it wasn't long before he conceived a solution.

Sparks produce "damped waves"—electromagnetic waves that fall rapidly in strength and soon vanish. Containing hidden frequencies, they splatter their energy across the radio spectrum, wasting power and bandwidth. Marconi discovered he could rig up a transmitter to generate sparks in rapid succession, eight per second, to create trains of damped waves. Then he inserted a telegraph key, turning the train off and on to form Morse code characters. It was a clever way of harnessing the spark transmitter's crude signals, but there was no hiding its deficiencies, and eventually spark transmitters would be banned for causing needless interference.

Fessenden envisioned a simpler and cleaner technology almost from the start—a technology that might one day lead to a mass market. He knew that if he could produce steady electromagnetic waves—the kind represented mathematically as pure sine waves—he could greatly boost efficiency, eliminate much interference, and impress the signals with speech and music. Fessenden's pristine signals became known as "continuous waves."

In fact, Reginald Fessenden was in some ways the Alexander Graham Bell of wireless. Though the details of his life are at times unclear, he is widely credited as first to demonstrate the transmission of voice and music over wireless. Why that remained unheralded and the name "Fessenden" languished in obscurity for so long are intriguing aspects of this remarkable inventor's life.

He was born in 1866 in the Canadian province of Quebec, the eldest of four children, all of them boys. His parents hoped Reginald would dedicate himself to serving others by becoming a minister (like his father Elisha) or teacher. In the eyes of his mother Clementina, inventing was surely the road to ruin; her father invested in a string of failed inventions, leaving her family penniless when he died. She was also a devotee of Britain's Queen Victoria, campaigned for the establishment of Empire Day, and for some time her fame overshadowed her son's—at least in some circles.

Reginald caught the inventor's bug anyway, and his youth was not completely devoid of inspiration in that direction. He read with fascination articles in *Scientific American* describing the work of Alexander Graham Bell. And despite his parent's misgivings, his uncle Cortez Fessenden encouraged him to pursue his passion.

Fessenden was an accomplished student. He attended Trinity College School in Port Hope, Ontario for two years and at the age of 14 was granted a mathematics mastership to Bishop's College in Lennoxville, Quebec. Four years later, he left Bishop's College without a degree, even though he completed "substantially all the work necessary." That didn't stop him from promptly finding a teaching position at the Whitney Institute in Bermuda, where he served as the sole teacher and principal. There he met Helen May Trott who would become his wife of 40 years.

Fessenden knew all along he was meant to be an inventor. Like most young men with such ambitions at the time, he dreamt of landing a job with the legendary Thomas Edison. After two years in Bermuda, he moved to New York City to pursue that goal. He boldly requested a meeting with the great inventor himself, but was denied. However, his persistence finally paid off; he happened to be present at the Edison Machine Works in 1887 when a tester suddenly left and Fessenden was offered the job on the spot. Developing a reputation as a highly competent troubleshooter, he was soon promoted to head tester.

During the early days of electrification, wealthy individuals such as J.P. Morgan built their own power plants. Fessenden recommended Morgan use conduit to protect against fires—an idea that eventually was universally adopted. Fessenden impressed the financial wizard, who complimented him to Edison, leading to another promotion.

Now Fessenden was working directly for Edison at the inventor's new Llewellyn Park laboratory in Orange, New Jersey. He was given problem-solving assignments ranging from chemistry to metallurgy to electricity. One of those assignments was to develop a better insulating material. Existing coatings tended to dry out and crack from exposure to heat. Edison sought a material with the insulation properties of glass and flexibility of India rubber. It was like requesting a breakthrough on demand. Fessenden didn't reinvent insulation, but he did make progress. His "dipole theory of elasticity" argued that electric forces—rather than gravity as suggested by Lord Kelvin—held rubber particles together. In 1890, Edison promoted Fessenden to Chief Chemist. From that lofty position, he gained access to an excellent technical library and found himself communing with industry luminaries such as electric power maven George Westinghouse.

Fessenden was thrilled by Heinrich Hertz's experiments demonstrating the existence of radio waves. He began conducting his own experiments and soon convinced himself there must be something better than spark-gap transmitters and coherer receivers. He had a hunch that wireless could enhance not only the telegraph, but the telephone. However, that required something more refined than sparks.

Specifically, he began thinking of ways to transmit voice over wireless. His hero and mentor Edison was skeptical. According to one anecdote, when Fessenden asked Edison about the prospects of transmitting voice wirelessly, Edison snarled: "What do you say are man's chances of jumping over the moon? I figure one is about as likely as the other."

Edison's gruff personality aside, Fessenden learned two crucial lessons working for the wizard. He learned to think in terms of systems rather than components, because systems lead to multiple inventions. He also learned the importance of securing patents. Unfortunately, he failed to acquire Edison's profound sense of market demand and timing.

There are conflicting accounts about why Fessenden left Edison in 1890. According to one account, business slowed and Fessenden was let go when Edison fired all but a few workers. But another claims Fessenden left to accept a job with Westinghouse. What is certain is that the battle between Westinghouse's alternating current (AC) and Edison's direct current (DC) approach to electric power distribution was in full swing, and Fessenden ended up supervising the development of power generators for Westinghouse. He must have felt financially secure at this point, because he promptly sent for Helen and got married.

Hiring Fessenden paid off on a grand scale when Fessenden developed improved lead-wires for light bulbs in 1892, enabling Westinghouse to secure a major light bulb manufacturing contract. Perhaps as a perk, Fessenden was sent to northern England to evaluate new steam turbines. He suggested they would be best suited to powering electric motors used to drive ships' propellers. Though the Navy showed little interest at the time, and Fessenden neglected to apply for a patent, his "turbo-electric drive" eventually became the standard for battleships.

Though Fessenden appeared to be on a steadily ascending trajectory career-wise, he must have felt something was lacking. He impressed people in academia as well as industry, and he wasn't sure which milieu he preferred. Upon returning from northern England he was offered a position as professor of electrical engineering at Purdue University in West Lafayette, Indiana that would allow him to investigate the transmission of sound via wireless. He accepted.

He must have left Westinghouse Corp. on good terms, though. While at Purdue he helped Westinghouse install the lighting for the 1893 World's Columbian Exposition in Chicago. The Exposition was a celebration of modern wonders, its halls filled with everything from neo-classical sculptures to electric motors and generators—all of it dazzlingly illuminated using AC power. To a nation just learning about electrification, it made the south shore of Lake Michigan look like the Las Vegas of a century later.

Not long after, George Westinghouse personally recruited Fessenden for the newly created chair of the Electrical Engineering department at Western University of Pennsylvania (now the University of Pittsburgh). Westinghouse sweetened the deal by offering him $1,000 (a significant sum in those days) towards equipping a laboratory inside Westinghouse's facilities. Under this arrangement, Fessenden performed work for Westinghouse and developed and patented a number of inventions in his own name. One of those inventions was microphotography, popular for many years as a document preservation technique.

Wireless continued to be Fessenden's core interest. In 1899, he demonstrated wireless transmission over 50 miles from Cobb Island, Maryland to Arlington, Virginia. The U.S. Weather Bureau liked what it saw, and hired him for $3,000 per year to help develop a wireless weather information network.

In 1900, Fessenden left the University of Pittsburgh to work for the Weather Bureau full time, hoping to prove that wireless was a viable alternative to telegraph lines. The contract gave the Weather Bureau access to all the devices Fessenden invented, while he retained ownership. Fessenden produced several important innovations, many of them aimed at enabling wireless transmission and reception of audio.

Fessenden demonstrated his genius when he modified a spark transmitter to handle minimally intelligible speech. It wasn't by any stretch of imagination a marketable solution, but it demonstrated that speech can be sent over wireless, and that doubters like Edison were simply wrong. Fessenden realized if he built a spark transmitter that sparked at a sufficiently high rate—faster than the audio frequencies it needed to handle—he could then modulate the signal by inserting a microphone between the transmitter and the antenna. Cutting tiny slits in a phonograph cylinder, he built a mechanical contraption for interrupting the spark-gap at a rate of roughly 10,000 times per second.

Reginald Fessenden transmitted speech wirelessly for the first time in history on December 23, 1900. The transmission took place on Cobb Island over a distance of one mile. His voice was badly distorted and accompanied by a loud noise. Reportedly, Fessenden's first words were "Hello, one, two, three, four. Is it snowing where you are, Mr. Thiessen? If it is, telegraph back and let me know." His assistant Alfred Thiessen, also a Weather Bureau employee, responded as requested.

In essence, Reginald Fessenden superimposed his voice on a wireless telegraph transmitting Morse code dots at an extraordinarily high rate. It was a primitive form of amplitude modulation. In amplitude modulation (AM) the transmit signal strength varies continuously in proportion to the source signal strength (in this case Fessenden's voice). Fessenden's system differed from AM, however, in that it used closely-spaced pulses rather than a continuous transmit signal.

Fessenden's historic demonstration also required a new type of receiver. He knew that existing detectors could not handle speech. In fact, to Fessenden the coherer was worse than useless, "…retarding the development of a practical detector." And he had a point. The coherer was simply a switch that can be thrown into the "on" position by a radio wave. Needed, instead, was a detector that continuously varied its resistance in proportion to the amplitude of the received electromagnetic waves and did not have to be tapped back.

Fessenden's solution was the hot-wire barretter detector (U.S. Patent 706,744 issued in 1902). The word "barretter" is derived from the French word for "exchanger." The device consists of a fine platinum wire embedded in a silver wire, drawn to a small diameter, etched to expose a length of platinum, and enclosed in a vacuum tube. A direct current heats the wire. It is essentially a very sensitive thermoresistor (a device that varies in resistance in accordance with temperature)—so sensitive that its resistance varies in response to Hertzian waves fed from an antenna.

While making one of his hot wire barretter detectors in 1903, Fessenden accidentally left the wire in nitric acid and discovered the even more sensitive electrolytic detector. The electrolytic detector (sometimes called the "liquid barretter") became the standard detector until it was replaced by the galena crystal and finally the vacuum tube in 1913. Using an electrolytic detector in place of the coherer, a radio operator could actually recognize individual wireless telegraph stations by their distinctive sounds.

The U.S. Weather Bureau renewed Fessenden's contract and expanded the scope of his work. Encouraged by his first wireless voice transmission, he began to pursue a conceptually simple but difficult-to-implement means of producing continuous waves: the high-frequency electric alternator. The idea that continuous waves might be produced by a dynamo feeding a tuned circuit was first suggest by G.F. FitzGerald. Fessenden hoped to build a device that generated alternating current at 100,000 Hertz or higher—frequencies way above those used for AC power distribution (typically around 60 Hertz).

Around the same time another source of continuous waves was discovered: the arc lamp. Prior to Edison's incandescent light, arc lamps were used for street lighting. However, arc lamps had an annoying characteristic: they produced an audible hum. In 1899, British electrical engineer William Duddell investigated the cause and showed that it was the result of regularly fluctuating current. He found he could increase the frequency of the oscillations to produce musical notes, creating the singing arc lamp. Duddell exhibited the device as an electronic musical instrument.

Then the Danish scientist Valdemar Poulsen found that by adding a tuned circuit he could drive the arc lamp's oscillations up to the 200 kHz to 1 megahertz (MHz) range. The arc itself produced moderately damped waves, but these could be used to drive a resonant tuned circuit putting out continuous waves. The oscillating arc transmitter was gradually perfected by Poulsen through advances such as operating in a hydrogen atmosphere. The oscillating arc would later give Fessenden's high-frequency alternator stiff competition.

Fessenden was sold on the high-frequency alternator. Discussing the idea with his uncle Cortez in 1897, he conceived a specific solution and obtained U.S. Patent 706737 (issued August, 1902). He knew that the output of an alternator (a device that converts mechanical motion into alternating current) resembles a pure sine wave. If such a device could be mechanically modified to produce alternating current at sufficiently high frequencies, the output could be modulated by an audio signal and fed into an antenna. There was reason for optimism: Nikola Tesla had already developed a 10,000 Hertz alternator—more than two orders of magnitude faster than standard AC power distribution systems. Fessenden just needed a ten-fold increase over what Tesla had achieved.

Fessenden's scheme was ridiculed by spark technology proponents. No less an authority than John Ambrose Fleming wrote: "...there was no HF alternator of the kind described by Fessenden and it is doubtful if any appreciable radiation would result if such a machine were available and were used as Fessenden proposes."

Undaunted, Fessenden hired General Electric to manufacture a prototype alternator running 100 kilohertz (kHz). In 1902, GE's Charles Proteus Steinmetz delivered a unit that ran at 3,750 revolutions per minute (rpm) to produce a 1,200 watt signal at 10 kHz—a frequency too low for speech or music. Still, Fessenden succeeded in transmitting tones the 50 miles from Buxton to Manteo in North Carolina.

That same year, a dispute arose between Fessenden and Weather Bureau Chief Willis Moore. According to Fessenden, Moore suddenly demanded a fifty per cent share for himself of all patents obtained by Fessenden while working at the Weather Bureau—contradicting the original contract between Fessenden and the Weather Bureau. In August of 1902, threatened with the loss of his job if he did not accede to Moore's demand, Fessenden decided to start his own business.

Fessenden founded the National Electric Signaling Company (NESCO) with the financial backing of two wealthy Pittsburgh businessmen, Hay Walker, Jr. and Thomas H. Given. The company's business mission was to compete with Marconi. To that end, wireless stations were built at Brant Rock, Massachusetts (which became NESCO's headquarters) and in New York, Philadelphia and Washington.

Since the high-frequency alternator was not ready for commercial introduction, Fessenden decided to pursue two transmitter designs simultaneously. The high-frequency alternator was a relatively low-power device, but it could handle both telegraphy and audio. The rotary-spark transmitter was a high-power device for long-distance wireless telegraphy. Fessenden was confident he could build a commercial-grade rotary-spark transmitter in short order (he used something like it to demonstrate wireless voice transmission two years earlier), and that would give NESCO something to sell while continuing to develop the HF alternator.

The rotary-spark transmitter addressed problems that arose as the industry moved to more powerful sparks: heat, erosion, and arcing. A rotating disk controlled the frequency and duration of the sparks, and ensured that each spark was quenched before the next spark. There were two major types of rotary-spark transmitters: asynchronous and synchronous. Asynchronous rotary-spark transmitters were less efficient but relatively easy to operate and maintain. Synchronous rotary-spark transmitters fired in time with the alternating current input to optimize the signal power delivered to the antenna, but required careful alignment.

The Brant Rock synchronous rotary-spark transmitter was completed in late 1905. It was a huge machine with a six-foot diameter rotor powered by a 40-horsepower steam engine. The synchronous rotary-spark gap fired on both positive and negative peaks of a three-phase, 35-kilowatt alternator running at 125 Hz, producing a 750 Hz spark rate. The device certainly didn't generate continuous waves, but it produced a fairly clear tone.

NESCO landed its first major contract with United Fruit Company, providing communication with ships at sea from stations in New Orleans and the company's plantations in Central America. It was a significant infrastructure project that was later spun out to create the fourth largest international telegraph company in the U.S., the Tropical Radiotelegraph Company.

Encouraged by that initial success, Fessenden aimed high, planning to introduce transatlantic wireless telegraph service between Brant Rock and an identical station in Machrihanish, Scotland (manned in early 1906 by his capable assistant, James C. Armor). Within two weeks, Armor reported via telegram that Brant Rock was being heard loud and clear. Fessenden installed 420-foot antenna masts at each end and methodically tested communications on three different frequencies. The results were recorded for various times of day and days of the month. People began coming out of the woodwork offering to buy NESCO gear, but Given and Walker refused to sell individual units, fearing that could jeopardize future package deals.

Amazingly, though Marconi achieved the first transatlantic wireless transmission in 1901, no one had yet achieved two-way transatlantic wireless communication. Fessenden performed the first two-way transmission in January of 1906. Two-way tests continued throughout the winter at a frequency of approximately 88 kHz. Fessenden also smashed Marconi's distance record when his signals were received 6,000 miles away in Alexandria, Egypt. However, Fessenden found it was impossible to communicate during daylight hours, and tests were suspended for the summer. In December of 1906, the Machrihanish antenna tower collapsed before commercial service could be inaugurated. It was never rebuilt.

Fessenden became deeply involved with his high-frequency alternator. He knew the rotary-spark transmitter was never more than a stop-gap measure, and was convinced that continuous wave transmitters producing pure sine waves at fixed frequencies would prove vastly more effective. He could continue to manufacture and sell NESCO's rotary-spark transmitter, but there was no sense in rebuilding the Machrihanish antenna tower.

Meanwhile, GE assigned Ernst Alexanderson to develop a faster and more powerful high-frequency alternator. He delivered a 50-kHz model to NESCO in 1906. The unit ran at an impressive 20,000 revolutions per minute (rpm) and generated a 2,000-watt signal.

Fessenden struggled to make Alexanderson's model operate at higher frequencies and power levels. Taking it apart, modifying it, and putting it back together, he managed to push it up to 90 khz and 50 kilowatts. (GE would later market a 200- kilowatt Alexanderson alternator.)

By mid-1906, Fessenden was routinely transmitting speech between Brant Rock and Plymouth, Massachusetts. In November 1906, Armor reported hearing from Scotland a conversation between the two Massachusetts stations regarding proper operation of the dynamo. It was the first time speech had been received across the Atlantic.

Once again, the only way Fessenden could modulate the transmit signal was directly. A high-power transmitter required a microphone capable of dissipating considerable heat. Fessenden inserted a water-cooled microphone between the transmitter and the antenna.

On December 21, 1906 Reginald Fessenden demonstrated wireless speech transmission to a group of telephone engineers. On December 24, 1906 Fessenden made the first broadcast of voice and music—a broadcast heard almost exclusively by radio operators onboard U.S. Navy and United Fruit Company ships equipped with Fessenden's receivers at various locations in the south Atlantic, north Atlantic, and the West Indies. During the broadcast, Fessenden made a short speech and played Handel's Largo on the violin. The broadcast was repeated on New Years Eve, 1906.

Though a key milestone in the development of wireless technology, Fessenden's audio broadcasts were hardly noticed. In fact, the only first-hand account appears to be by Fessenden in a letter he wrote on January 29, 1932 to former business associate, Samuel M. Kinter. The broadcasts were not even mentioned in the ships' radio logs. Apparently, Fessenden didn't make additional broadcasts (it was a new and unproven concept); he was busy trying to promote his high-frequency alternator for point-to-point wireless telephone service. That idea went nowhere fast: voice signals were difficult to tune in and less reliable than telegraph signals for communicating with ships at sea.

The use of continuous waves presented its own set of reception challenges. Continuous waves produced narrowband signals that were harder to find and tune in than the broadband signals produced by spark transmitters. Fortunately, Fessenden already solved the audio detection puzzle with his electrolytic detector, but he needed a version suitable for shipboard use. He developed a sealed electrolytic detector and obtained U.S. Patent 793684, issued December 1904.

Meanwhile, researchers including Karl Ferdinand Braun, Jagadis Chandra Bose, H.H.C. Dunwoody, G.W. Pickard and John Stone Stone developed rectifier detectors. These included point contact devices requiring careful positioning of a thin wire or "cat's whisker," later enabling simple crystal radios that practically anyone could assemble.

But there was another problem. Fessenden's synchronous rotary-spark transmitter produced a signal modulated at the spark rate. The output of the receiver's detector was a low frequency but audible hum; reading Morse code signals was easy. With his high-frequency alternator, Fessenden was creating pure continuous waves. Feeding such signals into a rectifier detector produced only feeble clicks. Reading Morse code signals was very hard.

Necessity is the mother of invention. Fessenden invented a solution with far-reaching ramifications. He combined two signals at different frequencies to produce their sum and difference frequencies. For example, combining a signal at 100,000 Hertz with another at 102,000 Hertz creates an audible "beat frequency" of 2,000 Hertz. By combining two continuous wave signals at either the transmitter or the receiver, Fessenden could produce a clear tone at whatever frequency he wanted.

Fessenden coined his invention the "heterodyne" from the Greek words "hetero" (meaning difference) and "dyne" (meaning force). His original heterodyne circuit is described in U.S. Patent No. 706740 issued in 1902 and his improved heterodyne circuit is described in Patent Nos. 1050441 and 1050728 issued in 1913.

The heterodyne would be easy to implement with vacuum tube oscillators. But vacuum tubes had not been invented yet. Fessenden's initial strategy was to use two continuous wave transmitters operating at different frequencies. But that doubled the power needed to run transmit stations. He soon concluded it made more sense to locate a low-power, second transmitter next to the receiver. However, with only high frequency alternators and negative resistance arcs to choose from, there were no inexpensive options.

Unfortunately, Fessenden's inventions rarely contributed anything positive to NESCO's business results. Disagreements with his partners boiled over in late 1910. While Fessenden attended a meeting in Pittsburgh, his partners attempted to shut down Brant Rock and remove his papers. Only quick action by his wife and a few loyal employees prevented this from happening. But it was only a temporary reprieve. Reginald Fessenden was officially ousted from NESCO in January of 1911.

NESCO began losing orders for synchronous rotary-spark transmitters to oscillating arc transmitters. Fessenden, the prophet of continuous waves, was still pushing sparks. Though the U.S. Navy had awarded a major contract to NESCO, its 100-kilowatt synchronous rotary-spark transmitters failed to perform as guaranteed. NESCO knew all along they would not, but believed the Navy would overlook the fact, seeing no better alternatives. When the Navy tested a 30-kilowatt oscillating arc designed by Cyril F. Elwell of Federal Telegraph Company in San Francisco, it was impressed.

Elwell secured the U.S. rights to Poulsen's oscillating arc for $450,000. That was a substantial amount in those days, but Elwell got Poulsen to finance the deal, requiring small payments at first, with gradual increases. Elwell claimed, quite correctly, that his oscillating arc transmitter was considerably more efficient than NESCO's rotary spark transmitter. He sold additional units to the Navy for installation in San Francisco and Honolulu, and both were promptly heard in Arlington, Virginia.

Ironically, it was one of Fessenden's inventions that tipped the balance in favor of Elwell's oscillating arc. When comparing reception of signals from the rotary spark and oscillating arc using a standard receiver, the Navy preferred the rotary spark's somewhat musical tone over the oscillating arc's hiss. However, when a receiver with a local heterodyne source was substituted, musical tones were generated from both types of signals. The only other difference of any importance was range; the oscillating arc won on that score and beginning in 1913, the U.S. Navy awarded order after order to Federal Telegraph Co.

It's not clear that Federal Telegraph Co. was ever profitable, though. Elwell left in 1913 due to disagreements with the firm's president Beach Thompson. Leonard Fuller, who had been laid off from NESCO, took over Federal Telegraph's engineering department. Fuller produced oscillating arc transmitters running up to 500 kilowatts for the U.S. Navy. Federal Telegraph Co. was acquired in 1928 and later became part of IT&T.

General Electric finally perfected the Alexanderson high-frequency alternator in 1915. By 1916 the Fessenden-inspired alternator was considered more reliable for transatlantic communication than any spark transmitter and RCA purchased several of the units. However, it was a short-lived success: high-frequency alternators were rendered obsolete by vacuum tubes in 1920.

From 1911 onward, Fessenden's involvement with wireless was primarily as a litigant. First he sued NESCO. Fessenden won and was awarded damages, but NESCO prevailed on appeal. So Fessenden sued General Electric, Westinghouse, and Radio Corporation of America (RCA).

NESCO went into receivership in 1912 and Samuel Kintner was appointed general manager. Marconi finally acknowledged Fessenden's intellectual property in 1914 by obtaining a license from NESCO. NESCO re-emerged in 1917 as the International Radio Telegraph Company, which was sold to Westinghouse in 1920. Westinghouse then sold its assets— including many Fessenden patents—to RCA in 1921. Finally in 1928, Fessenden received an out-of-court settlement from RCA of $500,000, of which forty percent went to his lawyers.

Fessenden jumped into a different but not completely unrelated field. He began experimenting with the transmission of sound waves under water for Submarine Signal Company in New London, Connecticut. He developed a fathometer, based on a primitive form of sonar technology, which was used to detect enemy submarines during World War I. The principle of operation was simple: a short burst of sound at frequencies up to 20 kHz was emitted from a transducer placed about 10 feet below the surface of the water. The signal was of sufficient strength to travel several miles, bouncing off solid objects such as icebergs, submarines, and the ocean floor. The distance to the object could be determined by measuring the time required to receive an echo. Fessenden amassed more than 30 sonar-related patents.

In the aftermath of the *Titanic* disaster of 1912, Fessenden announced his system could detect icebergs at a distance regardless of weather conditions. He demonstrated his system to the U.S. Navy in 1914. He was able to detect a large iceberg up to two miles away. Another test detected a moving submarine up to five miles away. The U.S. Navy employed Fessenden's sonar during World War I to evade submarine-born torpedo attacks. The technology was improved for both safety and exploration uses during the 1920s.

After WWI, Reginald Fessenden retired to a small estate called "Wistowe" in Bermuda, and turned his attention toward mysticism. In 1921, the Institute of Radio Engineers presented Fessenden with its Medal of Honor, and the next year the City of Philadelphia awarded him the John Scott

Medal. He won the *Scientific American* Gold Medal in 1929 for his work related to safety at sea.

Fessenden lived most of his life just above poverty. Unlike Marconi, he made little money from his patents (of which he obtained approximately 230), and was never really celebrated. He did, however, acquire a small fortune in the end.

Reginald Fessenden died on July 22, 1932 and was interred in the cemetery of St Mark's Church on Bermuda.

Fessenden's vision of continuous waves was right on target. Several years before he died, continuous wave transmitters already outnumbered spark transmitters. By 1924, the U.S. government began banning spark transmitters in parts of the radio spectrum. As voice, music, and even images were made to ride atop continuous waves, vast new industries and markets emerged.

Fessenden's business accomplishments, however, never came close to matching his technical achievements. Consequently, he received neither the fame nor fortune that the quality of his work should have commanded.

The life of Reginald Fessenden provides an important lesson. Fessenden spent too many years shifting from job to job, always looking for someone to hire him on his terms. He wanted to pursue his own inventions, but he also wanted a steady salary. He should have gone off on his own much earlier. When he finally did, he hedged his bets, pursuing both the rotary-spark and HF alternator, believing all the while that the former was racing towards obsolescence. He would have been better off pursuing the oscillating arc and HF alternator simultaneously, never missing an opportunity to promote continuous waves, and doubling his chances of being in the right place at the right time.

Reginald Fessenden kept making compromises. Instead, he should have followed his passion.

Chapter Eight
Diodes and Triodes

If advanced technology is indistinguishable from magic, the vacuum tube was witchcraft of the highest order. It didn't abrogate the laws of physics, providing something for nothing, but it certainly delivered more for less. With vacuum tubes, the challenges of amplifying weak signals and generating continuous waves seemed to vanish into thin air.

In laymen's terms, the vacuum tube receiver picked up weak signals, extracted the speech or Morse code, and made the audio loud. The vacuum tube transmitter produced beautiful continuous waves, added voice or music, and boosted the signal so it could be heard far away.

The vacuum tube was to electronics what the lever, wheel, and screw are to mechanics. It became a ubiquitous building block, often serving multiple purposes at the same time, and enabling a deluge of inventions. It became so essential, the pressure to size- and cost- reduce it was overwhelming, leading to the development of transistors followed by integrated circuits.

John Ambrose Fleming, Lee de Forest, and Edwin Howard Armstrong were the pioneers of the vacuum tube. Their backgrounds, temperaments, and skills differed, but their accomplishments were highly synergistic. Fleming invented the first "valve" but could not see beyond it. De Forest's small addition proved momentous. Armstrong revealed its hidden secrets.

* * *

During the years following his invention of the incandescent light bulb, in the early 1880s, Thomas Edison was annoyed by filament breakage and uneven glass blackening. He decided to investigate and instructed his engineers to fashion experimental light bulbs with extra wires, pieces of foil, or plates inside the bulbs. He noticed current flowed from the filament to a piece of foil when the foil was connected to the positive terminal of a battery, but not when connected to the negative terminal.

Always looking to augment his intellectual property portfolio, Edison proposed using the apparatus for indicating or automatically regulating voltage changes, and applied for and received a patent (U.S. Patent 307,031).

Edison never found a specific use for the invention—though he did receive eponymous credit for the "Edison effect."

Twenty years later, John Ambrose Fleming studied the Edison effect and used it to develop a superior radio wave detector.

Fleming was born in 1849 in Lancaster, England. He knew he wanted to be an engineer even before he reached adolescence, and through self-study became an accomplished mathematician and photographer. Beginning in his late teens, Fleming spent roughly a decade shuffling back and forth between work and higher education. He attended James Clerk Maxwell's lectures at Cambridge, and was himself appointed lecturer at the University of Cambridge, University of Nottingham, and University College London.

Fleming's expertise was rewarded; he was sought as a consultant by the leading companies of the day including the Marconi Wireless Telegraph Company, Edison Telephone, and the Edison Electric Light Company. He wrote scientific papers on batteries and transformers. Fleming helped design and build the high-power transmitter used by Marconi to signal across the Atlantic Ocean.

In 1904, Fleming discovered that the Edison effect could be used to detect and demodulate radio waves, converting alternating currents into direct currents, leaving behind only information about the waves' amplitude. He called his invention the "thermionic valve" because it used heat to control the direction of electricity flow just as a mechanical valve controls the direction of fluid flow. It became the standard radio detector for the next several decades. In 1919, British physicist William Henry Eccles renamed it the "diode" to denote its use of two electrodes.

Fleming's diode marked the dawn of modern electronics. But Lee de Forest's triode proved far more disruptive.

* * *

Born in Council Bluffs, Iowa in 1873, Lee de Forest had an unusual childhood. While Lee was still a child, his Congregational minister father was hired to run Talladega College, the country's oldest black college, founded by two former slaves shortly after the Civil War. The white citizens of Talladega, Alabama did not appreciate Henry de Forest's efforts to educate black students. Lee had a few black friends, but spent most of his time reading about great inventors.

Lee was eventually packed off to Mount Hermon School for Boys in Gill, Massachusetts where he had to work part time to supplement his scholarship. His father hoped he would follow in his footsteps and become a minister. Though Lee craved the recognition of his peers, he was not popular. In fact, he was voted "homeliest boy in school." Despite such humiliations, Lee was confident of his genius and destiny. He excelled in physics and delivered the Scientific Oration at his graduation.

In 1893, de Forest entered the Sheffield Scientific School at Yale University. He did not get off to an auspicious start; he almost got himself expelled when he tapped into Yale's electric power system and caused a campus-wide blackout. He financed his education in part with money earned from mechanical inventions and received a bachelor's degree in 1896. After a brief military stint during the Spanish-American War, de Forest obtained a PhD in 1899. His doctoral thesis focused on Hertz's experiments demonstrating electromagnetic waves.

In 1899, de Forest landed a job at Western Electric Co. in Chicago. Instead of working on the telephone as assigned, he worked on an improved wireless receiver. De Forest's "responder" employed a self-decohering detector. There was no need for a hammer to knock metal filings loose because the responder used a liquid electrolyte. Early versions did not work particularly well, though. Frustrated, he took a new job in 1900 with American Wireless Telegraph Company in Milwaukee. Refusing to share his inventions with his employer, he lasted only five months.

De Forest returned to Chicago and collaborated with Ed Smythe, a colleague from Western Electric, and Clarence Freeman, a professor at the Armour Institute, on perfecting the responder. The trio made enough progress to take a prototype into the field. De Forest tried to compete with Marconi in providing real-time coverage of the America's Cup yacht race. He created and received so much interference that the competing wireless teams were forced to take turns communicating. It was more of a setback for Marconi than a victory for de Forest.

De Forest had no clue about how to run a business—and he knew it. He hired Abraham White to handle everything else. Together, they founded the De Forest Wireless Telegraph Company in 1902 with White as president and de Forest as vice president. White immediately started lining up investors, promising to build wireless infrastructure nationwide. Instead, White built a few showcase stations, printed a fancy brochure, and erected the tallest structure at the 1904 World's Fair in St. Louis. At best, de Forest closed his eyes to what was happening.

Suddenly, de Forest was forced to face reality. He was charged with patent infringement for copying Reginald Fessenden's electrolytic detector and briefly fled to Canada to avoid arrest. White arranged a bail bond on the condition that de Forest let White buy him out for $1,000.

De Forest joined the faculty of the Armour Institute of Technology, now the Illinois Institute of Technology. He had been experimenting with Fleming's thermionic valve for a year or so. In 1906, he added a third element to create what he dubbed the "Audion." The third element, a zigzagging nickel wire, was inserted between the cathode (a tantalum filament) and the anode (a nickel plate) to influence but not block current flow between the two main electrodes.

The third element—which became known as the "grid"—was the key to amplification. It also made the Audion a "triode." A weak signal applied to the grid could be used to control the stronger current flowing between the cathode and anode. It amplified signals in much the same way that sunlight "amplifies" shadows just after sunrise and just before sunset. The grid allowed short signals to cast long electrical shadows.

Lee de Forest did not quite understand how the Audion worked. He believed residual gas was essential to its operation. In fact, the name "Audion" was devised as a contraction of "audio" and "ionized gas." Later, researchers showed that the residual gas was a nuisance. Understandably, de Forest assumed the Audion could only amplify direct current and never tried adding tuned circuits. After all, Fleming's valve was famous for changing alternating current into direct current. (De Forest failed to realize that an alternating current could be applied to the grid.)

De Forest merely set out to develop a better detector—this time without infringing on Fessenden's patents. He systematically tested modifications to Fleming's valve, much as Marconi tried every conceivable variation of Branly's coherer. He tried connecting batteries to the filament and the plate. Then he added a third wire drawn through the side of the glass bulb. When he discovered the third wire could influence the current flow, he increased its surface area by bending it back and forth, and saw that the effect became more pronounced.

The Audion attracted attention but was far from an instant hit. De Forest engaged automobile lamp maker Henry McCandless to manufacture Audions and sold them at $5 each—a hefty price in those days—mostly to amateur radio operators.

Strapped for cash, de Forest sold the invention to AT&T for $50,000 in 1913. It was a huge mistake. Testing the Audion in telephony applications, AT&T concluded the device was too finicky. Other engineers, however, began discovering ways to exploit it—using methods not covered by de

Forest's original patent. Some credit Fritz Lowenstein, an engineer formerly employed by Nikola Tesla, as first to transform the Audion into a working amplifier and continuous wave oscillator. Edwin H. Armstrong, however, did more than anyone else in characterizing the Audion's performance and putting it to practical use.

Lee de Forest was a brilliant inventor but poor executor. He knew instinctively that Fleming's diode portended another great invention, but failed to perfect his Audion. De Forest founded several companies, all of which failed. He foolishly copied Reginald Fessenden's electrolytic detector, and when Fessenden sued him and won, it gave Abraham White the opportunity to force De Forest out of his own company.

Unlike de Forest, White knew exactly what he wanted to do next. He founded United Wireless Telegraph, and promptly transferred all of De Forest Wireless Telegraph Company's assets (but not its liabilities) to the new firm. Thanks to that scheme, Fessenden was only able to collect a fraction of the damages awarded to him, and de Forest was frozen out of what was left of the business. Meanwhile, White reaped further gains in the wake of the false rumor that United Wireless Telegraph was about to take over Marconi Wireless Telegraph Company in England. (Though White is usually depicted as pure villain, he built United Wireless Telegraph into a large if financially unsound business.) White left the company a few months later, reportedly selling his 15,000,000 shares for well under one penny each. The new management, headed by C.C. Wilson, was convicted of mail fraud in 1911.

Lee de Forest was alternately annoyed and enraged by the work of the much younger Edwin H. Armstrong. Particularly galling was Armstrong's paper, submitted to the Institute of Radio Engineers (IRE), dismissing de Forest's "critical gas action" explanation of how the Audion functioned. De Forest took his revenge in late 1915 when he applied for a patent for the regenerative receiver—despite the fact that Armstrong was awarded a patent for the same in 1914. A lengthy legal battle ensued in which de Forest claimed he invented the regenerative circuit much earlier. The case was appealed all the way to the U.S. Supreme Court, which ruled in favor of de Forest in 1934. Most engineers, however, remained convinced that Armstrong was the true inventor.

De Forest was indisputably the originator of at least one major Audion application. De Forest's "reflex receiver," which he produced in the late 1920s with modest success, was the first to use the same vacuum tube to perform multiple functions. In this case, a single Audion simultaneously amplified radio frequency and audio frequency signals. De Forest's innovation reduced the number of vacuum tubes required and the amount of battery power consumed.

De Forest pursued the wireless business from a variety of angles. He attempted to compete with Marconi, providing wireless telegraph service. He went into manufacturing Audions and later complete receiving sets. He pioneered radio broadcasting, achieving two firsts, both in 1916. He broadcast the first radio advertisements and then the first presidential election results, covering Woodrow Wilson's re-election (reportedly picked up by 7,000 amateur radio operators). And de Forest tried to bring culture to the masses with live broadcasts from New York's Metropolitan Opera House.

De Forest was also interested in new art forms. He pioneered the technology for "talkies." Others tried to make movies talk by adding an external sound source, such as a phonograph. De Forest was convinced that an optical solution ("sound-on-film") was needed to ensure the images and audio remained synchronized. De Forest's Phonofilm process recorded sound directly on film as a series of parallel lines (after small adjustments for the difference in speed between light and sound). In essence, de Forest filmed the electric waveforms from a microphone so they could be played back over a loudspeaker while the movie was projected on the screen.

Meanwhile, Edison tried connecting the Kinetoscope to the phonograph to create what he dubbed the Kinetophone. However, recording actors' voices with sufficient volume and syncing the voices to the film proved to be bigger challenges than expected. *Variety* scoffed, "The talking, instead of enhancing the picture, simply annoys." After trying a number of refinements, Edison gave up. In 1926, despite the fact that most silent films were accompanied by live music, he declared, "Americans require a restful quiet in the moving picture theater." One year later, Warner Brothers released *The Jazz Singer*, proving otherwise.

De Forest founded the De Forest Phonofilm Corporation and filed for a patent in 1919. Though he could not interest Hollywood, he didn't let that deter him. He showed his talking movies in independent theaters such as the Rivoli in New York City, concentrating on short subjects such as Vaudeville acts.

Max and Dave Fleischer used Phonofilm in their Sound Car-Tune series of cartoons in 1924. De Forest also partnered with Theodore Case, whose patents he needed to perfect his system. But Warner Brothers' chose the Vitaphone sound-on-disc process and de Forest's company went under. Hollywood eventually standardized on a sound-on-film approach, though not specifically Phonofilm, and gave de Forest an Academy Award in 1960 for "his pioneering inventions which brought sound to the motion picture." Hollywood also gave him a bride: In 1930, de Forest wed the beautiful silent film actress Marie Mosquini.

De Forest received the IRE Medal of Honor in 1922 in "...recognition for his invention of the three-electrode amplifier and his other contributions to radio." He received the Edison Medal of the American Institute of Electrical Engineers in 1946 for "...the profound technical and social consequences of the grid-controlled vacuum tube which he had introduced." An annual medal awarded to engineers by the Institute of Electrical and Electronic Engineers (IEEE) is named the Lee de Forest Medal.

De Forest referred to himself as the "Father of Radio" and others called him the "Grandfather of Television." He predicted the use of microwaves for communications and cooking. However, he was somewhat skeptical of television and transistors. He amassed more than 300 patents and his inventions include a radio knife (for cold cautery), guided bomb, radar scanner, and portable diathermy machine.

Though de Forest was somewhat cynical, his irrepressible optimism deserves greater recognition. In distrusting everyone, he couldn't discern small but important differences in character, and failed to hold himself to a higher standard. But there is also no doubt he believed in his own ability to uplift humanity through his inventions.

Lee de Forest died in Hollywood in 1961 at the age of 87.

* * *

Edwin Howard Armstrong was very unlike Lee de Forest. Armstrong grew up in relative splendor in Manhattan. Born in 1890, he became known for his meticulous and comprehensive experiments conducted over a span of forty years, and the practical solutions that flowed from his work. Armstrong was pure inventor.

Armstrong is credited with four key inventions: the regenerative receiver, the superheterodyne receiver, the super-regenerative receiver, and frequency modulation. Though Armstrong lost numerous patent battles, there is no doubt he was a great inventor. He did not invent and quickly move on; he characterized and perfected each invention. His crowning achievement, frequency modulation (FM), was accomplished in the face of extreme skepticism and indolence.

He was called "Howard" by his relatives and, later, "The Major" by his friends. His father, John Armstrong, was the U.S. representative for Oxford University Press. At age nine, Howard fell ill with chorea ("St. Vitus' dance") and missed two years of school. Always surrounded by books, he was inspired in his early teens by two in particular: *The Boy's Book of Inventions: Stories of the Wonders of Modern Science* by Ray Stannard Baker and *Stories of Inventors: the Adventures of Inventors and Engineers* by Russell Doubleday.

Howard grew to be tall, lanky and strong. His bout of chorea left him with a noticeable twitch. His personal heroes were Michael Faraday and Guglielmo Marconi. Like Faraday, he had an extraordinary ability to design and conduct experiments. He became an amateur radio operator and, with his parents' approval and support, filled his third floor bedroom with Leyden jars, coils, coherers and condensers. He ran long wires along a nearby embankment for an antenna.

Armstrong built a 125-foot wooden antenna tower. That initiated a life-long fascination with dangerous heights. When a neighbor telephoned his mother to say she was mortified to see Armstrong working at the top of the tower, his mother calmly replied "Don't look, then." In 1923, he scaled an RCA antenna tower (station WJZ) as a publicity stunt, posing for a photographer he brought along.

When Armstrong told a neighbor that he discovered a "wrong" connection made his spark gap transmitter perform better, the man (Charles Underhill) countered "What do you care about what's in the book? You're an original thinker!" His rendering of American humorist Josh Billings' maxim became his mantra: "It ain't ignorance that causes all the trouble in this world. It's the things people know that ain't so." Armstrong spent his entire career questioning assumptions and conventional wisdom.

In 1909, Armstrong entered Columbia University's Electrical Engineering program. He rode to school on a red motorcycle, often at high speeds. It was the end of the decade in which Marconi achieved the first successful transatlantic wireless transmission and Fessenden made the first voice and music broadcast. It was also the decade in which the word "radio" (Latin for "ray of light") began to replace "wireless."

At Columbia, Armstrong studied under Michael Pupin. Pupin came to America at the age of 20 with five cents in his pocket. His accomplishments were legendary. Though the principle of operation had been established several years earlier by Oliver Heaviside, Pupin is credited with inventing loading coils used to extend telephone lines, for which Bell Telephone paid him $500,000 in 1900. Replicating Wilhelm Conrad Röntgen's experiments, Pupin discovered that by placing a sheet of paper containing fluorescent dyes next to a photographic plate he could reduce the exposure time for diagnostic x-rays from an hour to a few seconds.

Armstrong produced his first great invention in 1912 while still Pupin's undergraduate student. Through experimentation, Armstrong developed a clearer understanding of how de Forest's Audion worked, and applied that knowledge to better exploit the device.

He discovered that the anode's output could include alternating current. He tuned the "wing circuit" and fed some of the output back to the grid. Suddenly, he heard stations thousands of miles away loudly and clearly. He rushed into his sleeping sister's room, dancing around and shouting "I've done it!" His regenerative circuit amplified a weak signal until it was hundreds of times stronger—strong enough to drive a loudspeaker, eliminating the need for headphones.

Regeneration had one major drawback. It amplified both the signal and the noise. Up until then, engineers had limited experience with static. It would now become their constant companion until Armstrong developed wideband FM. In fact, when AT&T engineers visited Columbia's Philosophy Hall in 1914 to witness a demonstration of the new circuit, the first thing they asked about was the incessant clicking sound.

Armstrong noticed that too much feedback created a hiss. He ascertained that the circuit went into oscillation and was generating continuous waves at radio frequencies. Suddenly, noisy spark gaps and massive AC generators could be cast aside. Physicists already knew that the impulse of a spark was not necessary to throw radio waves out into the ether as once thought; there just hadn't been a simple and efficient means of generating continues waves.

Unfortunately, Armstrong was secretive to a fault. He did not share his discoveries with his instructors at Columbia, nor did he keep written records. To make matters worse, his father saw his inventions as a distraction, and refused to pay the $150 patent filing fee until after he graduated. This would all come back to haunt Armstrong when de Forest claimed he invented the regenerative receiver first, despite the fact that Armstrong filed for a patent years ahead of him.

Like his hero Michael Faraday, Armstrong worked primarily with physical concepts rather than mathematics. Unlike Faraday, he was neither a prolific nor an eloquent writer. Still, Armstrong managed to produce a number of papers over the years for organizations such as the Institute of Radio Engineers and Radio Club of America, proving he knew his theory backwards and forwards. For example, Armstrong clearly described how the vacuum tube triode works and invented the "characteristic curves" widely used to identify a specific model's performance sweet spot.

Thanks to his regenerative receiver breakthrough, Armstrong met the young David Sarnoff in 1913 and his boss Guglielmo Marconi in 1914. Assistant Chief Engineer Sarnoff called Armstrong's regenerative receiver "the most remarkable receiving system in existence." Sarnoff wanted the London headquarters to strike a deal with Armstrong. By the time Marconi made Armstrong a modest offer ($500 per month), de Forest had initiated a priority challenge that would ultimately involve 30 judges, 13 courts, and 21 years. Sarnoff, meanwhile, went on to build a radio and TV empire as chief executive of RCA and its broadcasting subsidiary, NBC.

With the outbreak of World War I, Armstrong enlisted and was assigned to the U.S. Signal Corps. Radio proved an important technology in the prosecution of the war. Armstrong was assigned to install radios on warplanes, and insisted on testing them in the air himself. Along the way, he met Henry Joseph Round of the Marconi Company in Britain. Round constructed cascades of up to 130 vacuum tubes to pick up weak German signals. Radio was used successfully to alert the Royal Navy in May 1916 that the German fleet was putting out to sea—leading to the battle of Jutland.

Round was looking for a way to pick up signals above 1.5 MHz; he asked Armstrong for suggestions. Most wireless systems at the time operated in the 100 kHz region. It wasn't because Germany was communicating at high frequencies—they weren't—it was because the ignition systems in German aircraft generated high frequency radio noise.

Could a receiver pick up noise generated by German aircraft ignition systems at a distance, serving as an early warning system? There were formidable technical challenges. For starters, triode amplifiers did not perform well at high frequencies. The circuits were also very touchy and hard to adjust. Armstrong's answer was his next great invention: the superheterodyne receiver.

The principle behind the superheterodyne receiver is simple. To overcome the limitations of triodes at high frequencies, the incoming signal was mixed with a signal from a local oscillator (using Fessenden's heterodyne principle) to produce a new signal at a lower frequency. The output could then be fed into a more reliable and effective regenerative circuit at a fixed low frequency, which became known as the intermediate frequency (IF). The superheterodyne not only made receivers for higher frequencies practical, it reduced the number of controls required, as the IF amplifier adjustments could be preset at the factory.

With the assistance of Sergeant Harry W. Houck, Armstrong developed the superheterodyne receiver in one year. The first design consisted of eight vacuum tubes: a two-tube frequency converter; five-tube IF amplifier; and one-tube audio amplifier.

The unit amplified the received signal voltage 5,000 to 10,000 times over its initial value. Armstrong hoped his superheterodyne receiver would be ready in time to help direct antiaircraft fire, but the war ended before it could be placed in service. Fortunately, bombing raids during World War I were not nearly as destructive as they became in World War II.

Armstrong applied for a patent in France, and in the U.S in 1918. France awarded him the *Chevalier de la Légion d'Honneur*. The US Army promoted him to major. And the Institute of Radio Engineers (now the Institute of Electrical and Electronics Engineers, or IEEE) awarded him its first Medal of Honor for the regenerative receiver.

Playing Westinghouse and RCA against each other, Armstrong made a small fortune when Westinghouse agreed to pay $350,000 for the rights to his regenerative and superheterodyne receiver patents, with a $200,000 bonus if Armstrong prevailed over de Forest in court. Westinghouse had been frozen out of the market by RCA, GE, and AT&T and was desperate to get in. Westinghouse mainly wanted access to regeneration, but Armstrong insisted on a package deal including the superheterodyne. Armstrong's attorneys also managed to license regeneration to about 20 manufacturers at a 5% royalty rate.

In late 1921, Armstrong once again showed "It's the things people know that ain't so" that often get in the way. He successfully sent a message from the U.S. to Scotland with just 1,000 Watts of power at a wavelength of 200 meters. Up until that time, the conventional wisdom was that transatlantic wireless communications required transmitters running hundreds of kilowatts at much longer wavelengths. The government assumed frequencies above 1 MHz were useless. Amateur radio operators ("hams") such as Armstrong proved otherwise.

(The origin of the term "ham" is unclear. According to one narrative,[8] the word "ham" was synonymous with "unskilled" as in "ham actor." Somehow the term lost its negative connotation and became a nickname for amateur radio operator.)

---

[8] See http://earlyradiohistory.us/sec022.htm

Thanks to Armstrong's technical innovations and David Sarnoff's business acumen, by late 1922 there were 580 commercial radio broadcast stations, hundreds of firms manufacturing receivers, and one million listeners. Receivers based on Armstrong's superheterodyne circuit went into mass production in 1924.

At first, Armstrong saw the superheterodyne as the Rolls Royce of radios. Vacuum tubes were expensive and consumed considerable battery power. That began to change with the introduction of low-power filaments and dual-purpose tubes. The first RCA superheterodyne receiver was the model AR812. It was followed by the Radiola Super-VIII, housing the same electronics in a fine cabinet. By 1933, largely thanks to Armstrong's innovations, the number of radios in use grew to 19,250,000.

Armstrong's next invention was super-regeneration. Using a simple technique (known as "quenching"), super-regeneration enabled receivers that could amplify signals up to 100,000-fold. But super-regeneration exhibited poor selectivity, was only well-suited to AM transmissions in specific frequency bands, and generated local signals that could interfere with other nearby receivers. Now Sarnoff saw Armstrong's growing patent portfolio as a threat to RCA. Sarnoff hoped to neutralize Armstrong's position by acquiring a similar patent owned by John Bolitho in the U.K., but the wily Armstrong anticipated as much, and personally tracked down Bolitho in Egyptian Sudan to buy him out before Sarnoff could reach him.

Sarnoff understood the value of patents and, more importantly, the advantages of collecting rather than paying license fees. Recognizing Armstrong's immense talent, Sarnoff bit the bullet and paid Armstrong $200,000 plus 60,000 shares in RCA—making Armstrong RCA's biggest shareholder. Armstrong justifiably gloated in a telegram to his friend H.J. Round, "Arriving in England on Saturday with the contents of the Radio Corporation's safe."

The next year, Armstrong received another 20,000 shares for a simpler receiver design—a design enabling receivers with just two tuning knobs and one volume control. When Armstrong met collaborator Harry Houck for lunch at Morey's Bar and Grill, he shocked Houck by writing him a check for $100,000 on the spot.

Armstrong's relationship with Sarnoff paid off in other ways. In 1924, the 32-year old Armstrong married 22-year old Marion (Minnie) McInnis, an RCA secretary. Armstrong gave her the world's first portable radio as a wedding gift.

As a harbinger of things to come, Armstrong returned from his honeymoon to find his patent war with de Forest renewed. In September 1915, de Forest applied for his "oscillating Audion" patent, claiming he was first to discover regeneration for both receive (amplification) and transmit (oscillation) functions. Earlier, Armstrong applied for separate receive and transmit patents. This enabled de Forest to attack what he suspected was the more vulnerable of two patents.

Armstrong lost his superheterodyne patent in 1928 due to a patent interference ruling. Most of his claims were transferred to a patent owned by AT&T and acquired from Lucien Lèvy of France. Lèvy applied for a patent in France on August 4, 1917—seven months ahead of Armstrong. However, Lèvy touted the superheterodyne for its superior selectivity. Armstrong correctly saw it as the key to accessing higher frequencies (better sensitivity and broader frequency range) and simplifying receiver tuning. It's obvious that whoever was first, Armstrong had a much clearer idea of the invention's purpose and value.

But there was some good news: the dispute with de Forest began to go Armstrong's way. Judge Julius M. Mayer of the Southern District of New York Federal Court was not impressed with de Forest's argument or "faulty memory." De Forest's own documents showed he had an assistant in 1912; Herbert Van Etten failed to corroborate de Forest's claim that he used feedback to create RF oscillations.

In fact, in his zeal to refute one of Armstrong's earlier papers, de Forest went on the record stating that regeneration did not produce RF oscillations. Judge Mayer asked: if de Forest conceived the use of feedback for producing RF oscillations on Aug. 6, 1912, why did he wait until Sept. 1915 to apply for a patent, two years after his claimed discovery, one year after Armstrong's patent, and six months after Armstrong explained how the triode RF oscillator worked? On March 13, 1922, the three judges in the Federal Circuit Court unanimously rejected de Forest's appeal.

But Armstrong made a terrible mistake by not being magnanimous in victory. He refused to waive costs to the nearly bankrupt de Forest, and further refused to let de Forest license the regenerative circuit. He even taunted de Forest by flying a flag from his home displaying Patent No. 1,113,149—high enough so de Forest could see it from his home in the Bronx.

Aside from goading de Forest, Armstrong's foolish actions delayed the final decree. In the spring of 1924, de Forest filed suit with the District of Columbia Circuit Court—the court with jurisdiction over the U.S. Patent

Office. Recall that de Forest sold the Audion to AT&T; he had a potentially powerful ally with massive financial resources. Allegedly, AT&T's lawyers were permitted to make a small and seemingly innocuous change to de Forest's original patent: they inserted the word "electrical" in front of "oscillations."

Circuit Court Judge Josiah Van Orsdel may have been in over his head. De Forest had noticed low frequency (audio) oscillations. However, he treated these as a nuisance to be eliminated. Judge Orsdel interpreted this as evidence that de Forest was aware his Audion could produce high frequency (radio) oscillations. The judge disregarded three Patent Office rulings and the not-yet-final New York court decision. On May 8, 1924, he took Armstrong's ten-year old patent away from him and handed victory to de Forest.

Armstrong was distraught but did not give up. He took the dispute all the way to the U.S. Supreme Court. (Armstrong sold most of his RCA stock at $114 just before the market crash.) He lost the battle in 1934.

Anyone who has participated in a major courtroom proceeding understands that the description presented above is at best a rough sketch. No doubt there were elaborate arguments, physical evidence, the testimony of witnesses, and questions of credibility to consider. It's possible that de Forest was first to recognize that the Audion could serve as an RF oscillator. It's possible that de Forest expressed this to colleagues at the time. And it's possible that de Forest set the record straight in his admittedly tardy patent application.

But what can't be disputed is that Armstrong was first to systematically study regeneration, to explain how it worked, to show how it could be applied in practice, and to apply for patents. The Audion was de Forest's invention. But the regenerative circuit and associated RF oscillator were Armstrong's inventions.

Most of the electronics industry felt the judicial system had made a mistake. In view of the Supreme Court decision, Armstrong tried to return his gold medal (awarded in 1918) to the Institute of Radio Engineers (IRE). The Institute refused to take it back in a public meeting at which nearly one-thousand engineers gave Armstrong a boisterous standing ovation.

Armstrong's campaign to defend his regeneration patent may have ended badly, but Armstrong was by no means finished inventing. He continued to see opportunities flowing from others' false assumptions. Bell Labs' John Renshaw Carson, a pioneer of bandwidth-efficient "single sideband" transmission, showed that narrowband frequency modulation (FM) offered no advantage in squeezing more stations into an existing radio band.

Carson assumed spectral efficiency was the most important considera-tion. Consequently, he assumed the only type of FM worth considering was the kind that required the least bandwidth per station, narrowband FM. But what if there were other reasons to use FM, and other types of FM to explore?

Armstrong and many others had searched for ways to reduce the static endemic to amplitude modulation (AM). While there were ways to reduce noise—for example by using special filters—it was impossible to eliminate; both the noise and the desired audio consisted of variations in amplitude. Armstrong wondered if a different modulation scheme would prove more effective in combating static.

Carson was extremely pessimistic: "...static, like the poor, will always be with us." Most engineers responded to Carson's findings by deserting FM development. To Armstrong, such attitudes served as a provocation. Armstrong began experimenting with frequency shift keying (FSK), a frequency-dependent system for sending Morse code or other data. No doubt, he soon realized a receiver looking for changes in frequency would, if properly designed, be relatively insensitive to common static.

Then it hit him: the best way to exploit frequency modulation's insensitivity to noise would be to ensure that changes in frequency were sufficiently pronounced. To do so required broadband (for example, 200-kHz channels) rather than narrowband channels. He also understood the importance of eliminating all traces of AM. Armstrong developed a limiter to keep out AM and a discriminator to convert FM back to audio. He was delighted to find that his FM system yielded a vast improvement in the signal-to-noise ratio (SNR). And he made a fundamental discovery in the process: the way to increase the SNR of an AM signal is to use a narrower channel; the way to increase the SNR of an FM signal is to use a wider channel.

As a major RCA stockholder, Armstrong decided to demonstrate his embryonic FM technology to Sarnoff in 1933, giving RCA the opportunity to jump on it first. But Sarnoff did not want to undercut RCA's existing businesses based on AM technology. Plus, he was already firmly committed to developing television. In fact, Sarnoff believed TV would completely replace AM radio, so he wanted it to be a controlled process. FM radio could have a destabilizing effect.

Armstrong's only choice was to pursue FM on his own. It was a tall order; while his previous inventions were circuits used in other products, FM was an end-to-end solution. And he had reason to worry about how long it would take. After all, he had searched for a cure for static for twenty years. Pressing ahead, he recruited three recent Columbia graduates as assistants. One of them was John Bose, who later collaborated with Armstrong to develop FM multiplexing used in stereo and other applications.

The now 47-year old Armstrong demonstrated wideband FM on Nov. 5, 1935 to the Institute of Radio Engineers in New York City. The audience was stunned by how quiet the receiver was when no sound was being broadcast. It was almost as if the receiver had been switched off. "The shimmering afterglow hangs in the room with uncanny, lambent clarity," one listener reported.

While FM was challenging, it offered multiple benefits for a variety of applications, as Armstrong demonstrated using spectrum in the 42.5 to 43.5 MHz band that the FCC allocated for FM on an experimental basis. Armstrong showed that a low-power (two kilowatt) FM transmitter operating in the 40-MHz band performed comparably to a high-power (50 kilowatt) AM transmitter in the 1 MHz band over the same distance (85 miles). He also demonstrated FM multiplexing—combining audio and telegraphy transmissions on a single FM "carrier."

Later, General Electric discovered the "FM capture effect." While the apparent strength of an AM signal varies from very weak to very strong, once an FM signal exceeds a certain threshold it sounds just as good as a stronger signal.

By this time, Sarnoff realized that FM's triumph was inevitable. However, he still didn't want to undercut the AM radio business. So he embraced FM as the audio technology of choice for nascent television, asked his engineers to develop their own version of FM, and continued to throw obstacles in the way of the emerging FM radio business.

Armstrong sued RCA for infringing on the five most basic of his ten FM patents. RCA's strategy, in contrast, was merely to outlast Armstrong. Ironically, Armstrong defended Sarnoff at a stockholder's meeting in 1935 even as he was suing him.

Armstrong built the first FM broadcast station in Alpine, New Jersey in 1940, investing $300,000 of his own money. He likened the battle between FM and AM radio to the earlier battle between AC and DC power distribution. GE invested in FM on the recommendation of Ernst Alexanderson, who was convinced RCA had made a strategic mistake. In 1940, the FCC allocated 42 - 50 MHz to commercial FM; enough bandwidth for 35 commercial and 5 non-commercial stations per market.

Armstrong showed that FM radio technology was excellent for relaying program content from studios to transmitter sites—threatening AT&T's leased line business. FM was also ideal for mobile use; police, emergency services, and the military began using it. During World War II, Armstrong worked on the development of FM-based long-range radar. After the war, he bounced an FM signal off the moon.

Meanwhile, the FCC began contemplating changes to the FM service. To increase capacity, the FCC examined reducing channel bandwidth to 100 khz. Armstrong saw three potential problems: it would increase noise; receivers would be more likely to lose signals due to oscillator drift; and it would kill off multiplexing. Was the government trying to help or hinder FM?

In 1945, War Department engineer Kenneth Alva Norton predicted FM would suffer from interference due to sky wave propagation in the 42-50 MHz band; the FCC responded by reallocating FM to the 88-108 MHz band. (Tellingly, the FCC had no problem reallocating the offending 42-50 MHz frequencies to TV.) Next, the FCC was persuaded by CBS to limit the power of FM stations and to allow AM simulcasts of FM programs. These moves were clearly designed to strengthen the AM radio industry. Finally, FM stations were restricted to "single-market" use—meaning they could not participate in networks as AM stations did. The relocation of FM rendered 50 broadcast stations and 500,000 receivers obsolete. Afterwards, FCC Chairman Charles R. Denny went to work for RCA.

Sarnoff agreed FM was the audio system of choice for television. Armstrong refused to sell his patents, so RCA tried to develop ways around his patents, most of which were set to expire in 1950. RCA also licensed Bell Labs' "ratio-detector," a single-tube version of Armstrong's limiter and discriminator circuits. RCA's legal strategy was to assert that Armstrong's FM patents were too broad. However, Armstrong made broad claims because FM was an end-to-end system. Receiver manufacturers played the other side of the coin, claiming they did not infringe on Armstrong's system because they only made receivers.

Not until the 1960s did FM really catch on. The introduction of stereo phonograph records was the major impetus. The FCC authorized multiplex transmission for stereo music in 1961. Prior to that, FM struggled to survive by providing commercial-free "storecasts"—background music for stores, doctors' offices, and elevators.

Armstrong was again hailed by the industry. The Franklin Institute awarded him a medal for pioneering regeneration, the RF oscillator, the superheterodyne receiver, and wideband FM. Before it was all over, Armstrong acquired 42 patents. Armstrong had received an honorary Doctor of Science degree from Columbia University in 1929, and was appointed a professor by Columbia to replace the ailing Michael Pupin in 1934. It was an inventor's dream job; Armstrong was so wealthy he refused a salary, and Columbia was so delighted to associate his name with the University that he was excused from all teaching and administrative responsibilities.

Vacuum tubes were improved when the American Irving Langmuir developed a way to produce a better vacuum. Edwin H. Colpitts and Ralph V.L. Hartley, both working at Western Electric, made further advances in oscillator and amplifier circuit design. However, by the late 1930s, radio had evolved about as far as vacuum tube technology could take it. Fundamental improvements awaited the invention of the transistor.

Fortune magazine described Armstrong in 1948 as, "...the greatest American inventor since Edison and the most important of all radio inventors, including Marconi." Armstrong, however, always exhibited humility. He learned whatever he could from every engineer he encountered, and shared his own knowledge freely. Not one of Armstrong's inventions was entirely his own. And yet it would be unthinkable to say they were not his inventions.

Posthumously, Armstrong was elected to the pantheon of electrical greats by the International Telecommunications Union (ITU), joining figures such as Ampere, Bell, Faraday and Marconi.

Armstrong was totally dedicated to inventing. Starting and growing a business was never among his goals. He did, however, want everyone to recognize the true value of his inventions, and nothing said that better than patents, licensing deals, royalties, and stock options. Unfortunately, he seemed to have a knack for losing one court battle after another.

On January 31, 1954, a deeply depressed Armstrong gave up the fight. He wrote a two-page suicide note, put on his hat and coat, and jumped out his 13th story window. His widow Marion continued the legal battle, winning a stunning victory in 1959 in NYC federal district court. She sealed the victory in 1967 when the U.S. Supreme Court refused to review the lower court's judgment against Motorola.

Edwin H. Armstrong died a defeated man, but his memory lives on in victory.

Chapter Nine

The Father of Broadcasting

In the Russian shtetl of Uzlian in the province of Minsk (now in Belarus), young David Sarnoff was being groomed to be a rabbi. He spent his childhood steeped in the Talmud, learning to dissect problems, sort through proposed solutions, and make decisions. The lessons would serve him well.

His father, a menial laborer, had arrived in New York City in 1895 to earn the money for his family's passage. David was only nine when he made the trip five years later with his mother and two younger brothers, but he already had American moxie. Their trip had taken them through Liverpool, where passengers bound for America were transferred from a small freighter to a large steamship. The family's kosher food hamper got mixed up with the luggage, and was about to disappear in the hold when David jumped from the deck to retrieve it. The seaman who threw him a rope said, "Boy, you're going to do alright in America."

Still, the young boy had to learn a new language and a new way of life. His father's dingy $10 per month flat on the Lower East Side must have been a disappointment to David and his mother. As if there were not enough challenges, his parents soon added another brother and a sister to the family.

Like many Jewish immigrant boys, Sarnoff discovered he could make money hawking Yiddish newspapers. But he quickly surpassed his peers, acquiring his own newsstand and lining up other boys to run his routes. His father worked at painting jobs when he was healthy, and his mother took in sewing. Sarnoff enrolled in English classes.

Despite the crowded tenements of the Lower East Side, Sarnoff still saw America as a land of opportunity. He came from a place where a man was considered rich if he had a shanty with wooden floors, a horse, and a few sticks of furniture. Now he was surrounded by skyscrapers, electricity, and combustion engines. Best of all, as he observed later, "We had no Cossacks to fear." It was a wondrous time in American history, when a poor immigrant could believe in any dream—and make it come true. The young newspaper-peddler imagined himself a journalist or an editor—or even a publisher.

Sarnoff completed the eighth grade with marks good enough for a college preparatory school. However, his father was ill and the family desperately needed a steady paycheck. Sarnoff decided to go to the *New York*

Herald and ask for a job. Entering the building, he walked straight into a ground floor office. They offered him a job as a bicycle messenger boy and he took it. But it wasn't with the *New York Herald*; he had walked into an office leased to a transatlantic cable company. Sarnoff soon found himself mesmerized by the Commercial Cable Company's telegraphs. However, he was fired just a few months later when he insisted on taking an unpaid leave for the Jewish High Holy Days.

He needed money, but now he wanted a career in wireless, not just another job. The Commercial Cable Company's older telegraph operators encouraged him to apply for a job as a junior telegraph operator at Marconi's office in Manhattan. When he asked Marconi's traffic manager George De Souza if he needed a junior telegraph operator, De Souza said he needed an office boy. Sarnoff accepted the $5.50 per week job without hesitating.

His zeal was inspired by a comment attributed to Marconi, "My chief trouble was that the idea was so elementary, so simple in logic, that it seemed difficult for me to believe that no one else had thought of putting it into practice." David Sarnoff felt the same about the opportunities he saw all around him.

And just as Michael Faraday educated himself by reading the books he worked with as an apprentice bookbinder, Sarnoff learned from the documents he was asked to file. The American branch of the Marconi Company struggled to achieve market traction and had fewer than a dozen employees. Sarnoff was expected to handle diverse tasks. He enthusiastically delivered spare parts to Marconi-equipped ships visiting New York, managed the office's small technical library, and occasionally filled in when a local telegraph operator was ill.

From his first day, Sarnoff made it his goal to meet and talk with the great Marconi. His big chance came in December of 1906. Sarnoff had stayed at the William Street office after regular business hours to study technical papers. Marconi unexpectedly showed up. While Sarnoff did not dare approach the great man in the office, he heard Marconi was en route to his Front Street office, and followed him. Just as Marconi unlocked the front door, Sarnoff stepped forward to introduce himself as the American branch's newest employee. Marconi invited him in and Sarnoff gave him a brief account of his life. He quickly established a rapport with the older Italian. "We were on the same wavelength," Sarnoff crowed as he recounted the story years later.

Sarnoff offered to assist Marconi in whatever capacity desired, though he probably never anticipated his main assignment. Marconi sent his young employee to pickup and deliver candies and flowers to his many lady friends. Realizing that Marconi trusted his discretion and judgment, Sarnoff exploited the opportunity to its fullest. A few months after Sarnoff turned 16, he was promoted to junior telegraph operator and his salary was increased to $7.50 per week. That was not bad money in 1907.

Sarnoff was given assignments on ships and at other Marconi-equipped locations. At the age of 18, he became Marconi America's chief telegraph operator. He possessed what telegraph operators call an expert "fist." (In other words, he could tap out clearly formed Morse code messages as fast as most operators could read them.) At the age of 20, he resigned as chief operator to volunteer as wireless telegraph operator on an arctic seal hunting expedition, remaining all the while a Marconi employee. Keeping a diary, he wrote about the trip in clear and eloquent fashion, perhaps embellishing the story here and there. He wrote about eluding an attack by an angry seal after attempting to take close up pictures of its young; crossing dangerous ice floes to repair the wireless equipment on a sister ship; and relaying instructions from his ship's doctor to treat an injured sailor one hundred miles away.

After the expedition, Sarnoff seized the opportunity to manage Marconi's wireless station at the John Wanamaker department store in New York. With his evenings now free, he enrolled in and completed a course in electronics offered by the Pratt Institute.

Like Marconi, Sarnoff had a flair for public relations. Years after the British luxury liner *Titanic* sank in 1912, Sarnoff portrayed himself as the lone operator of the Wanamaker department store station in direct communication with the *Olympic*, *Titanic*'s sister ship. In reality, Sarnoff took turns with two other operators, receiving reports relayed from other Marconi stations.

Wireless played an important role in the disaster, but perhaps not as positive as it could have been. The *Titanic* was equipped with the latest Marconi gear. Unfortunately, frivolous messages to and from passengers kept the wireless system tied up 24 hours a day. Iceberg warnings were not always considered urgent by the sending ships.

The *Titanic*'s overworked operators were terribly young; John "Jack" G. Phillips was 25 and Harold Blake was only 21. For two hours, they begged for help from other ships, most of which were too far away to arrive in time. The *Carpathia* nearly missed their desperate plea. She had only one wireless operator, Harold Cottam, who was about to end his shift when his headphones crackled with the first distress signal at 12:25AM. "Require immediate assistance. We have collision with iceberg. Sinking. Can hear nothing for noise of steam." At 1:45AM, the *Titanic* sent its last message, "Come as quickly as possible old man: the engine-room is filling up to the boilers."

When the *Carpathia* finally arrived, it was almost 4:00AM. By then, there was nothing left of the *Titanic* but her lifeboats. The last survivors boarded the *Carpathia* at dawn. Phillips was not among them. Bride survived by jumping in the water at the last instant. It was his reports from the *Carpathia*--relayed by other stations—that Sarnoff and his colleagues picked up at the Wanamaker store.

The spectrum hadn't yet been divided, and the airwaves were cluttered with transmissions on the same frequency. Relatives and friends were reassured by false reports that all passengers had been rescued. To their credit, the *Titanic*'s wireless operators remained onboard even after the captain gave the "abandon ship" order. Without their heroism, all of the passengers would have perished. The public was deeply impressed and shipboard wireless soon became a safety requirement.

As 1912 drew to an end, Sarnoff was promoted to inspector for all Marconi-equipped ships entering the port of New York and instructor at the Marconi Institute. He was learning every aspect of the business and his salary was growing. For the first time, he realized he wanted to be a manager rather than an engineer. As he explained to the Institute of Radio Engineers' first president, Robert Marriott, engineering is where money goes out; management is where money comes in.

1912 was a pivotal year for another reason: the Radio Listening Act (RLA) was passed. It regulated transmitters and transmissions by requiring licenses, assigning call letters to stations, and dividing the spectrum into three frequency bands (one for commercial use, one for government use, and the highest frequencies for amateur radio operators).

The government also reserved the right to take control of the airwaves in the event of war. And that's exactly what it did during World War I. Manufacturers were permitted to ignore patents and churn out as much radio gear as possible. Amateur radio operators were told to shut down their transmitters.

At the outset of the war, Marconi hired cable executive Edward J. Nally to lead his American subsidiary. The move was intended to give American Marconi a more independent and American character. Sarnoff helped bring Nally up to speed and quickly became his trusted assistant.

As the war drew to a close, government policymakers sought more extraordinary powers. Given the vulnerability of undersea cables, some considered it imperative that the U.S. acquire and protect the lead in wireless technology by, for example, developing high frequency alternators. Others believed a government monopoly of wireless was necessary.

In retrospect, both camps were wrong. High frequency alternators gave the U.S. the lead in continuous wave technology, but everything changed with the invention of vacuum tube oscillators. Competition was clearly driving innovation. As Congressman William S. Greene remarked, "I have never heard before that it was necessary for one person to own all the air in order to breathe."

Still, the government could not resist catering to protectionist sympathies. The sale of high frequency alternators to Marconi was blocked. A patent holding spin-off from General Electric (GE) called Radio Corporation of America (RCA) was established on December 1, 1919. RCA bought Marconi America in what amounted to a forced sale; Sarnoff and the other Marconi America employees now worked for RCA.

The ownership change worked in Sarnoff's favor. About four years earlier, he suggested to his superiors at Marconi the possibility of creating a mass market for wireless. In his now-famous "Radio Music Box" memo of September 1915, Sarnoff described a business based on one-to-many transmission—broadcasting—that would require high-volume production of receivers for consumers. He envisioned broadcasts of recorded music and live sports events, concerts, and lectures.

The memo began "I have in mind a plan of development which would make radio a 'household utility' in the same sense as the piano or the phonograph. The idea is to bring music into the home by wireless." He described the use of transmitters with a 25 to 50 mile coverage radius. And he provided a financial justification, explaining that if just one million out of 15 million U.S. households bought a $75 music box it would generate $75 million in revenue—a huge sum in those days.

Keep in mind that the word "broadcast" was not yet in use. Nor was there much evidence of market demand (Lee de Forest had been broadcasting to a limited audience). Sarnoff understood that Marconi had created the maritime market for wireless; why couldn't he create a household market for wireless?

The memo was generally dismissed. Many engineers thought interference would make such a scheme unworkable. Mainly, Sarnoff's timing was wrong; in 1915, Marconi's resources were being consumed in post-*Titanic* ship-to-shore communications. And vacuum tubes were not yet perfected.

With World War I over and Marconi America absorbed by RCA, Sarnoff revived his Radio Music Box idea. There were still formidable obstacles, however. The radio patents of De Forest, Armstrong, and Pupin had been acquired by AT&T and Westinghouse. Sarnoff recommended cross-licensing deals with both firms. It was accomplished, but at a steep price: Westinghouse now owned 20.6% of RCA.

Sarnoff didn't invent broadcasting. The first person to conduct regular broadcasts to the public was Frank Conrad, an amateur radio operator (and Westinghouse employee) near Pittsburgh. Conrad leveraged vacuum tube technology to broadcast good fidelity voice and music. A receiver was set up in Horne's department store in Pittsburgh to promote home sets selling for $10 and up. (That was a serious chunk of change in those days, but it only made owning a receiver more of a status symbol.)

Conrad was asked by Westinghouse executive H.P. Davis to build a more powerful station in time for the presidential election. Westinghouse was granted a license for station KDKA in 1920, the first commercial broadcast station. Now owned by CBS, it is still on the air with the same call letters. Westinghouse would subsequently add WJZ, WBZ, and KYW.

Wired telegraph stations began using "call signs" much earlier as a simple way of identifying themselves without having to repeatedly spell out their locations. The 1906 Berlin International Wireless Telegraph Convention issued regulations stating that all coastal and ship stations should adopt three-letter call signs. The U.S. did not formally ratify the Convention's regulations until 1912. The country was divided into two geographical regions; stations in the east were given call signs starting with "K" and stations in the west were given call signs starting with "W." Amateur radio operators were assigned call signs containing a number (originally 1 through 9) indicating their radio district.

Radio was becoming a craze. People were listening with simple crystal sets they could build themselves, but that required headphones. Manufacturers were springing up everywhere, some paying no regard to patents. Sarnoff realized that broadcasting, an application he anticipated four years earlier, was taking off without RCA. But he wasn't just trying to get back in the game; Sarnoff put together a visionary and comprehensive business plan for radio broadcasting.

At this critical moment, second- and third- level GE managers began harassing Sarnoff, who had risen above most of them in the organization. Unwanted visitors (e.g. crackpot inventors) were automatically routed to him. Invitations to social events were misplaced or misaddressed. Make-work projects were dumped in his lap. Sarnoff suspected anti-Semitism.

Sarnoff's response underscored his wisdom and maturity—and proved a turning point in his career. Instead of complaining, he made the most of the meetings and projects. Then he invited RCA Chairman Owen D. Young to dinner in a private room at Delmonico's restaurant. Sarnoff began by recounting his humble origin and the opportunities he discovered in America just as he once did with Marconi. He spent most of the remaining evening describing the magnificent future he envisioned for RCA. Sandwiched between these inspiring topics, he mentioned the problems he was experiencing. The dinner lasted four hours.

Young got the message. Within days, word spread that when Sarnoff spoke, he spoke with Young's authority. Any further harassment of Sarnoff would be considered attacks on Young. It was clear that Sarnoff was the Chairman's protégé and immune to the envy of less capable managers.

Young made the 30-year old Sarnoff General Manager of RCA and encouraged him to take on Westinghouse's broadcast network. Sarnoff recognized that he needed to stage a high profile broadcast to win mindshare for RCA. He picked the heavyweight boxing championship between Jack Dempsey and France's Georges Carpentier scheduled for July 2, 1921.

Sarnoff put together the broadcast despite limited time and funds. He placed radios with loudspeakers in public venues such as Rotary and Elks Clubs, movie theaters, and school auditoriums. Finally, he selected RCA employee and boxing aficionado Andrew J. White as the blow-by-blow announcer. As it turned out, White's descriptions made it no further than the transmitter shed, where technician J.O. Smith relayed White's descriptions. Fortunately, Dempsey scored a knockout in the fourth round shortly before the transmitter overheated.

The broadcast was a huge success. It was heard by three hundred thousand Americans. Congratulatory telegrams and letters poured into RCA. Nally telegraphed Sarnoff from London: "You have made history."

Radio started to boom. Receivers were manufactured by companies such as Atwater Kent, Grebe, Philco, Stromberg-Carlson, and Zenith. For those who really wanted to splurge, receivers with ornate cabinets could be bought for as much as $400—more than the cost of a Ford automobile. Despite surging demand, RCA's Radiola receiver was late; the firm missed the Christmas retail season.

Sarnoff had to do something about patent infringers. He wisely targeted select companies to make examples of them, going after A.H. Grebe first. He also dropped distributors that only ordered tubes—a sure sign they were supplying unlicensed manufacturers. Predictably, RCA was accused of anti-competitive practices.

Young decided RCA needed someone with an impeccable background to navigate increasingly hazardous waters. Though Sarnoff had sufficient talent, Young selected a World War I hero, Major General James G. Harbord. Young, Sarnoff, and Harbord had worked together before, lobbying the Federal Trade Commission (FTC) and Congress in support of RCA's patent pool. Harbord took the reigns January 1, 1923.

Naturally, Sarnoff was disappointed. But he respected Harbord, who was no mere figurehead—he had won the Distinguished Service Medal for directing army logistics. And Harbord wisely permitted Sarnoff to continue running operations in areas that Harbord lacked experience.

The FTC filed a formal complaint against AT&T, GE, RCA, United Fruit (an enterprise user that launched its own wireless business in 1913), and Westinghouse, accusing them of restraining competition and engaging in monopolistic practices. Eventually, the charges were dropped, but RCA was party to a series of consent decrees over the next forty years.

Radio grew at an unprecedented rate. The number of broadcast stations increased from one in 1920, to 30 in 1922, and 556 in 1923. The number of radios produced grew from just a few in 1921 to 100,000 in 1922 and 500,000 in 1923. RCA's market share—16.5% in 1923—was by no means dominant.

Sarnoff continued to fight patent infringers. Independents complained that RCA left them with only two choices: infringe or go out of business. Sarnoff decided to make an offer that he hoped would improve RCA's image and put infringement to an end. He offered licenses at a 7.5% royalty rate and soon reduced it to 5%. With its portfolio of 4000 patents, RCA licensed 90% of radios manufactured in the U.S.

The period 1922-1926 proved crucial to development of American broadcasting. Sarnoff originally saw broadcasting as a local enterprise, but now he saw the possibility and need for a nationwide network. This would be his greatest accomplishment. However, he opposed the advertising business model advocated by others and even joined hands with Herbert Hoover in trying to prohibit it. Instead, he thought radio stations should be operated as public institutions, much like libraries. (Sarnoff may have been motivated by something other than civic-mindedness, however; he may have feared that advertising growth would limit receiver sales.)

The technology continued to advance. Louis Alton Hazeltine, an American engineer and founder of the Hazeltine Corporation, invented the neutrodyne circuit, eliminating high-pitch squeals by stabilizing radio frequency amplifiers, in 1924. Austrian engineer Alexander Meissner and Western Electric engineers Ralph Hartley and Edwin H. Colpitts made enhancements to the superheterodyne receiver. Speakers and microphones were also improved. Originally, all commercial broadcasters were forced to timeshare one frequency: 833 kHz. Frequencies from 550 to 1500 kHz would be allocated to broadcasting by the Federal Radio Commission (FRC) in 1927.

AT&T, meanwhile, was disappointed with its wireless transmitter business. Only a small fraction (35) of the 600+ broadcast stations bought AT&T transmitters. AT&T experimented with its New York City station, WEAF, letting local businesses sponsor airtime (some called it "tollcasting"). A local realty firm paid $50 for ten minutes, receiving just a brief mention for its money.

AT&T believed its phone lines gave its radio stations a competitive advantage. Though phone lines could be used to stage broadcasts from almost anywhere in a city, the ability to feed the same content to multiple stations (in multiple cities) was even more important. The company proceeded to build the first radio network consisting of WEAF and 12 other stations extending as far west as Davenport, Iowa. RCA began to build a competing network, but when they approached AT&T for phone lines the company refused to lease them. RCA tried to use telegraph lines, but found them inadequate.

AT&T became increasingly bold, using a clause in the cross-licensing agreement to break into the receiver business. To some, it looked as though AT&T was trying to destroy RCA. During the dispute, AT&T's VP of Finance Walter S. Gifford tried to convince Young to replace Sarnoff. Young was not about to let AT&T tell him how to run his company.

RCA threatened to go to court. During arbitration (as suggested by the original cross-licensing agreement), AT&T agreed to exit broadcasting while RCA formed a separate broadcasting subsidiary, National Broadcasting Company (NBC) using AT&T phone lines for interconnection. Both RCA and AT&T were anxious to avoid being branded monopolies. And when Gifford ascended to AT&T's presidency, he didn't want the dispute hanging over his wireline empire.

NBC was officially incorporated in September of 1926. There were now five million receivers in use. Full-page ads signed by Young and Harbord assured the public that RCA was not interested in acquiring a broadcasting monopoly. The company promised to cooperate or compete with independent stations, whichever they preferred.

In fact, RCA built two separate radio networks. The Red network consisted mostly of former AT&T stations. The Blue network was composed of stations owned by GE, RCA, and Westinghouse. Sarnoff, whose salary had grown to $60,000 per year, was made Chairman of the NBC Advisory Council. The Red and Blue networks were launched November 15, 1926 with a four-hour broadcast. Programming included the New York Symphony Orchestra featuring Met opera star Tito Ruffo; the dance bands of Ben Bernie and Vincent Lopez; and Will Rogers doing an impersonation of President Coolidge from Independence, Kansas. Sarnoff finally agreed the advertising business model made most sense; after all, now he was in both the broadcasting and receiver manufacturing businesses.

Other radio networks emerged. CBS, with William Paley at the helm, was formed in 1927 to compete with NBC. Marconi and others combined forces in 1922 to create a radio network in the UK; that network became the British Broadcasting Company (BBC—later British Broadcasting Corporation) and was taken over by the British government. In 1943, the FCC forced RCA to sell the Blue network, which became the American Broadcasting Company, ABC.

Much of the early radio broadcasting was live; stations did not want to pay royalties for recorded music. WMAQ began providing play-by-play coverage of Chicago Cubs baseball games in 1925. The concept caught on. (WMAQ radio didn't do as well, signing off the air for good in 2000.)

By 1929, a wide assortment of radios sold for anywhere from $25 to $500 each. Manufacturers were now producing 75,000 radios per month. Radio company stocks surged in value. In the previous year, RCA went from $80 to $420 per share and split five for one. Though Sarnoff had a modest stock portfolio, he was more interested in the progress of his career. When Harbord took a leave of absence in 1928 to campaign for Herbert Hoover, Sarnoff's salary was increased to $80,000—putting him in the same league as baseball's Sultan of Swat, Babe Ruth.

(While most entrepreneurs and business owners primarily sought wealth, David Sarnoff was an example of the new breed of professional managers who primarily sought power and prestige. He presaged today's high-tech management, which often takes over from the founders, who either retire in splendor or move on to start other businesses.)

Sarnoff continued to explore new markets such as talking movies, car radios, and radio-phonograph combinations. RCA's sound-on-film solution, Photophone, competed with AT&T's Vitaphone. Two hit movies, *The Jazz Singer* and *Lights of New York,* forced the major studios to take talking movies seriously. By the time RCA's system was ready, AT&T's system had grabbed 90% of the market. In 1928, Sarnoff teamed up with Joseph. P. Kennedy, who enticed his movie production company Film Box Office (FBO) to merge with Keith-Albee-Orpheum. The new company, Radio-Keith-Orpheum (RKO), used RCA's Photophone technology. RKO quickly became profitable and made ten musicals starring Fred Astaire and Ginger Rogers. Sarnoff fell behind early, but instead of giving up he made a shrewd business deal that proved a boon to RCA's technology.

Sarnoff had had his eye on car radios since 1922. But it wasn't until 1929 that an opportunity emerged. General Motors developed a scheme for embedding radios in automobile dashboards and Sarnoff struck a deal with the automobile manufacturing giant.

Many years after Edison invented it, the phonograph was not a particularly successful product. Its audio was weak and distorted. The phonograph did not come into its own until Bell Labs scientist J.P. Maxfield began adding vacuum tube-based electronics. However, the phonograph was soon losing sales to radios. The management of Victor Talking Machine quietly secured licenses from Western Electric to manufacture radios, but failed due to weak marketing and distribution. Sarnoff engineered a deal that saved Victor, increased RCA's manufacturing capacity, and led to combination radio-phonograph products. (It also prolonged the life of Victor's trademark terrier, Nipper.) In the spring of 1929, the RCA Victor Company was incorporated with David Sarnoff as Chairman.

But after a triumphant summer for the new corporate entity, all hell broke loose. On October 24, 1929, panicked investors began a run on the stock market. By Black Tuesday, October 29, RCA's stock collapsed from $110 to less than $20 per share. Sarnoff kept the firm on an even keel, however, and was appointed President of RCA in early 1930.

Then another challenge arose. On May 30, 1930, Sarnoff was handed a complaint from the Department of Justice. After dinner, he and a group of RCA executives met to map out a strategy. Sarnoff concluded over a period of months that protracted litigation was not in RCA's best interests. Besides, Sarnoff wanted RCA to be independent of GE and Westinghouse. He proposed a break up. Later, he often said, "The government handed me a lemon and I made lemonade of it."

Around 1934, Sarnoff began seriously thinking about the next potential household appliance: television. There was no way to send an image en bloc; television required a method of sending pictures piece by piece. Thanks to a basic characteristic of human vision, persistence, people would not notice that images were built dot by dot and line by line if it could be done quickly enough.

In 1884, German inventor Paul Nipkow received a patent for a mechanical system using synchronized spinning disks in the transmitter and receiver. The concept was simple: the image was scanned so that one dot impinged on a selenium photocell at a time. The photocell measured the relative brightness of each dot. At the receiver, the image was recreated dot by dot. The system posed two challenges: scanning the image quickly enough to create the illusion of a complete picture, and keeping transmit and receive disks synchronized. It's not known whether Nipkow ever tried constructing such a system.

The first mechanical television was built by Scottish engineer John Logie Baird in the 1920s. He demonstrated in his laboratory in 1924 and to the public at Selfridges department store in 1925 that he could recreate a moving silhouette. Then he added halftones and transmitted 30 vertical lines per frame at a rate of five frames per second, producing a fuzzy picture. As the number of lines per frame and frames per second gradually increased, picture quality improved.

Cumbersome names such as "radiovision" and "telephonography" were proposed before the industry settled on "television." There were also different ideas about how the invention would be used. Publisher of the first science fiction magazine Hugo Gernsback envisioned a two-way videophone he dubbed "telephot." CBS' William Paley thought televisions would mainly be set up in movie theaters to show live events.

Sarnoff was convinced that television would become the ultimate in mass media. The first American-produced TV was demonstrated in 1925 by Charles Francis Jenkins. His system—also mechanical—used rotating prisms instead of disks. Jenkins produced receivers retailing for $85 to $135. However, at the start of the Great Depression, Sarnoff felt television's quality was not yet good enough, and funds for further development became scarce.

The mechanical system was the most obvious approach to television, but the receivers were certain to require frequent maintenance and repair. The first all-electronic television was proposed by British engineer Alan Archibald Campbell-Swinton in 1908. Instead of spinning disks, Campbell-

Swinton's television would use cathode ray tubes; the cathode rays would be deflected using electromagnets to build the picture. RCA's Vladimir Zworykin was also convinced the all-electronic system was the best way to go. In 1929, Sarnoff asked him how much money he needed for development; Zworykin requested $100,000. That proved $50 million short of the actual amount spent.

Zworykin was not the only person in the U.S. who saw the necessity of an all-electronic system. Philo T. Farnsworth, a farm boy from Idaho, envisioned a system that electronically scanned each scene line by line and recreated the image line by line at the receiver. Farnsworth's innovative camera using an image scanning tube would prove a key piece to the puzzle.

* * *

Philo T. Farnsworth was born in a log cabin at Indian Creek, Utah in 1906. His parents were Mormon farmers. One of nine children, he must have learned early how to ask for what he wanted. As a high school freshman, he talked his way into a chemistry course for seniors taught by Justin Tolman, who became his mentor.

Farnsworth began tinkering at an early age. He won a magazine contest for his "magnetized anti-theft ignition system." He began to think about television after reading an article about a French engineer's efforts to transmit photographs between St. Louis and New York City via radio. Edouard Belin first demonstrated his invention using phone lines between Paris and Lyon in 1907. Farnsworth, like Belin, saw the transmission of moving pictures as the next goal.

In 1923, Farnsworth began taking courses at Brigham Young University in Provo under a special arrangement while still enrolled at Brigham Young High School. Two years later, he started a business selling and repairing radios in Salt Lake City. The radio business struggled, however, and Farnsworth worked part-time for a couple of fundraisers, George Everson and Leslie Gorrell. Farnsworth took every opportunity to buttonhole Everson, who was looking for a high stakes investment opportunity, about the possibility of electronic television. In 1926, Everson put up $6,000 for the 20-year-old Farnsworth to patent and develop the idea.

Farnsworth's scheme required an electronic camera he called the "image dissector." The idea was to focus the image on a light-sensitive plate and scan the plate line by line; the resulting electronic signal could be transmitted and used to recreate the scene line by line at the receiver on Farnsworth's "image oscillate," a type of cathode ray tube (CRT).

Farnsworth set up a laboratory with a closet serving as his tube-making "annex." He quickly concluded that selenium photocells were too slow for scanning. He needed a material that could convert light into electricity almost instantaneously. Farnsworth determined that a coating of potassium hydride could do the job.

Constructing an image dissector posed three major challenges. First, he needed to produce a structurally sound vacuum tube with an optically clear glass plate at one end. Second, he needed to devise a method of coating the inside of the evacuated tube with his photoelectric chemical. Third, he needed to get the right type of electrical leads into and out of the tube.

With the help of his brother-in-law Cliff Gardner, Farnsworth produced image dissector tubes the experts said could not be built. The industrious Gardner kept working until he became an expert glassblower. On one occasion, a half-built tube exploded in Gardner's face. Luckily, he wasn't seriously injured.

In addition to creating a working prototype, Farnsworth needed to patent his solution. He scheduled the first demonstration for his partners in the summer of 1926. The prototype dissector exploded. (Fortunately, the teamed learned from Gardner's first accident to keep their distance.) However, by then Farnsworth had burned through Everson's $6,000 investment.

Farnsworth was dejected, but Everson and Gorrell were hopeful. They had been successful charity fundraisers, so there was no reason to think they couldn't be effective as venture capitalists. They went to Crocker National Bank in San Francisco seeking the advice of bank vice president Jesse McCargar, who had chaired a past fundraiser. McCargar, it turned out, was on vacation. As they began to leave, they were approached by executive vice president James Fagan. The next day, Crocker offered $25,000 in funding and laboratory space in San Francisco.

Farnsworth filed his first patent application in 1927 and it was granted in 1930. He finally got his prototype working on Sept. 7, 1927. He slowly progressed from transmitting a straight line to a triangle to a dollar sign.

Farnsworth formed a public company and welcomed visitors. De Forest, Marconi, and Zworykin all trooped through his lab. Unlike Farnsworth, Zworykin kept what he was doing close to his chest. Zworykin had the better receive tube, while Farnsworth had the superior transmit tube. Farnsworth was interested in teaming up with a big company. But Zworykin believed he could master the transmit tube on his own. Zworykin used electrostatic focusing instead of Farnsworth's magnetic coils. Otherwise, the systems were based on essentially the same operating principles.

Sarnoff saw Farnsworth as the only serious technological competitor. The wireless mogul also knew that the company that controls the patents controls the industry. Sarnoff visited Farnsworth's lab at 202 Green Street in San Francisco while Farnsworth was in New York City. He pretended RCA could perfect TV without Farnsworth's patents, while offering to buy them for a paltry $100,000. In reality, Zworykin was using Farnsworth's dissector tube concept.

Farnsworth's big break came—or so he thought—when he received an offer from radio manufacturer Philco in 1931. Philco was looking for a competitive advantage over RCA. Farnsworth would be granted royalties on television set sales, but he had to move his lab to Philadelphia. He had a difficult time adjusting to Philco corporate culture, however, which required that he and his team wear suits and ties even while glassblowing. Farnsworth was granted an experimental television broadcast license for station W3XE and began broadcasting cartoons.

Meanwhile, Zworykin continued to improve his camera tube. He desperately needed a way to isolate the tiny drops of light-sensitive chemicals to create a mosaic. One of his engineers stumbled on the answer by accidentally over-cooking silver-covered mica sheets. The "iconoscope" camera proved the final link in RCA's all-electronic system.

Farnsworth's prospects rapidly diminished. When the Farnsworths' youngest child died from strep throat in 1932, his wife was forced to travel alone to Utah to bury him, because Philco refused to grant Farnsworth time off. Allegedly, in 1933 RCA threatened it would not renew Philco's radio manufacturing license unless the firm ended its alliance with Farnsworth. Fortunately, Crocker National Bank's McCargar agreed to establish Farnsworth Television, Inc. in Philadelphia on the condition that Farnsworth cut his staff and expenses to the bone.

Farnsworth publicly demonstrated his system at the prestigious Franklin Institute in the summer of 1934. A few months later, he went to London and convinced John Logie Baird of the superiority of the all-electronic approach. Baird decided to join forces with Farnsworth; however, the BBC selected the Marconi-EMI system based on RCA's technology. In 1936, Farnsworth and his wife sailed for London in a last-ditch effort to make Baird's system competitive. Good progress was made in just a few weeks. Exhausted, Farnsworth and his wife departed for the French Riviera to rest. There he received the devastating news that Baird Labs had been destroyed by fire.

Farnsworth tried to salvage the trip by seeking licensees in Germany. He got out of Germany just before the war left him stranded.

RCA began challenging Farnsworth's patents. The testimony of Justin Tolman, Farnsworth's teacher and mentor, proved insufficient. But RCA's case was far from airtight as Zworykin's iconoscope was not yet perfected.

One of Sarnoff's strategic options was to simply delay commercial TV. Sarnoff was in no hurry to undercut radio, though he knew television was inevitable and that the way to control the transition to television was to lead it. RCA and NBC began experimental television broadcasts as Sarnoff wrestled with the FCC over TV standards. Sarnoff officially introduced television to the public at the 1939 World's Fair in grand style. RCA had its own radio tube-shaped building at the fair, with halls devoted to television technology and the role of television in the home of the future. Visitors saw their own images displayed on prototype television sets. Topping it all off, NBC broadcast President Franklin D. Roosevelt's speech at the opening ceremonies via television.

While Sarnoff was dazzling the world, Farnsworth was headed towards a nervous breakdown. With no real options left, he threw in the towel, selling his more than three dozen television patents to RCA Victor for $1 million in September of 1939.

Today, Philo T. Farnsworth is remembered as the inventor of the first all-electronic television. Though he was no match for the sophistication and power of Sarnoff and RCA, that fact only seems to have made him more of a hero to his admirers; his life has been the subject of numerous books and even a screenplay. He spent the remainder of his days researching nuclear fusion. Philo T. Farnsworth died of pneumonia in 1971 at age 64.

* * *

All-electronic television based on the cathode ray tube (CRT) invented by Karl Ferdinand Braun in 1897 (the same Braun who shared the 1909 Noble prize with Marconi) continued to progress. The receiver's operation was simple: the cathode was heated to emit electrons, the trajectories of which were controlled by two pairs of parallel plates (one pair for up/down and the other for left/right). The intensity of the electron beam controlled brightness.

During the same period, Edwin H. Armstrong developed and demonstrated frequency modulation (FM). Sarnoff immediately recognized it was an important technology but did not jump on it for two reasons. He did not want to disturb the thriving AM market. And he saw FM as the audio solution for TV which was still years off in the future. While seeking ways to bypass Armstrong's patents, RCA (as well as CBS) did what it could to delay FM's commercial success.

Everything was put on hold when World War II broke out. Sarnoff tried to enlist during World War I, but was told his work was too important. However, the military represented his most cherished virtues: order, power, daring, and discipline. He joined the reserves in the 1920s and served in England prior to D-Day. Working under Eisenhower, Sarnoff was assigned to centralize and enhance military and news communications. He was promoted to Brigadier General.

David Sarnoff was no tin soldier. He was grateful for the opportunities that America afforded him. He wanted to serve his country and distinguished himself when the opportunity arose. From then on he let others know he was proud to be called "General."

Trans-Atlantic communication capacity was 130,000 words per day when Sarnoff took command. He planned an increase to 500,000 words. The system carried 570,000 words on D-Day. Sarnoff was awarded the Legion of Merit medal.

Television was perfected by combining the iconoscope (invented by Zworykin) and image dissector (invented by Farnsworth) for transmission and kinescope for receiving. The National Television System Committee (NTSC), established in 1940 to set television technical standards, created the 525-line standard as a compromise between the systems advocated by RCA and Philco.

By 1946, television was ready for commercial rollout. Ten thousand TV sets were sold that year. The TV market grew rapidly: there were 175,000 TVs in use by the end of 1947; nearly one million by the end of 1948; nearly three million by the end of 1949; and seven million by the end of 1950. The first RCA Victor TV, the model 630TS, sold for $375. RCA grabbed roughly 50% of the market and easily recouped its $50 million investment.

The battle for a color TV standard began even before black & white TV was a success. Bill Paley of CBS announced a color TV system in 1940. Amazingly, it was based on Peter Goldmark's mechanical system. Sarnoff opposed it because it was not all-electronic and was incompatible with existing black-and-white sets (the signals could not be displayed in black-and-white on black-and-white sets). He dismissed it as "horse and buggy era mechanical color."

Meanwhile, RCA's engineers developed five different color TV schemes. Remarkably, four out of the five appeared to work. In 1949,

Sarnoff demonstrated color TV to the FCC. It was a disaster: "The monkeys were green, the bananas were blue, and everyone had a good laugh," said Sarnoff.

RCA selected the three-gun shadow mask approach, conceived by engineer Alfred Schroeder, as its color TV solution. Separate electron guns were employed to excite phosphors for the three primary colors. A thin sheet of perforated material—the mask—was positioned to prevent each gun from exciting the wrong phosphors. A properly working system was demonstrated in 1950.

By 1956, however, color TV still hadn't taken off. By 1959, RCA had spent nearly $130,000,000 developing color television. There were just 500,000 color sets in use compared with 45 million black-and-white sets. It wasn't until 1965 that color TV achieved critical mass; prices dropped from $1,000 to $500 each and five million sets were sold. By the end of 1968, there were 20 million color TV sets in use.

Later, RCA entered the computer business, but sold the unsuccessful division to UNIVAC. RCA may have been better positioned to develop computer technology than IBM, but IBM understood the market.

* * *

If Sarnoff's forerunners were inventors and entrepreneurs like Edison and Marconi, he in turn would be the forefather of generations of executives managing high-tech businesses. Sarnoff believed in the need for managers who understand the technology but concentrate on planning, developing and marketing products and intellectual property.

As a manager, Sarnoff was skilled at resolving technical disputes and making key engineering decisions. He wasn't afraid to meet with the engineers, ask a series of probing questions, and lead them to the solution. When NBC engineers made an embarrassing mistake—the audio during live coverage of a former British Prime Minister's speech at the Lotus Club was terrible—he grilled the engineers to determine exactly what went wrong. When they admitted their mistake and promised to not let it happen again, he was satisfied and moved on to other issues.

Sarnoff arrived on the scene just as product development shifted from individual inventors to corporate research and development teams. It was simply a matter of specialization. The engineers solved technical problems, while senior executives ran the business. Sarnoff understood that technology can produce value where none existed before. He believed big companies are best able to create new markets because they possess the R&D, production, and sales resources. But he also knew when to delay, block or oppose change. He wasn't afraid to take risks for necessary developments; he also understood that new markets take time.

Sarnoff was something of a contradiction. He was ambitious, but he could also be selfless. He was a workaholic and often exaggerated his role in historic events. At other times, however, he was happy to let the company take the credit for his achievements. To Sarnoff, loyalty to the company was a cardinal virtue. But he also knew when to put defeats behind him. He opposed government-protected monopolies, but wasn't above manipulating the system for his firm's benefit. He was a street fighter, but spoke in a quiet and reasoned manner.

Was Sarnoff a 20th century robber baron? He has often been accused of destroying Edwin Armstrong and Philo Farnsworth. However, it's not that simple. Sarnoff was a tough-minded businessman, but he never set out to ruin anyone. He was entrusted with advancing the interests of RCA's employees and investors, and could hardly have been expected to thwart his company's business model. RCA made Armstrong wealthy, and eventually paid Farnsworth. But there is also compelling evidence that RCA under Sarnoff used its influence in Washington, DC to stall FM radio and that Sarnoff used deception in dealing with Farnsworth.

One thing we can be sure of is that amassing personal wealth was not Sarnoff's primary goal. If he was driven by lust, it was lust for position and prestige—not wealth. He could justly claim to be the father of radio and television broadcasting. He built an empire that included manufacturing, licensing, broadcasting, and content production.

In 1955, General Sarnoff received The Hundred Year Association of New York's Gold Medal Award "in recognition of outstanding contributions to the City of New York." During his lifetime, he also received 27 honorary degrees.

David Sarnoff retired in 1970, at the age of 79, and died the following year, at age 80. He is interred in a mausoleum featuring an elliptical atom on its front door and a stained-glass vacuum tube in Kensico Cemetery in Valhalla, New York.

PART III

Chapter Ten

Going Mobile

Mobile radio was not a single invention; it was the result of multiple developments. It defined an ecosystem consisting of mobile infrastructure, mobile user devices (enabled by components that were smaller and consumed less power), mobile communication protocols, and mobile services. And its progenitors were a diverse group that included bootstrap entrepreneurs, Nobel Laureates, and a movie star.

The first mobile radios were not small and personal like today's ubiquitous mobile phones. In the early days, a palm-size radio seemed as unlikely as a pocketsize refrigerator. A "mobile" radio was simply a radio that could be installed on a ship or an airplane, or in an automobile. In fact, the first cellular telephones were strictly car phones (requiring special installation) and bulky bag phones.

Ironically, the very first radios were mobile. Guglielmo Marconi avoided like the plague any hint that wireless was intended to replace telegraph lines. The last thing he wanted was to provoke the big telegraph companies, their investors, and their friends in high places. He knew the cable giants could squash wireless both politically and financially. So he focused on an application for which wireless was the only option: maritime communications.

Not that Marconi's wireless gear was something you could just throw in a tote bag. It was big yet delicate, and even more space was needed for the antenna. Fortunately, ocean-going ships—the kind of vessels that desperately needed communications—were large enough to accommodate wireless equipment and trained operators. A quarter of a century passed before wireless gear was small enough for automobiles.

Putting wireless on the streets was no trivial task. Under the inspired leadership of Commissioner William P. Rutledge, the Detroit Police Department began experimenting with mobile radio in 1921—the same year broadcasting was introduced. The maiden application resembled paging, a one-way system, more than two-way mobile radio. The Detroit PD wanted to alert specific officers in the field to call a dispatcher from the nearest telephone.

The challenge was building receivers small and rugged enough for patrol cars. More specifically, the receivers had to withstand shock and vibration, and they needed enough power to keep their tubes' filaments burning. The Detroit PD wrestled with the problem for six years, testing voice and even Morse code. Instability and lack of sensitivity limited coverage. By 1927, an exasperated Detroit PD finally threw up its hands and shut down its mobile communications program.

It wasn't shut down for long, though. Robert L. Batts, a student at Purdue University, developed a rugged superheterodyne receiver. With no manufacturers in sight, Commissioner Rutledge created a small electronics assembly plant within his own department. A one-way system went on the air in the spring of 1928 and this time proved successful. The Cleveland Police Department followed suit in 1929.

The first two-way mobile radio system was developed in the early 1930s and placed in operation by the Bayonne, New Jersey Police Department. By then, the biggest challenge was defining a fast, efficient, and orderly method for a central dispatcher and many squad cars to talk to each other. In other words, a communications protocol was needed. The Bayonne PD implemented what is now known as the push-to-talk (PTT) protocol. Everyone listened on the same frequency and spoke only when granted permission by the dispatcher. It was important to keep transmissions short and say "over" when done speaking.

The pioneers of mobile radio soon realized that the hardware demands were minor compared to the propagation challenges. Signals may be blocked by buildings or hills (an effect called shadowing). Signals can bounce off the ionosphere, traveling greater distances than desired, causing interference to distant users (skipping). The biggest problem, however, is that signals often take multiple paths of differing lengths from the transmitter to the receiver, interfering with each other when they arrive at the receiver (fading). Together, these impairments cause mobile signals to vary from very weak to very strong.

Despite the hardware and propagation challenges, by 1934 there were 194 municipal and 58 state police radio systems serving more than 5,000 radio-equipped police cars. In 1937, the new Federal Communications Commission (FCC) expanded the number of channels allocated for police use from eleven to forty.

The establishment of the FCC by the Communications Act of 1934 was largely a response to tectonic shifts in the wireless industry, such as the rise of radio networks and radio advertising. But it was also an admission that the FCC's predecessor, the Federal Radio Commission (FRC), had a reputation for being arbitrary and even corrupt.

A confluence of technologies enabled further growth of mobile radio. Frequency modulation, paging, the transistor, trunked radio, and spread spectrum debuted in separate roles. Together, they set the stage for the breakthrough that would change everything, cellular radio.

* * *

By the late 1920s, a growing percentage of Americans were buying their own automobiles. But it would be years before features we now take for granted would be included such as air conditioning, power steering, and radios. In 1929, the Galvin Manufacturing Company decided to fill in the gap by creating an after-market car radio. Paul Galvin, the company's founder, wanted a catchy name that would evoke taking RCA's famous Radiola on the road. He called his new product line "Motorola."

Galvin was born in the small Midwestern town of Harvard, Illinois in 1895. After working his way through two years at the University of Illinois, he concluded that he wasn't getting enough out of his education to justify the cost in time and money. First he went to work as a clerk in a local railroad station. Then he went to work for Commonwealth Edison in Chicago.

Anticipating the United States would enter World War I Galvin enrolled in an officer's training program, became an artillery officer, and served on the front lines in France. The war must have taught him perspective: after a conflict that claimed 20 million lives, what was a mere business setback? It was a good lesson, since he would face many during his career. From his tour of duty, he also learned about leadership, discipline, and loyalty—ideas that helped shape Motorola. The company became known for its dynamic organization—and stalwart presence on the market's front lines.

Upon his discharge from the military in 1919, Galvin went to work for D&G Storage Battery Company. Two years later, he and Edward Stewart (also from Harvard, Illinois) started a storage battery manufacturing company in Marshfield, Wisconsin. The company failed in 1923 mainly due to high shipping costs from its rural location. Galvin later claimed he had just $1.50 in his pocket when he returned to Illinois with his wife and infant son. He found a job in Chicago as personal secretary to Emil Brach of the Brach Candy Company. He also must have learned from Brach, who built a successful candy manufacturing and distribution business after losing his entire $15,000 savings in a failed venture.

Working closely with a successful entrepreneur made Galvin determined to make another attempt at starting his own company. In 1926, he teamed up with Edward Stewart again to manufacture storage batteries—this time in Chicago, a major transportation hub, and during an economic upswing. What could possibly go wrong? Only the most basic element: The product had a serious defect. Customers deserted the firm before it could be rectified. The company went out of business and its property was seized by creditors.

However, in a last-minute attempt to avert going out of business, Galvin, Stewart, and one of their engineers developed a battery eliminator. This device enabled battery-operated equipment, such as the first consumer radios, to instead be powered from an electric power outlet in the home. Chicago-based Sears Roebuck agreed just in the nick of time to sell the product. Because the battery eliminator was developed by the failed business, however, the creditors had the right to auction it off. That is exactly what they did. With Sears as his anchor customer, Galvin was able to raise $1,000, and was the highest bidder for the battery eliminator design, tools, and plan at $750.

The Galvin Manufacturing Corporation was founded on September 25, 1928 with five employees. Initially, the firm survived by repairing rather than selling battery eliminators. Then Galvin jumped into manufacturing AC-powered radios for private label customers—customers that put their own brand names on the radios. Galvin managed to line up about twenty such customers, mostly small companies trying to tap a fast-growing market.

Business was touch and go. The company sometimes relied on last-minute cash sales to meet its payroll. It worked out because Paul, who handled sales, and his brother Joe, who managed production, inspired loyalty among their employees. The Galvins knew their company could only succeed in the electronics business as a tight-knit team, and their small town upbringing taught them to treat the other members of their team with respect.

In the spring of 1929, the company's home radio business started to boom. Unfortunately, in the fall of 1929 the stock market went bust. As demand for radios plummeted, manufacturers of name-brand radios began dumping their inventories. The selling prices of name-brand radios fell below the cost of Galvin's radios for private label dealers. Once again, Galvin faced a looming business collapse.

Galvin sought refuge in the emerging car radio market. Even during the worst year of the Great Depression, 1932, the U.S. produced 900,000 automobiles. By 1935, annual production climbed back to over 2,000,000 automobiles. Galvin didn't need to dominate the market—he just needed sufficient sales to hang on.

Up until that time, the market for car radios was small because car radios required custom installation. You could have one installed in New York for $240. Galvin saw an opportunity for low-cost, mass-produced car radios. The race was on to develop a saleable car radio before the company went belly up. Galvin marshaled all of his resources to build a prototype in time for the 1930 Radio Manufacturers Association Convention in Atlantic City. Just days before the convention, a working prototype was built and installed in Galvin's personal automobile. He drove his Studebaker the approximately 850 miles over rough roads. Having no booth space, Galvin and his wife Lillian demonstrated the prototype outside the convention hall.

Galvin's car radio was not an immediate success, but several dealers bought a few each, and that gave Galvin reason for optimism. The bad news was that the company finished 1930 with a loss of $3,745 on sales of $287,000. The good news was that it had a new product with a promising future: the model 5T71 car radio selling for approximately $120—half the price of custom-installed units.

Though the 5T71 was easier to install, that doesn't mean all it took was a couple of screws. As Motorola employee Elmer Wavering (who also invented the automobile alternator) recalled, "[We'd] go in and rip out the brand new headlining in the car, drill holes into the floor for our batteries, and rig up a whole complicated electrical system with a network of wires."[9]

Despite that, people wanted radios in their cars. Radios had become common appliances in homes, and automobiles were a big part of the changing American landscape. Cars provided young couples with mobile privacy, and car radios provided the background music. As the nation improved and extended its roadways, commutes lengthened, and car radios helped combat the monotony.

Galvin's relationships with private label dealers paid off: they started ordering car radios. However, Galvin learned from experience that the private label business is risky and he resolved that this time he would diversify. Continuing to sell private label sets, he created the "Motorola" brand and began selling sets under that name as well. Galvin signed up seven wholesale distributors in 1931—distributors that drove business to Motorola for many years to come.

The car radio market took off worldwide. Blaupunkt in Germany and Crosley in the U.K. began manufacturing car radios for their respective domestic markets. By 1933, there were more than 500,000 car radios in use.

---

[9] http://www.motorola.com/content.jsp?globalObjectId=8432-10811

In 1936, the Delco subsidiary of General Motors began producing the first dashboard-installed car radios.

Galvin was not yet out of the woods, but things were looking up. He launched two new car radio models in 1934. An agreement with B.F. Goodrich Company put Motorola radios in hundreds of stores. The company began advertising in *Collier's* and the *Saturday Evening Post*. A highway billboard advertising campaign was launched, too.

At the suggestion of his distributors, Galvin re-entered the home radio and phonograph businesses in 1937. Most car radios were produced during the first six months of the year; sales to the home market peaked in December. Later that year, Galvin sensed an oncoming economic recession and convinced his distributors to reduce their inventories with a well-timed but modest price-reduction. Motorola was forced to lay off two-thirds of its workforce.

What happened next shows that merely surviving during tough times can lead to success. The Philco Company was hit by a major labor strike and was forced to contract with other companies to produce its radios. Motorola was one of the companies selected; Philco's business helped Motorola weather the recession of 1937.

Motorola introduced a car radio modified to monitor police frequencies in 1936. Three years later, Galvin decided to enter the police two-way radio market. Motorola's famous SCR536 "Handie-Talkie," a handheld two-way AM radio, was developed in 1940 and began shipping in 1941. Having diversified into car and police radios, Motorola was well positioned to serve the military "field radio" market.

In 1936, Galvin took his family to Europe. Touring Germany, he was impressed by the country's autobahns and remarked, "These roads have not been built just for autos. They are war roads." Convinced another war was coming, he instructed the company's engineers to begin developing radio technology for military use.

Sure enough, the U.S. Army approached Motorola about backpack-style field radios in 1940. The Army Signal Corps, in particular, wanted a portable AM transmitter-receiver combination. Since transistors had not yet been invented, the units would have to include vacuum tubes and the large batteries needed to heat their filaments. Dr. Dan Noble, Motorola's Director of Research, traveled to Fort Monmouth to discuss the Army's requirements. He suggested it would be wiser to use the new frequency modulation technology developed by Edwin H. Armstrong. (Most police departments had already switched to FM mobile radios.)

The Army liked what it heard. Western Electric was already supplying the military with FM mobile radios. German Panzers, meanwhile, were still using the less reliable AM technology. It was a bold idea from Noble and Motorola. FM was clearly the superior technology, but putting it in a backpack would be a challenge.

The SCR-300 backpack FM transceiver development team included Henry Magnuski, Marion Bond, Lloyd Morris, and Bill Vogel. Operating in the 40-MHz band, the unit had to communicate at least three miles while weighing no more than 35 pounds. The Motorola team understood the urgency and ruggedness requirements. In particular, the units would have to withstand the high temperatures and humidity in the Pacific theater.

The SCR-300 was a success. Its unique features included a single tuning control for both the transmitter and receiver and automatic frequency control. The unit beat the three-mile communications requirement with ease, routinely working at distances of 10-20 miles. Nearly sixty years later, the Institute of Electrical and Electronics Engineers (IEEE) honored the Motorola engineer who conceived the breakthrough SCR-300 portable, two-way, FM radio by establishing the IEEE Daniel E. Noble Award for contributions to emerging technologies.

Starting in 1943, Motorola produced nearly 50,000 SCR-300 units, with the first units arriving just in time for the invasion of Italy. The SCR-300 also helped re-establish order in the Battle of the Bulge's aftermath. Specifically, it helped restore supply lines, intelligence gathering, and tactical communications. The Army awarded Dan Noble a Certificate of Merit for his outstanding contributions.

As World War II drew to a close, Motorola emerged as the undisputed leader in two-way radio. Even as things were going well, Galvin saw a need for further diversification. He targeted the emerging television market. As the potential of transistor technology became apparent, and on the urging of his son Robert (who replaced his father as CEO in 1958 and grew sales to 30 times the level he inherited) and the advice of research director Noble, he entered the semiconductor design and fabrication business. The military electronics laboratory that Motorola established in Phoenix, Arizona in 1949 evolved into a leading supplier of semiconductor devices. Motorola moved aggressively to employ transistors in new product designs.

The television market was particularly challenging. Having introduced a television with a ten-inch screen in the $300 range, RCA had a significant lead. Galvin realized that Motorola would need to develop a comparable or superior product it could sell for less. To make it happen, Galvin created something that became a Motorola hallmark for the next few decades—he established competing R&D teams within his own firm. One team developed a unit with a seven-inch screen at much lower cost. Motorola set a retail price of $179.95 for the Golden View model VT71 and quickly sold 100,000 units. The firm took fourth place in unit sales volume with its very first television product.

The use of competing R&D teams was undoubtedly hazardous. On the upside, it made developing great products more urgent and personal. But there was a risk of demoralizing engineers on the teams whose products were not selected. The ideal outcome must have been to incorporate at least some of their ideas in the final product.

Motorola continued to make progress in the car radio market. Having acquired Detrola Company, a Detroit-based maker of both tabletop and car radios, Motorola enjoyed 50% of Ford's car radio business and significant shares of Chrysler's and American Motors' car radio businesses, too. Motorola tried without success to produce automotive units that played 45 rpm disks or tapes. Only after Philips launched the compact cassette in 1964 could automobile owners play the content of their choice.

By 1954, Motorola had grown so large it had to be reorganized into separate product divisions. Two years later, Paul Galvin became chairman and CEO and appointed his son Robert president. By 1960, Motorola approached $300 million in annual sales. That same year, Motorola introduced the first fully transistorized, "large-screen" television. (Customers bought bragging rights: "Come watch the game on our gigantic 19 inch screen!") The following year, Motorola entered the broader automotive electronics market, where its solid-state designs gave the firm a competitive advantage. Motorola went on to become a leading provider of mobile phones and mobile phone network infrastructure.

Though the company succession was assured, Paul Galvin never lived to enjoy retirement. He died of leukemia on November 5, 1959 at age 64.

Galvin was the quintessential entrepreneur. He never gave up despite a string of failures. Instead, he turned each failure into a learning experience. He learned how to control costs, when to develop new products, when to reduce prices, the importance of product diversification, and how to leverage distribution channels. According to one biographer, Galvin never intended to be more than a successful small businessman. However, he discovered the only way to ensure survival was to keep growing. In high-tech industries such as wireless, that meant accepting risk-taking as a necessary activity.

* * *

The mobile telephone service (MTS) was introduced in St. Louis shortly after World War II. AT&T was the first licensed operator. However, MTS was nothing like today's mobile phone offerings. MTS served only a tiny slice of America's elite. It was a mobile phone service for millionaires and movie stars with chauffeur-driven automobiles.

MTS operated in the 150-MHz VHF band, just below TV channel 7 in the United States. The system used FM radio technology and had very limited capacity. Because cellular radio was not yet practical, MTS used what is known as a star topology. A single base station was placed roughly in the center of the service area, and communicated with mobile users up to 30 miles away. The mobiles used up to 50 watts of transmit power—way more power than the 0.6 watts maximum used by today's handheld cell phones.

Within a year, MTS spread to 25 cities. The lack of market penetration wasn't due to high costs; rates were high for the time at about $15 per month for a basic subscription plus 15 cents per minute of usage, but for those who could afford it MTS was a much sought after luxury. Market penetration was limited because the systems were quickly loaded to capacity. New applicants were placed on waiting lists. Unlike today's cellular service, MTS calls were operator-assisted and half-duplex; only one person could speak at a time.

The first direct dial mobile phone system (permitting users to dial without operator assistance) was deployed in 1948 in Richmond, Indiana by the Richmond Radiotelephone Company. By contrast, AT&T didn't provide automated dialing until 1964.

Prices rose as it became clear that mobile phone demand far outstripped supply. The phones cost $2,000 and up; usage charges rose to between 70 cents and $1.20 per minute and basic subscriptions increased to as much as $100 per month. Mobile phones became a status accessory; James Bond used a car phone.

Waiting lists provided some incentive for increasing capacity. Three methods of boosting capacity were used over the next two decades. Channel splitting doubled capacity, but it became harder and harder to squeeze intelligible conversations into narrower channels. The original MTS channels were 120-kHz wide and were split into 60-kHz and then 30-kHz channels.

Capacity was also increased by allocating additional spectrum. The FCC allocated 50-kHz channels in the 450-MHz band in 1950. These were split into 25-kHz channels in the 1960s. However, the new 450-MHz channels did nothing to relieve congestion for 150-MHz users.

Trunking was another capacity-boosting technique. In the original MTS scheme, a mobile user wishing to place a call had to first contact the operator on a dedicated channel. Over the course of a day precious channels lay idle for considerable periods; it took time for the operator to identify an available channel and assign it to the next user.

Trunked systems identify and assign available channels automatically—eliminating the delays associated with operator intervention. By adding processing power to both the mobile and base station radios, idle channel time was drastically reduced. (The first radio to feature a microprocessor was the Motorola MX-300, a portable trunked radio.) By the 1960s, the time lag between the end of one call and the start of another was often reduced to less than one second. However, while trunking can boost efficiency by 20%, it doesn't come close to multiplying capacity.

The improved mobile telephone service (IMTS) was introduced in 1964 and incorporated direct dialing, full-duplex operation (allowing users to talk and listen at the same time but requiring twice as much bandwidth per call), and 32 channels distributed across three different frequency bands. Capacity was increased, but not nearly enough: In 1976, New York City had 543 subscribers on its 12-channel system and 3,700 people on its waiting list.

Today, most MTS and IMTS frequencies have been "refarmed." Many were grabbed up by paging operators, who have themselves succumbed to cellular competition. Before cell phones became ubiquitous, paging provided a cost-effective way of letting individuals know that someone was trying to reach them. The first "beepers" merely told the user to call a paging operator. More advanced paging systems delivered the caller's phone number directly to the display on a pocketsize device. Because paging was primarily a broadcast service, it could serve millions of users with relatively little radio spectrum.

There were MTS systems still operating as late as 2006 in extremely remote areas, such as Canada's Yukon Territory, where there is no economic incentive to deploy cellular technology. Otherwise, MTS will be remembered as little more than a preview of genuine mobile phone service—and an old movie prop.

* * *

Motorola has faced many competitors, but one stood out as mobile radio matured and cellular telephone emerged: LM Ericsson of Sweden. Ericsson was a much older company, but unlike Motorola, which started as a radio company and evolved into mobile phones, Ericsson started as a telephone company and diversified into mobile radio.

Ericsson claims it built the first fully automated mobile phone system in 1956 for the Swedish operator TeliaSonera. This system was called Mobile System A (MTA). In 1965, it was rendered obsolete by a more advanced, transistorized system called Mobile System B (MTB). MTA was shut down in 1969, having acquired all of about 150 subscribers. However, Ericsson went on to become a leading supplier of private mobile radio systems for police and utility companies, and it continues to be a leading provider of mobile telephone systems.

Lars Magnus Ericsson was born in Värmskog, Sweden in 1846. His father died when he was twelve years old and he had to go to work when he was just fourteen. Lars saved enough money to move to Stockholm in 1867. There he found employment as an instrument maker at Öllers & Co., a firm specializing in telegraph equipment. Working at Öllers during the day, he studied English, German, mathematics, and technical drawing at night. Ericsson earned a scholarship to study instrument making abroad, which he did from 1872 to 1875, working with Siemens and Halske (forerunner of the European engineering conglomerate of today, Siemens AG) during part of that time.

When he returned to Sweden in 1876, Ericsson started a mechanical workshop with his friend Carl Johan Andersson. For the first few years, the company mostly repaired telephones. Then the company began manufacturing telephones (competing with Alexander Graham Bell's products which Ericsson had come to know intimately through his repair work) and was reorganized as the Ericsson Corporation in 1883.

Lars Magnus Ericsson retired at age 54 in 1900 having built a highly successful telephone manufacturing company. He and his wife Hilda moved to a farm in 1906. In 1910, Ericsson created what could be called the first mobile telephone—though it was not wireless. Lars did not enjoy touring in the couple's horseless carriage, but his wife loved driving. Wanting to make sure she could communicate in an emergency, Lars gave her a telephone with its wires attached to two long poles. When his wife needed to make a call, she could pull over to the side of the road, use the poles to touch the wires to overhead phone lines, and crank the phone's dynamo handle to signal the operator at the nearest exchange.

Ericsson's "mobile telephone" was not really a new invention; telephone companies already had portable telephones that they used to test phone lines. Similarly, the military sometimes commandeered phone lines using phones produced by Ericsson for precisely that purpose. But the device Ericsson rigged up for his wife may have been the first portable phone for a civilian automobile owner.

Ericsson was contemptuous of patents and he freely copied others' products whenever he could get away with it. For example, Bell Telephone had not bothered to obtain patents in Scandinavia, and Ericsson saw this as his personal invitation. Unfortunately, the same attitude also worked against him; Norwegian firms made copies of his copies. In any event, Ericsson's telephones became known for both their performance and attractive designs, and later became highly collectible.

Towards the end of Ericsson's tenure, his two biggest telephone service provider customers (Telegrafverket and Stockholm General Telephone Company) began assembling their own telephones. Ericsson was forced to pursue foreign markets and did so with success. The firm exported phones to Norway, Denmark, Finland, Australia, New Zealand, South Africa, the United Kingdom and Russia. By 1897, Britain accounted for 28% of LM Ericsson's sales. Ericsson made both telephones and exchanges and grew to approximately 500 employees.

Ericsson's telephones were first-rate but its exchanges were inferior to those made in the U.S. By 1910, the company could no longer ignore this weakness and the next decade was spent refining and enhancing its infrastructure products and business. LM Ericsson introduced its first dial telephone in 1921. However, in 1930 the company experienced weakness in its export markets—particularly the new Soviet Union. LM Ericsson was rescued from bankruptcy by Swedish industrialist Marcus Wallenberg Jr. with help of friendly banks (owned by his family) and the Swedish government. Ericsson gained control of several telephone operating companies which, from that time onward, were certain to purchase a great deal of Ericsson gear.

Once LM Ericsson's financial condition stabilized, the company began leveraging its foreign factories and reducing its ownership of operating companies. For example, the Beeston factory in the U.K. helped LM Ericsson win the lion's share of British Post Office contracts for switching equipment made under license from Strowger.

Lars Ericsson sold all of his shares in 1905. Like Paul Galvin, he inspired fierce loyalty, and built an organization that took on a life of its own. Ericsson died 26 years after retiring, on December 17, 1926. By his explicit request, he was buried in an unmarked grave.

* * *

The development of semiconductor components was a breakthrough for mobile communications—and all portable electronics. Semiconductor devices did away with power-hungry, heat-generating filaments. Employing materials in direct contact, semiconductors eliminated the need for bulky and fragile glass tubes. Best of all, semiconductors put the electronics industry on the road to continuous cost, size, and power-consumption reduction.

Semiconductors lie somewhere between conductors and insulators. The two most common semiconductors are silicon and germanium. Impurities can be added to these materials to change their electrical properties in ways that have proved exceedingly useful.

The transistor was one of Bell Laboratories' finest achievements. It was a small, low-power device that could do almost everything that vacuum tubes could do—though at first not always as well. Transistors could be used in amplifiers, oscillators, modulators, switches, and regulators. As they shrank in size, transistors enabled digital electronics and modern computers.

The transistor is often associated with controversial Nobel Laureate William Shockley, but several researchers contributed to its development. One of the most important was Russell Ohl, who came to Bell Labs in 1927. He had a hunch that semiconductors would prove useful in the development of high-frequency receivers. However, his initial research yielded nothing of value, and Bell Labs' management wanted to put him on other projects. He repeatedly convinced management to let him continue investigating semiconductor crystals.

Ohl stumbled on the P-N junction, which proved a momentous discovery, by accident. He was trying to produce pure silicon crystals. By 1939, Ohl was achieving 99.8 per cent purity. He already knew the crystals could act as rectifiers, permitting the flow of current in one direction only. On February 23, Ohl began studying a crystal with a crack down its middle. One morning while measuring current flow in opposite directions, he noticed the amount of current changed when the crystal was held over different objects: a bowl of water, a hot soldering iron, and an incandescent lamp. By early afternoon, he realized the changes were caused by light.

On March 6, Ohl showed his silicon experiment to Bell Labs' research director (and future president) Mervin Kelly, who alerted experimental physicists Walter Brattain and Joseph Becker. Ohl demonstrated that shining a flashlight on the crystal caused the voltage to jump half a volt. The relationship between light and electricity was not new, but the extent of the voltage increase (10x anything seen previously) was. Brattain understood immediately that there must be some sort of electric barrier associated with the crack.

Further research revealed that there were different impurities on opposite sides of the crack. One side produced an excess of electrons and the other side produced a dearth of electrons. It all started to make sense. Because opposite charges attract each other, the excess electrons were drawn to the crack, creating a thin electrical barrier. Electrons could easily cross the barrier in one direction but not the other. The crystal behaved much like a vacuum tube diode.

Photons from the flashlight imparted just enough additional energy to the electrons to push them across the barrier. That suggested something even more exciting. The semiconductor P-N junction resembled Fleming's vacuum tube diode. The addition of a third element transformed the vacuum tube diode into the vacuum tube triode amplifier and oscillator. Could another element be added to the semiconductor diode to create a semiconductor triode?

Brattain teamed up with colleague John Bardeen, working under Bell Labs executive William Shockley, to experiment further with germanium and silicon crystals. Bardeen earned his PhD in mathematical physics at Princeton in 1935. Having studied quantum physics, Bardeen was just the person to identify and explain semiconductor behavior. His mastery of theory was the perfect complement to Brattain's experimental investigations. A quiet, unassuming, "regular Joe," Bardeen would become the only person to twice win the Nobel Prize in Physics.

One of the many stories from that time is that Brattain and Bardeen allegedly failed to keep Shockley fully informed of their discoveries. When the pair invented the point-contact transistor, Shockley commandeered it and created the junction transistor, causing a permanent rift in their relationship with their imperious boss. Patent applications were submitted for both inventions in 1948, but Shockley's junction transistor quickly became the preferred solution.

Though Shockley would end his career in failure and disgrace, there is no question that he was a brilliant scientist. Having earned his PhD at MIT, he developed a reputation as Bell Labs' quickest and most imaginative problem solver. For example, Shockley and James Fisk (who would succeed Kelly as Bell Labs' president) were assigned by Bell Labs to explore nuclear fission as a potential energy source. Shockley came up with the idea of producing a controlled chain reaction. He and Fisk were among the first to design a nuclear reactor. When they sent their report to Washington, DC it was immediately stamped classified, and the pair were prohibited from seeking a patent.

During World War II, Shockley devised successful strategies for destroying German U-boats and helping allied convoys evade German bombers. He also improved bomber crew efficiency. Shockley earned a National Medal of Merit for his contributions to the war effort.

Shockley discovered the field effect in 1945 while trying to create a semiconductor amplifier. (The field effect transistor (FET) uses an electric field to control a conductive channel in semiconductor material; modern FETs are used extensively in digital integrated circuits.) His first device consisted of a cylinder with a thin coat of silicon mounted next to a metal plate. The device didn't work, so he asked Bardeen the theoretician and Brattain the tinker to figure out why. In late 1947, Bardeen discovered that the electrons drawn to the surface of the crystal created an electric barrier.

The point-contact transistor developed by Brattain and Bardeen consisted of strips of gold foil on a plastic triangle in contact with a germanium slab. Shockley developed his sandwich transistor (which evolved into the more advanced junction transistor) in a hotel room in Chicago, where he was attending the American Physical Society convention. He wasn't trying to take credit away from Bardeen and Brattain, but having come close to inventing the first transistor (in 1945) he was desperate to match or exceed their success. And he did: The junction transistor was more rugged and easier to manufacture than the point-contact transistor. Still, there were stories that Shockley tried to take credit for the work of Brattain and Bardeen; these stories were probably fueled by Bell Labs' policy of always including the team leader in photographs and press releases. In the end, the point-contact transistor patent was credited to Brattain and Bardeen and the junction transistor patent was credited to Shockley. Shockley's book, *Electrons and Holes in Semiconductors*, became the bible of semiconductor science for a generation of researchers.

The transistor received little attention at first—though Shockley saw its tremendous potential. He left Bell Labs and founded Shockley Semiconductor in Palo Alto, California. However, Shockley's personality created friction and eight of his smartest engineers soon left to found a competing company, Fairchild Semiconductor. (In fact, Shockley's company never produced a viable product.) Two of the eight, Robert Noyce and Gordon Moore, went on to establish Intel Corporation. In the April 19, 1965 issue of *Electronics*, Moore made the famous prediction that has become known as "Moore's Law": the number of transistors that can be packed into a single chip at the minimum component cost will double every two years.

Shockley put together a great team but was clueless about how to leverage their talent. Several team members went on to create tremendous wealth based on semiconductor technology while Shockley watched helplessly from the sidelines. After briefly teaching at Stanford, Shockley floated the theory that incompetent people multiply while intelligent people use birth control. During an interview, he pointed out that on average African Americans scored 15 points lower on IQ tests and suggested that the cause was genetic.

Brattain, Bardeen, and Shockley made very little money from their invention—though Shockley was instrumental in establishing Silicon Valley. Bardeen left Bell Labs for the University of Illinois and won a second Nobel Prize for his work in superconductivity in 1972. Brattain stayed at Bell Labs for several more years before leaving to teach at Whitman College.

Though the three physicists went their separate ways, they were reunited in 1956 in Sweden when they received the Nobel Prize and spent a cordial evening together. They met again in 1972 at a celebration of the 25th anniversary of the invention of the transistor, hosted by Bell Labs. It must have been an interesting night: Bardeen, by all accounts a man without a trace of egotism, had just won his second Nobel Prize.

The transistor was first used as a replacement for vacuum tubes in military applications. Within less than a decade, however, the transistor— along with polyethylene plastic developed by DuPont chemist W.H. Carothers—was widely used in portable radios. Like "solid state televisions," "transistor radios" were something most consumers knew they wanted, if only because they were told there were no vacuum tubes to replace. Several more years passed before transistors were etched into integrated circuits and applied to digital processing.

Predictably, the vacuum tube industry dismissed transistors as cheap substitutes. Sony Electronics' founders Masaru Ibuka and Akio Morita encountered little competition for their handheld transistor radios. The battery-powered radios brought technology to even the poorest people in the most remote areas. However, for many years audiophiles insisted that vacuum tubes produced better sound quality.

In 1958, Robert Noyce of Fairchild (and later Intel) and Jack Kilby of Texas Instruments produced the first integrated circuits (ICs). In 1971, Ted Hoff of Intel put the central processor of a computer on a single IC, creating the first microprocessor. Hoff was responding to a request from a Japanese company that wanted to build a calculator using ICs. The customer expected to use twelve separate ICs, but Hoff consolidated the functions onto a single chip.

When he received the Nobel Prize for Physics in 2000, Kilby commented, "I graduated in 1947, just one year before Bell Labs announced the invention of the transistor. It meant that my vacuum tube classes were about to become obsolete, but it offered great opportunities to put my physics studies to good use."

* * *

Another seminal technology, spread spectrum radio, was implemented by the military in the 1950s. However, commercial applications awaited its declassification in 1981 as well as the development of digital ICs. Today, spread spectrum is a fundamental technology used in applications such as the Global Positioning System (GPS), wireless local area networks, and third-generation mobile phone networks.

Spread spectrum technology has several benefits—only some of which were known to early investigators. Spread spectrum was conceived to provide secure communications—both in terms of evading jamming (intentional interference) and ensuring privacy. Other advantages, such as allowing cellular networks to reuse all frequencies in all cells, were not discovered until later.

The invention of spread spectrum is often attributed to an unexpected source: the movie star Hedy Lamarr and her friend George Antheil, composer of the nearly impossible to perform *Ballet Mécanique*. For many years virtually unknown, the story of their unlikely technology patent has spawned almost its own genre of books, articles and references. It's easy to understand why: We've seen many men rise from humble roots to become great scientists and entrepreneurs, but there aren't any precedents for a Hollywood movie goddess and avant-garde music composer teaming up to patent a telecommunications technology that was ahead of its time.

For all of the fascination with Lamarr and Antheil, it may disappoint fans to learn that the earliest description of frequency hopping is actually found in Nikola Tesla's U.S. patents 723188 and 725605 issued in 1903. Tesla conceived frequency hopping as a means of providing secure and reliable communications for remote control of a submersible vessel.

Still, Hedy Kiesler Markey (Lamarr's married name at the time) and George Antheil did obtain U.S. Patent 2,292,387 entitled "Secret

Communication System" issued August 11, 1942. The patent describes the use of frequency hopping for the remote control of torpedoes. Basically, the shipboard transmitter and torpedo-based receiver hop from one frequency to another as a means of evading enemy signal jammers. The transmitter and receiver hop to the same frequencies at the same time by using synchronized player piano-style rolls; each roll is capable of indicating 88 different frequencies (also the number of keys on the standard piano keyboard).

Hedy Lamarr was born Hedwig Eva Maria Kiesler in 1913 in Vienna, Austria. She achieved notoriety when she appeared nude in the film *Ecstasy* in 1933; other Lamarr films include *Samson and Delilah* and *White Cargo*. The first of her six husbands was Austrian industrialist Friedrich (Fritz) Mandl. While married to Mandl, she often heard about the arms business, and learned that torpedoes were radio-guided but easily jammed. She fled Austria and her husband in 1937.

She signed a contract with Louis B. Mayer of MGM in Hollywood, where she met composer George Antheil at a dinner party. Antheil experimented with automated musical instruments. Unfortunately, at the time synchronizing instruments with sufficient accuracy proved impractical. While Antheil influenced Lamarr, he acknowledged that frequency hopping was her invention. Lamarr's idea was simple: if the shipboard transmitter and torpedo-based receiver hop from frequency to frequency, then it will be difficult for someone operating another transmitter to interfere with the communications. Most likely, by the time that person finds the current frequency and retunes his transmitter to it, the system will have hopped to the next frequency.

Lamarr donated the patent to the war effort. The use of identical player piano rolls to synchronize hopping was probably workable. However, there is no evidence the Navy attempted to implement it. The idea continued to percolate, though.

In the 1950s, the Hoffman Radio Corporation won a contract to build sonobuoys (dropped in the water to detect submarines) and matching aircraft receivers. The sonobuoys and receivers used mechanical spools to control the roughly 36 hops per second. In the 1960s, Hoffman developed the first digital frequency hopping system for unmanned surveillance drones used in Vietnam.

Ideally, a pseudorandom code should be used to control the frequency hopping. In other words, an observer should not be able to recognize a pattern. Generating pseudorandom codes was a major challenge for early spread spectrum systems. Player piano rolls were acceptable for one short transmission, but they would have to be looped for multiple transmissions, and that would create an obvious pattern.

Federal Telecommunication Laboratories (FTL) developed a better mechanical solution: the noise wheel. A noise-like image is recorded on a circular piece of film. Then the light from a slit lamp is passed through the film and detected by a photoelectric cell. Noise wheels were faster and could handle a larger number of frequencies than player piano rolls.

Synchronizing the receiver to the transmitter was another challenge. Lamarr's system required mechanical synchronization, which is inherently unreliable. Some early frequency hopping systems avoided mechanical synchronization by transmitting the hopping instructions on a separate frequency. A major drawback to that approach is that it uses a fixed control channel that can itself be jammed.

The term "spread spectrum" is credited to Madison Nicholson and John Raney of Sylvania Buffalo. As the name implies, the signals are spread out over a wide frequency range. To a conventional (non-spread spectrum) receiver, a spread spectrum signal looks like background noise. Nicholson and Raney headed a military project appropriately codenamed "Hush up" leading to construction of the first airborne spread spectrum radio, the ARC-50.

The ARC-50 was flight tested at Wright Patterson Air Force Base. The spread spectrum ground terminal was installed about 100 yards from the base's control tower. Though the ground terminal communicated with aircraft up to 100 miles away on frequencies overlapping the tower's frequencies, tower personnel were never aware of the spread spectrum communications.

The ARC-50 was eventually manufactured by Magnavox. It consisted of two boxes: a UHF radio and a spread spectrum modem, and employed roughly 600 transistors. The ARC-50 consumed two aircraft chassis slots usually reserved for a vacuum tube radio and an identical back up. In those days, the standard Air Force vacuum tube radios had limited Mean Time Before Failure (MTBF), so pilots felt they needed to carry two radios in case one failed during the flight. Though the transistorized ARC-50 had a much longer MTBF, 400 hours, the pilots felt safer with two vacuum tube radios. Approximately 1,000 ARC-50s manufactured in 1961 ended up sitting in a warehouse, victims of an unshakeable habit.

* * *

Much was learned during mobile radio's early days about signal propagation, radio networks, and communications protocols. But vacuum tubes could only take mobile radio so far. The invention of transistors, integrated circuits, and microprocessors set the stage for two momentous developments: cellular radio and digital radio.

Chapter Eleven

Birth of the Cell Phone

Flash back to the end of World War II. It was the beginning of the baby boom—and an unprecedented period of industrial growth. The U.S. became the world's economic powerhouse; during the 1950s millions of middle class families purchased automobiles. Mobile radio for business, public safety, and transportation was growing, and mobile telephone service was rolling out.

But anyone who did the math could see that the existing spectrum allocations and technology offered little room for growth.

Petitioning the government to allocate more mobile radio spectrum was one option. But that was a task for the political echelon. The engineers' challenge would always be squeezing more users into available spectrum. There was an obvious way to instantly double capacity: split each radio channel—the bandwidth allotted to individual conversations—into two channels. Unfortunately, the gain in capacity was matched by a loss in audio quality. Make the channels too narrow and speech would become unintelligible.

The cellular concept was first described in late 1947 in a Bell Laboratories' internal memorandum written by Douglas H. Ring with assistance from W. Rae Young. The memo laid out the essential elements of cellular radio: divide a city into cells, use low-power transmitters, and handoff calls from one frequency to another as the mobile user travels from one cell to another.

Instead of splitting the channels, Ring proposed dividing the geography. It was a brilliant idea enabling frequency reuse. For example, a city could be parceled into 70 cells and the available channels divided into seven groups. Each group could be assigned to one cell in a cluster of seven cells—with the clusters arranged so that adjacent cells never use the same frequencies. Employing low-power base station and mobile transmitters, each channel could be reused ten times throughout the city.

The moment such a cellular radio network was switched on it increased the traffic capacity of the assigned spectrum by a factor of ten.

In theory, the cells could be divided again and again to achieve ever-greater capacity. In practice, cell-splitting has limits. Cellular radio also required more sophisticated radios and networks than could be built using vacuum tubes. Still, no other technology came close to matching cellular's capacity.

Ring examined the traffic capacity of alternative cellular architectures. He considered systems based on triangular, square, and hexagonal cells and found the latter was most efficient. He concluded that cell handoffs required further study. The transistor was not yet available, and microprocessors were decades away. Handing off a call from one base station to an adjacent base station was not by itself a major challenge, but switching the mobile transmitter and receiver to new frequencies at precisely the right moment was a risky proposition.

Commenting later, Young reportedly said Bell Labs' engineers were confident that they could overcome all of the obstacles identified by Douglas Ring. That's not surprising. By that time telecommunications engineers were routinely solving a wide range of difficult problems. Inventions such as the superheterodyne receiver, frequency modulation, and television were the result of a little ingenuity, but mainly they were the result of methodical problem solving.

Apparently, Ring's colleagues weren't bowled over by his telephonic surname. The immediate reaction to his memo was lukewarm. Bell Labs' engineers may have been confident the difficulties could be surmounted over time, but they certainly weren't promising any delivery dates. Though Douglas Ring accrued a dozen patents between 1934 and 1960, the inventor of cellular radio faded into obscurity (most cellular telephone histories refer to him only as "D.H. Ring"), dying in the year 2000 at the age of 93.

Precious little cellular radio research and development was performed during the 1950s and 1960s. In 1953, the Bell System[10] published a paper that touched on the cellular concept. The 21-page article "Frequency Economy in Mobile Radio Bands" by Kenneth Bullington appeared in the *Bell System Technical Journal.*

Henry Magnuski, one of the co-developers of the Motorola SCR-300 portable FM transceiver for the military, received U.S. Patent U.S. 2,734,131 for "Communication System with Carrier Strength Control" in 1956. Eleven years later, R.A. Channey of Bell Laboratories received U.S. Patent 3,355,556 for "Automatic Radio Telephone Switching System." While these patents described methods for handing off calls between base stations, they did not employ frequency handoffs, an essential element of cellular radio.

---

[10] The Bell System was a trademark of American Telephone and Telegraph Company, better known as AT&T.

Practical cellular telephone networks and subscriber devices awaited the development of advanced semiconductor components. The first baby steps were taken during the 1950s. The transistor radio, using silicon transistors made by Texas Instruments (TI), was introduced in 1954. In 1958, Jack Kilby of TI invented the integrated circuit—a slab of germanium 7/16 x 1/16 inches containing a single transistor and several other components.

Meanwhile, lines were forming for early mobile phone service (MTS and subsequently IMTS). Though demand exceeded supply, a full 37 years elapsed before the launch of commercial cellular telephone service in 1983. Not all of the delay could be chalked up to technology hurdles, though. There was also a major political roadblock: most of the prime mobile spectrum had been allocated to VHF and UHF television. And there was market uncertainty, as well. Though there were waiting lists for capacity-starved MTS, they did not add up to huge numbers.

The Federal Communications Commission (FCC) presented one of the obstacles. Regulation of the wireless spectrum has always been contentious, and though course corrections have been made over the years, it has never kept up with rapidly evolving technologies and markets. Some see the wireless spectrum as a precious resource that must be closely guarded against forces bent on dominating it. Others believe the industry and market can sort things out themselves and only minimal regulation is required. One thing both camps agree on, however, is that the market and technology were both ready for cellular telephone long before the FCC was ready for it.

A little history may help explain the FCC's inertia.

In the wake of the *Titanic* disaster, the Radio Act of 1912 divided the spectrum between commercial, military, and amateur use; mandated licenses and call signs for interstate and international communications; and spelled out rules for communication between ships and coastal stations. The Radio Act of 1927 established the Federal Radio Commission to end the chaos of too many stations trying to be heard on too few frequencies. The rise of radio networks and radio advertising, among other things, led to the Communications Act of 1934, which created the FCC.

Given its lineage, it's not surprising that the FCC saw policing the radio spectrum as its main job. Consequently, the FCC did not have much motivation for introducing new services. The FCC dragged its feet not only on cellular telephone, but FM radio, television, unlicensed radio, and high definition TV.

Because cellular radio promised much greater capacity than MTS/IMTS, it deserved a generous helping of spectrum—enough to show just how much it could achieve. However, the broadcast industry did not want to give up any of its spectrum—even though large tracts were sitting around collecting electromagnetic dust. In 1961, FCC chairman Newton Minow famously called television "a vast wasteland." But it would be several more years before the FCC mustered the courage to take back some of the broadcast industry's spectrum.

(When cellular telephone proved a big success the FCC adopted a completely different attitude. It no longer saw itself as the radio police. In fact, the FCC embraced the opposite extreme, fancying itself a facilitator of new technologies and services, and an auctioneer of valuable spectrum. Suddenly, the government agency that delayed cellular telephone was taking credit for cellular's success. Manhattan Institute senior fellow Peter Huber would have none of it, however; he argued that the FCC is unnecessary and we would be better off without it.)

Even the Bell System was initially ambivalent about establishing the cellular telephone service. The first time the FCC allocated more channels for mobile radio (in 1949), half of the channels were assigned to the Bell System and half were reserved for competitors. The non-Bell operators became known as radio common carriers (RCCs) and were more aggressive about creating and marketing new services such as paging and radio dispatching. By 1978, the RCCs had acquired 80,000 mobile users. The powerful Bell System, always fearful that wireless would cut into landline revenues, had signed up just 40,000 mobile users. Given those numbers, why would a company that already had a landline telephone monopoly push for a cellular telephone service that could end up introducing more competition?

(The Bell System's fear proved unfounded—at least, for several years. During its first decade, cellular telephone did not cut into landline phone revenues. The two services were complementary. It was not until around the year 2000—when the combination of low prices and flat rate plans made mobile service too attractive to pass up—that a "replacement effect" became noticeable. Young people, in particular, started using mobile phones exclusively.)

But the telecom landscape was already changing. In 1956, AT&T and the Department of Justice (DoJ) settled another in a string of anti-trust suits. AT&T agreed not to extend its business beyond voice and data transmission over telephone networks. Specifically, Bell Laboratories and Western Electric agreed not to enter the computer business and to discontinue manufacturing radio equipment. As a quid pro quo, the Bell System was allowed to retain its telephone monopoly. And contractors such as ITT-

Kellogg, Motorola, and Secode were allowed to build radio equipment to Bell System specifications.

That same year, AT&T began providing operator-assisted mobile phone service in the newly assigned 450 MHz band, and Motorola introduced its first transistorized product, a car radio. The radio spectrum's commercially viable frequency ceiling was rising—and continues to climb today. The fully transistorized radio was smaller, more rugged, and consumed less battery power than its vacuum tube predecessors. These were key developments on the road to cellular telephone.

By 1958, the Bell System began to see mobile phone service as a business opportunity; it petitioned the FCC for 75 MHz of spectrum in the 800-MHz band for mobile use. However, the FCC dragged its feet for another ten years. By 1968, it could longer ignore the many requests for additional mobile phone spectrum.

Meanwhile, the cellular concept continued to percolate at Bell Laboratories. Additional internal memoranda were written in 1958 ("High Capacity Mobile Telephone System - Preliminary Considerations," by W.D. Lewis) and 1959 ("Multi-Area Mobile Telephone System," by W.A. Cornell and H. J. Schulte). Both documents recognized the need for frequency handoffs, and the second asserted that existing technology could do the job. But there was no urgency to these documents, because cellular telephone had not yet been allocated spectrum. The two memoranda were distilled into papers published in the IRE's *Transactions on Vehicle Communications* in 1960.[11] The cellular telephone concept was finally being promoted to the wider engineering community.

* * *

By the mid-1960s, the transistor created high expectations for product miniaturization, and fictional handheld wireless phones began to appear in television programs. From Maxwell Smart's shoe phone to Captain Kirk's communicator, the idea of small and untethered phones captured the public's imagination. The company that became the world's leading supplier of handheld mobile phones, Finland-based Nokia, began to take shape.

---

[11] The Institute of Electrical and Electronics Engineers (IEEE) was formed in 1963 through the merger of the Institute of Radio Engineers (IRE) and American Institute of Electrical Engineers (AIEE).

Nokia's roots trace back more than a century. In 1865, mining engineer Fredrik Idestam started a paper mill based on a more cost-effective process he imported from Germany. It was an immediate success. Idestam changed the company name to Nokia AB in 1871. "Nokia" was the local name for the marten, a northern weasel hunted for its sable-like fur. A cousin to the wolverine, it is also a carnivorous predator. Perhaps Idestam wanted people to think of Nokia as valuable to investors and customers and fearful to competitors. Or perhaps he just liked furry critters.

Paper mills use large amounts of water and energy, so it's not surprising that Nokia diversified into electricity generation in 1902. The firm expanded into cable, rubber, and electronics manufacturing in 1967 when it merged with Finnish Rubber Works and Finnish Cable Works to form Nokia Corporation. Finnish Cable Works entered electronics in 1962, developing a pulse analyzer for nuclear power plants. The company began developing radio telephones for military and public safety markets in 1963. Building on this experience, Nokia entered the television market and by 1987 was Europe's third largest TV manufacturer.

Somehow, the company that started as a paper manufacturer metamorphosed into a consumer electronics powerhouse.

Though Nokia owes its spectacular growth to digital cellular, the firm pioneered analog cellular phones in 1979 with Mobira Oy, a joint venture of Nokia and Finnish television manufacturer Salora. Nokia developed a digital telephone switch and the Mobira 450 Nordic Mobile Telephone (NMT) car phone in 1982. Two years later, it introduced the Mobira Talkman, a portable mobile phone for the NMT system. This was followed in 1987 by the 800-gram Mobira Cityman, the first handheld NMT phone. Nokia also expanded into manufacturing NMT infrastructure.

Nokia succeeded, in part, because Finland had a more competitive telecommunications market than other European countries, where telephone service was often a government-run monopoly. The decision to aggressively pursue portable and handheld phones early—despite initial high costs and limited demand—positioned Nokia to benefit from the explosive subscriber growth ignited by digital cellular several years later. Today, Nokia supplies more than one-third of the more than one billion mobile phones shipped each year.

* * *

The FCC's inaction may have allowed Nokia to pull ahead in mobile phone technology. But developers in the U.S. were by no means idle. In 1971, AT&T proposed a cellular radio system with frequency reuse based on a patent filed in 1970 (U.S. Patent 3,663,762 issued in 1972) by Amos E. Joel, Jr. and Bell Telephone Laboratories. By this time, the Bell System had field experience with frequency reuse, having implemented a simple cellular radio system in 1969 for payphones on Metroliner trains connecting New York City with Washington, DC. The trains ran more than 100 mph; six channels in the 450-MHz band were reused in the nine cells along the 225-mile route.

The AT&T proposal was designed to sell the FCC on the firm's unique cellular telephone vision. The paper, entitled "High-Capacity Mobile Telephone System Technical Report," covered the basic technology, features, coverage, capacity, service quality, and costs. It was intended to establish AT&T as the last word on cellular telephone technology and business.

Cellular telephone was quickly becoming practical thanks to fundamental developments in electronics, most notably the invention of low-cost microprocessors (used to control channel assignment and frequency handoffs) and frequency synthesizers (enabling reliable automatic frequency switching).

Motorola responded to AT&T's full-court press by launching a major R&D effort of its own. The radio giant obtained US Patent 3,906,166 in 1975 for its "Radio Telephone System" attributed to Martin Cooper, Richard Dronsuth, Albert J. Mikulski, Charles N. Lynk, Jr., James J. Mikulski, John F. Mitchell, Roy A. Richardson, and John H. Sangster. The competition between Motorola and Bell Laboratories was growing intense. Cooper and his team at Motorola were first to demonstrate a working cellular radio base station and telephone in 1973. Motorola presented a paper titled "The DYNA T.A.C Concept" to the FCC to demonstrate it was at least as knowledgeable about cellular telephone as AT&T—if not more so.

Both companies were eager to conduct field trials. In 1975, the FCC approved AT&T's request to build trial networks in Newark and Philadelphia, though the company was not allowed to operate them until 1977. Motorola and American Radio Telephone Service Inc. (ARTS) filed an application for a trial cellular system in Washington/Baltimore, also in 1975.

The AT&T and Motorola cellular visions differed in several key respects. While AT&T focused exclusively on car phones, Motorola was convinced handheld subscriber devices were coming. Motorola proposed lower FM frequency deviation (swings of up to 5 kHz) compared to AT&T

(12 kHz). The Motorola approach would enable 25-kHz channel spacing, while AT&T's approach required 40-kHz spacing. Consequently, Motorola believed robust cellular telephone service could be achieved in as little as 13-MHz of spectrum. Caught between the dueling experts, the FCC compromised, adopting 8-kHz deviation and 30-kHz channel spacing. The two approaches were eventually merged through meetings hosted by the Electronics Industries Association (EIA).

Motorola continued to pioneer cellular technology. The Motorola vision of cellular radio was further described in the paper "A System Plan for a 900-MHz Portable Radio Telephone," by James J. Mikulski, which appeared in *IEEE Transactions on Vehicular Technology* in 1977. The paper discussed how a system primarily serving handheld units would be architected— including the use of cell sectorization as a means of reducing interference. The paper also revealed that Motorola engineers believed signal strength (rather than knowledge of the user's precise location as proposed in AT&T's 1971 Technical Report) was the best guide to cell handoff decisions.

Keep in mind that the mobile phones used with MTS and IMTS were strictly car phones. There was no question of walking around with such phones; they had to be permanently installed in vehicles. And the first cellular telephones were almost all car phones, too. In the U.S., there were heavy portable models called "bag phones." Palm-size mobile phones didn't come into widespread use until the 1990s.

Motorola's vision of handheld mobile phones, brought to life by Martin Cooper, heralded a future much like that predicted by William Ayrton over a half century earlier. As Cooper later observed, cellular telephone brought about a shift in which telephones became associated with individuals rather than locations (such as homes and offices). On April 3, 1973, Cooper placed the first official call from a portable cell phone, ringing up one Joel Engel— his counterpart at corporate rival Bell Labs. Cooper astonished New Yorkers as he walked around the city talking on his portable wireless phone; this was even before the advent of limited-range cordless phones. Today, people would be equally astonished to see someone using a mobile phone weighing almost two pounds; perhaps that's why Motorola's engineers called it "the brick."

Cooper's team had to solve a number of technical problems to create the DynaTAC portable phone. One of the biggest challenges was that cellular telephone required mobile radios that could switch on command to any of hundreds of frequencies. Up until then, mobile radios used crystals to lock onto exact frequencies. With hundreds of channels per system the use of crystals was impractical; the devices would be too bulky and expensive (the manufacturing of crystals for exact frequencies was costly). Needed was an electronic frequency synthesizer—a circuit that could generate and lock onto the desired frequencies. Since integrated circuits were relatively new, the DynaTAC required thousands of discrete components and, consequently, a large battery. Fortunately, Cooper just needed to show the government and industry that a portable cellular telephone was technically feasible. Almost no one noticed the DynaTAC offered only 20 minutes of "talk time."

* * *

The big regulatory breakthrough came 16 years after the Bell System first petitioned for a sizable chunk of mobile spectrum. On May 1, 1974 the FCC decided to reallocate 115 MHz, primarily in the 800-MHz band, for future cellular telephone and other mobile radio uses. The FCC took back spectrum allocated for UHF-TV channels 70-83. Though that spectrum was hardly being used, clearing out the existing stations nationwide would take time.

While AT&T waited for permission to switch on its trial networks, cellular telephone field tests were already underway in Japan.

Meanwhile, another regulatory battle erupted. There was widespread concern that the FCC would simply allow AT&T to extend its landline telephone monopoly to cellular telephone. The RCCs took legal action. Sensing that the RCCs' would prevail, the FCC wrestled with two difficult questions: How many cellular systems should be licensed in each metropolitan area? And should existing wireline telephone operators be allowed to obtain cellular licenses?

The number of licenses awarded per city had both technical and political ramifications. A cellular telephone network needed a large number of channels if it was to fully exploit the cellular architecture and achieve significant capacity. Competing systems, therefore, would require more channels than a single system. While the pre-cellular mobile phone systems were allocated just 54 channels nationwide, the new cellular radio service was allocated a total of 666 channels.

If the Bell System was a landline telephone monopoly, then shouldn't it be excluded from cellular telephone? That seemed both unfair and unwise. The Bell System spent a fortune on cellular telephone R&D and on fighting for additional spectrum. It was one of the few companies that knew how to build, operate, and maintain vast telephone networks. It possessed much-needed financial and technical resources. More to the point, would it make sense to exclude the dominant landline telephone operator when most cellular telephone calls would likely be placed between mobile and landline users?

Lurking in the background was yet another question: Who should be allowed to manufacture cell phones? When the Bell System issued a request for bids for the 135 phones to be used in its trial system in Chicago, it received responses from American firms including Motorola and E.F. Johnson. However, the contract was awarded to Oki Electric of Japan. Motorola complained bitterly that Oki was subsidized by the Japanese government. Fears lingered that cellular would be established as a monopoly, and that a single cell phone manufacturer would quickly come to dominate the market.

While the FCC mulled these issues, the rest of the world continued to move forward. The first commercial cellular telephone networks came online in Bahrain, Japan, and Mexico. But these were extremely limited systems. For example, the first known cellular telephone network, placed in commercial service in May of 1978 by the Bahrain Telephone Company, had just two cells. Provided by Matsushita of Japan, it served approximately 250 subscribers using 20 channels in the 400-MHz band.

Two months after the Bahrain launch, the Bell System began a field trial of advanced mobile phone service (AMPS), the U.S.'s first generation cellular telephone standard, using the new 800-MHz mobile telephone allocation in Newark, New Jersey and Chicago, Illinois. The Chicago network consisted of ten cells covering 21,000 square miles. The test began with 90 Bell employee-users; a market trial with paying customers began in December. In addition to the first 1,000 phones purchased from Oki Electric, the Bell System ordered an additional 2,100 units from E.F. Johnson and Motorola.

The AMPS system worked like a champ. It proved that the base stations, mobile switch, and car phones could all work together as envisioned. It demonstrated the feasibility of frequency handoffs and frequency reuse. More to the point, it provided a justification for building large-scale commercial cellular telephone networks.

Meanwhile, two more countries claimed to have beaten the U.S. to market. A cellular network was switched on in 23 districts of Tokyo, Japan in late 1979. However, the system only worked with coin-operated phones installed in taxis and buses. Operated by Nippon Telegraph and Telephone (NTT), the network consisted of 88 cells, used equipment supplied by Matsushita and NEC, and was expanded to provide nationwide coverage in

1984. Another "cellular" telephone network was launched in Mexico City in 1981, though initially it had just one cell.

Though the networks in Bahrain, Japan, and Mexico did not fully embody the cellular vision, they were steps in that direction, and they showed that the U.S. was at risk of falling behind. Then the U.S. truly fell behind. The first cellular telephone services similar to those planned in the U.S. were launched in Scandinavia in 1981. The NMT networks would also be first to introduce portable cell phones and automated international roaming.

The U.S. Department of Justice's latest anti-trust suit against the Bell System was one of the reasons the launch of cellular telephone service was delayed. A settlement was concluded on January 8, 1982 that required AT&T to divest its local telephone business. In return, AT&T was allowed to enter the computer market. This resulted in the creation of seven independent, regional Bell operating companies (RBOCs).

The DoJ pursued the case with a self-righteousness that did not square with the fact that the government helped to create the Bell System monopoly. For example, the government blocked construction of (and even eliminated) competing facilities as wasteful. The result—a single service provider—was accepted as a quid pro quo for regulated rates and subsidized universal service. The Bell System did not obtain its monopoly through ruthless business practices; it was granted its monopoly by policymakers eager to achieve other objectives.

Though the decision to break up the Bell System was long overdue, it did not lead to telecom competition. It was more an admission that a regulated nationwide monopoly was not needed to ensure universal service at affordable rates. The Telecommunications Act of 1996 went further, attempting to jumpstart competition by requiring incumbent local exchange carriers (ILECs) to open up their networks for access by rivals. However, the new competitive local exchange carriers (CLECs) found it difficult to make a profit using facilities provisioned and maintained by a powerful competitor.

When cellular telephone service finally launched in the U.S. it was clearly not a threat to landline operators. Mobile operators were starting from scratch. Before they could compete with existing services, they had to build expensive networks, create brand awareness, acquire a critical mass of customers, and prove they could deliver reliable service on a consistent basis. Operators wisely positioned mobile telephone as a premium service, and the phones and service plans were priced accordingly. Only years later, thanks to handheld phones, enhanced coverage, and a host of standard features did cellular telephone begin to compete head-on with landline phone service.

(Mobile phone service packages include features such as caller ID, call waiting, three-way calling, and voice mail. Landline operators usually charge setup and monthly fees for the same features. Plus, basic mobile phones provide features such as date/time, address book, and speed dialing; more expensive models include multimedia features that are rarely, if ever, available on landline phones.)

The lesson of these events is that governments can't create competition by decree, but they can facilitate an environment in which competition is more likely to emerge.

Cellular telephone is a case in point. The FCC originally proposed to license just one cellular operator per city. Under that proposal, the licenses would have gone to the dominant local telephone service provider—usually the Bell System. The radio common carriers (RCCs) were furious and filed suit to prevent the plan from being implemented. The FCC cleverly responded by modifying its proposal to allow any "qualified" carrier to obtain a cellular license. That did not mollify the RCCs, because determining which carriers were "qualified" rested with the FCC.

In 1981, after much debate, the FCC issued cellular telephone rules in its Report and Order for Docket 79-318. The rules specified two competing mobile phone licenses in each service area. One license was reserved for the local landline telephone company; the other was for anyone other than the local telephone company. That meant, quite literally, that an RBOC could obtain "wireline" (also known as "system B") licenses within its home territory and "non-wireline" licenses (also known as "System A") in areas outside its designated region. In many cases that is exactly what happened. (Five RBOCs ended up obtaining about 30% of the non-wireline system licenses.)

The FCC defined 90 urban markets for cellular telephone service. Each licensee would get 20 MHz of spectrum. The FCC decided to award the licenses through comparative hearings. That meant the Commission would examine all of the applications and decide which applicant in each market was most deserving.

When the FCC received more than 200 applications for the largest 30 markets, it knew it had its work cut out. But the Commission was not prepared to handle the 700 applications it received for the 30 smallest markets. These weren't standardized forms a few pages in length; these were thick documents that needed to be stored, read, compared, and discussed. The

FCC was forced to abandon comparative hearings for all but the 30 largest markets. Licenses for the remaining 60 markets would be decided by lotteries. What went wrong? The public realized that radio spectrum is a valuable asset—much like real estate. The comparative hearing process was flawed in that it invited abuse; a cottage industry emerged to prepare credible license applications for anyone willing to pay a small fee. Lotteries were based on blind chance and, therefore, provided a quick fix. But no one considered lotteries fair; many licenses went to individuals who knew nothing about building and operating mobile phone networks. The applicants were betting they could either find others to build and operate networks for them or turn around and sell their licenses.

The FCC created what was soon labeled a "duopoly." During the first years, these systems barely competed with each other. Operators often divided fast-growing markets by informal agreement. It was not until the establishment of the Personal Communications Service (PCS) in 1994 (way up in the 1900-MHz region of the spectrum) that U.S. mobile phone service became truly competitive. There were soon five or more mobile phone operators in every major city.

The first fully-commercial U.S. cellular telephone service was launched in October of 1983 by Ameritech in Chicago, Illinois. The car phones, supplied by Motorola, were introduced at retail prices in the $3,000-$4,000 range. Nevertheless, cellular telephone service grew rapidly over the next few years. American Radio Telephone Service launched commercial service right after Ameritech, using the trial network it built in Washington, DC. Additional networks were constructed by the dozen. Motorola's mobile phone business grew from zero to nearly $200 million in annual revenue within one year. By the late 1980s, the industry was worried about running out of capacity in the largest cities, as the total number of U.S. subscribers approached five million.

While some countries (particularly in the Americas) adopted the AMPS standard, other countries developed their own standards. The UK's total access communications system (TACS) was similar to AMPS but not compatible with it—a TACS phone would not work on an AMPS network nor would an AMPS phone work on the TACS network. NMT was launched in Denmark, Sweden, Finland, and Norway; it gradually expanded to Switzerland, The Netherlands, Hungary, Poland, Bulgaria, Slovakia, Slovenia, Serbia, Croatia, Bosnia, Russia, and a few other countries.

The global cellular telephone market looked very different in the first years than it would twenty years later. The U.S. had a single, nationwide standard supported by competing operators. Europe had competing standards and, in most countries, a single government-owned service provider. When Europe and the U.S. upgraded to digital cellular—so-called second generation (2G) systems—the situation was almost reversed; Europe moved to a single standard while the U.S. permitted competing standards. Plus, most European countries licensed multiple 2G operators to compete with the existing analog cellular operators.

Though Europe has roughly twice as many inhabitants as the U.S., the two markets grew to about 15 million subscribers each in the first decade. By 2007, however, the U.S. had an estimated 240 million subscribers while Europe had grown to 558 million subscribers. The European cellular market's mercurial growth is usually attributed to its adoption of a single standard. But annual growth figures suggest each market took off after genuinely competing operators launched service.

One reason the U.S. was slow to embrace digital cellular was that AMPS worked fairly well. Operators were reluctant to replace a technology that had been fine-tuned over a period of years with a technology certain to require debugging. The primary motive for migrating to 2G in the U.S. was to increase capacity. Networks in the largest cities (most notably Los Angeles) were in danger of running out of capacity.

Not everyone in the U.S. was convinced the upgrade to digital was necessary, however. Motorola developed a more spectrally efficient analog solution called narrowband AMPS (N-AMPS) that split each existing AMPS voice channel into three voice channels. Getting additional spectrum allocated to mobile phone service was another option and the FCC did just that in the 1990s when it allocated spectrum for the Personal Communications Service (PCS). The commission dealt analog radio advocates a blow by mandating the use of digital radio technology in the new PCS band.

The U.S. mobile phone industry became quite a bit more interesting and complex thanks to a couple of dynamic entrepreneurs—and a more flexible FCC. Fleet Call, co-founded by former FCC attorney Morgan O'Brien in 1989, was a specialized mobile radio (SMR) operator created to serve business applications such as field service and truck fleet management. The company requested changes to the SMR rules that would, in effect, allow it to enter the mobile phone market. O'Brien realized that Fleet Call's spectrum, adjacent to cellular telephone frequencies and obtained at relatively low cost, was potentially very valuable. He worked with Motorola to develop a digital technology called iDEN (an acronym for "integrated dispatch enhanced network").

In 1993, Fleet Call changed its name to Nextel. The operator supported a couple of unique features that were greatly appreciated by its customers— almost all of them organizations rather than individuals. "Direct connect" allowed users to connect to specific team members at the push of a button. Today, the generic term for this capability is "push to talk" (PTT). "Group calling" was an audio conferencing solution popular with public safety agencies and emergency repair crews.

Nextel and Motorola ran into serious technical problems with iDEN. In 1996, wireless entrepreneur Craig McCaw invested in the rapidly sinking venture and turned it around. Nextel grew to more than 15 million subscribers and merged with Sprint in 2005 to form Sprint Nextel, the third largest mobile phone operator in the U.S.

Craig McCaw started in telecommunications during the 1970s, rebuilding his father's cable television business (McCaw Cable Vision). When the FCC distributed cellular licenses by lottery, McCaw moved quickly to buy up as many as he could, believing they were undervalued even in the gold rush atmosphere. He also realized that a nationwide cellular carrier would have advantages over regional and local operators. He made a fortune when AT&T bought McCaw Cellular for $11.5 billion in 1994.

McCaw's business successes were not just good luck. He understood the inherent value of service provider businesses and recognized bargains. He built each business based on a differentiated and tested long-term vision. Former employees described meetings run by McCaw as "intense." Reportedly, McCaw applies his own brand of critical path analysis to strategic business planning. The mildly reclusive McCaw is currently chairman of Clearwire Corporation, a broadband wireless Internet service provider.

While Nextel was evolving its business, the mobile phone industry was also changing. Sales were shifting rapidly from car phones to handheld phones, and the industry was beginning its migration to digital cellular. One of the pioneers of handheld mobile phone technology was Donald C. Cox of Bellcore—the part of Bell Labs assigned to the RBOCs as part of divestiture. Recognizing that cellular telephone would play a larger role in the future, either complementing or competing against landline telephone, Cox performed seminal research on extending cellular coverage to residential areas and inside buildings. His mobile radio propagation studies helped guide the development of both infrastructure and handsets. Cox was co-recipient of the Marconi prize in 1983 and won the Alexander Graham Bell medal in 1993.

Though cellular telephone products were mainly developed by teams, other individuals made key theoretical and practical contributions. Bell Labs engineers Joel Engel and Richard Frenkiel were awarded the National Medal of Technology for their work developing cellular network infrastructure. Engel and Frenkiel also won the 1987 Alexander Graham Bell medal along with William C. Jakes, who put together a classic text on cellular radio technology. Martin Cooper, who went on to found ArrayComm, a developer of smart antenna technology and systems, is recognized for leading the development team at Motorola. And there were pioneers in other parts of the globe, particularly Scandinavia.

Cellular telephone is a complex system and its development was clearly collaborative. But don't be fooled: development is the methodical problem-solving process that follows acts of discovery and creation. Teamwork and carefully planned technology roadmaps don't abolish innovation—they exploit it.

Not everyone thought cellular telephone would be a success, and almost no one imagined just how successful it would be. Some—including Martin Cooper—wondered if cellular telephone would survive. The first studies predicted a limited market; research commissioned by AT&T forecast 900,000 subscribers by the year 2000.

Though the first cellular telephone networks were based on analog radio technology, they also made use of digital electronics. Specifically, cellular networks contain digital switches and mobile phones include microprocessors, and AMPS actually employed a combination of analog voice channels and digital control channels. (The control channels are used for call set-up, handoffs, and call termination.)

The first generation cellular telephone technology launched a new industry and market. By 1995, the number of cellular telephone subscribers in the U.S. reached 25 million. (However, by then it was growing at a torrid pace—46% per year.[12]) Worldwide, the number of subscribers rose from just 11 million in 1990 to 91 million in 1995.[13]

---

[12] U.S. mobile phone subscriber figures are per the CTIA-The Wireless Association, http://www.ctia.org/

[13] Worldwide mobile phone subscribers are per the International Telecommunications Union (ITU), http://www.itu.int/net/home/index.aspx

But analog cellular could not outgrow its reputation as a toy for the rich and necessary but expensive tool for professionals such as doctors, lawyers, and real estate agents. Analog cellular networks didn't have enough capacity to drive down per minute usage rates. And while the cost of analog phones declined sharply, they could not take full advantage of Moore's Law.

By enabling personal communications and blurring the line between phones and computers, digital cellular ignited explosive growth. Digital technology not only drove down the cost of providing a minute of airtime, it dramatically reduced the size, cost, and power consumption of handsets. By 2007, the market swelled to more than 2.5 billion subscribers worldwide—almost all of them using digital handsets on digital networks.

Chapter Twelve
Digital Airways

Europe's digital mobile phone standard is one of the greatest success stories in the history of technology. In just fifteen years, the number of subscribers using the global system for mobile communications (GSM) standard soared to over two billion. GSM drove down the cost of mobile phones and networks and brought telephone service to the masses.

However, GSM's extraordinary success came at a price. It gave ammunition to those who believe new technologies should be designed by committees, that governments should select and mandate standards, and that it is acceptable for governments to protect markets from competing technologies. GSM is an exception and not the rule; most successful standards evolve out of proprietary technologies.

(Here are a few examples: Ethernet local area network technology was developed at Xerox PARC. The Internet Protocol (IP) was created by DARPA, an agency within the U.S. Department of Defense. Three wireless technologies discussed later in this chapter—CDMA, Wi-Fi, and Bluetooth—were conceived by private companies. The AMPS analog cellular standard was a compromise between systems developed by AT&T and Motorola. Committees are good at normalizing solutions, a process requiring negotiation and compromise, but they are rarely a source of innovation.)

The manufactured cost of low-end GSM handsets has dropped to around $30. The cost of service is as low as $10 per month. In developed countries, the mobile phone market is nearly saturated. Looking ahead, most subscriber growth is expected in developing countries such as China, India, Brazil, and Russia. Thanks largely to GSM, the number of mobile phone subscribers worldwide is expected to hit three billion by 2010.

It would be hard to exaggerate the cultural impact of GSM. Roughly one hundred years after William Ayrton predicted ubiquitous personal communications, it has come to pass. GSM has hastened the speed at which business is conducted. It has delivered unprecedented convenience for consumers. Though some complain the omnipresent mobile phone has made life a bit ruder.

GSM delivered more than basic telephone service. It transformed the mobile phone into a handheld computer capable of composing and receiving text messages; downloading and playing games, music, and even short videos; and accessing the Internet. The spectacular success of GSM, a second-generation (2G) mobile phone technology, inspired the development of third-generation (3G) wireless technology based on code division multiple access, CDMA.

The GSM story began in 1982. The organization of European telecom operators, the Conference Europénne des Postes et Télécommuniçations (CEPT), allocated spectrum in the 900-MHz band for a pan-European mobile phone standard that it originally dubbed Groupe Spécial Mobile (GSM).[14] Though the goals included "high spectrum efficiency" and "state of the art" subscriber devices, the leap to digital radio technology was by no means a given.

The difference between analog and digital transmission is profound. An analog system encodes a continuously varying input (such as human speech) as a continuously varying output; a digital system encodes a continuously varying input as a discrete output. For example, in an analog telephone system speech is converted from continuously varying sounds into continuously varying electric currents; in a digital telephone system speech is converted from continuously varying sounds into predefined electric waveforms representing specific combinations of 1s and 0s. In the analog system, the information received is at best a good approximation of the information transmitted. In the digital system, the information received is often an exact copy of the information transmitted.

Some audiophiles may object that analog recordings sound better than digital recordings. That is a legitimate complaint, but the source of the problem is analog to digital conversion, not digital transmission. Speech and music are converted to digital through a process of sampling and quantizing. For example, to produce a compact disc the audio is sampled 44,100 times each second; the value of each sample is recorded at 16-bit resolution.

The problem is easy to visualize. First imagine a perfectly smooth sine wave. Then imagine a sine wave that looks the same from a distance, but from close up looks like a series of tiny steps. The perfectly smooth sine wave is the original (analog) sound. The stair-step sine wave is a digital approximation. Note that the digital version is *always* just an approximation

---

[14] Government-sponsored standards committees are largely responsible for the acronyms and jargon that make it difficult for anyone other than insiders to comprehend the technologies.

of the analog signal. However, only the digital version can be transmitted so that an exact copy of itself appears at the destination.

* * *

Digital cellular has two key advantages. It enables wireless to exploit the ongoing price/performance gains of integrated circuits described by Moore's Law, yielding products that are both more capable and more affordable. The bill of materials for a basic digital mobile phone is following a trajectory that should take it below $15. Digital cellular also permits more robust signaling, taking advantage of statistical communications theory.

Less well-known but just as important as Moore's Law is Cooper's Law, which states that the number of conversations that can be conducted in the same area via radio frequency communications doubles every 30 months. Cooper's Law was developed by Martin Cooper, who had placed that first call from a portable "brick" when he was general manager of Motorola's Communications Systems Division. Cooper's research shows that the trend has been exhibited since the days of Marconi's spark gap technology.

Various disciplines contributed to making Cooper's prediction a reality. Physics brought an understanding of the electromagnetic spectrum and how it could be exploited. Engineering brought the design, implementation, and optimization of the necessary equipment. Mathematics tied it all together, as researchers showed how different signaling techniques could be used to achieve greater capacity and higher data throughputs.

Modern communications theory traces back to the pioneering work of Harry Nyquist, Ralph Hartley, Norbert Wiener, Stephen O. Rice, and Claude Shannon. In the 1920s, Harry Nyquist developed what is now known as the Nyquist sampling theorem. The sampling theorem says that to faithfully recreate a continuous (analog) signal such as voice using digital encoding, the analog signal must be sampled at a rate of at least twice its bandwidth. For example, an analog telephone channel usually occupies 4-kHz of bandwidth. The Nyquist theorem says it should be sampled at least 8,000 times per second. Nyquist's colleague at AT&T's Department of Development and Research (the precursor to Bell Laboratories), Ralph Hartley, authored the paper "Transmission of Information" for the *Bell System Technical Journal* in 1928.

Norbert Wiener's classic 1930 paper "Extrapolation, Interpolation and Smoothing of Stationary Time Series with Engineering Applications," also known as "Yellow Peril" due to the color of its cover and the subject's difficulty, discussed signal prediction and optimization. Wiener's most important contribution was showing how to optimize the filtering of signals out from noise and interference.

Wiener is best known as the father of cybernetics, the study of feedback and control in engineering, biology, and society. Born in Columbia, Missouri in 1894, Wiener was a child prodigy, earning his BA in mathematics from Tufts College at the age of 14 and a PhD from Harvard at age 18. Wiener's parents did not tell him about his Jewish ancestry; he learned the truth by accident. However, his parents did help arrange his marriage to German immigrant Margaret Engemann, who became a fervent Nazi supporter during the 1930s. They remained married until Wiener's death in 1964.

Stephen O. Rice's 1944 paper "Mathematical Analysis of Random Noise" in the *Bell System Technical Journal* examined the mathematical probability of receiving a signal in the presence of noise.

Distantly related to Thomas Edison, Claude Shannon is widely considered "the father of information theory." The impact of Shannon's work ranges from digital circuit design to genetics to telecommunications.

Among Shannon's many classic papers, two became particularly influential. "A Mathematical Theory of Communication" was written for the *Bell System Technical Journal* in 1948. Using elements of probability theory developed by Norbert Wiener, this landmark article examines the most efficient ways of encoding information for transmission over a communications channel. It employs the concept of "information entropy" for measuring the uncertainty in a message. Shannon also examined the number of bits per second that can be accurately transmitted over a noisy or otherwise impaired communications channel. Shannon's 1949 paper "Communication Theory of Secrecy Systems" was a major contribution to the field of cryptography.

Shannon joined Bell Laboratories during World War II and, starting in 1956, served on the faculty of the Massachusetts Institute of Technology (MIT) for more than 20 years. In addition to his prodigious theoretical work, Shannon was interested in juggling, unicycling, chess, and whimsical inventions. One such invention was the "Ultimate Machine," a featureless box with a single switch on its side. When the switch was turned on, the lid opened and a mechanical hand reached around the side of the box to flip the switch off, disappearing back into the box as the lid shut. Shannon was a creative thinker with a sense of humor. He died in 2001 at the age of 84.

The use of statistical communications theory to enhance performance is illustrated by the famous algorithm developed by Andrew Viterbi. The Viterbi algorithm helps decode faint signals received over noisy channels.

It's implemented in virtually all cell phones and satellite receivers, and has found use in applications including deep space communications, speech recognition, and DNA sequence analysis.

Viterbi came to America at the age of four, when his parents decided it was time to flee Italy and Benito Mussolini's increasingly anti-Semitic policies. They arrived just in time; five days later Germany invaded Poland to start World War II. Viterbi made up his mind at an early age that he wanted to attend nearby MIT and become an engineer. After earning a BS and MS in Electrical Engineering, he accepted a position at the Jet Propulsion Laboratory (JPL) in Pasadena, California where he worked on the problem of acquiring signals from distant spacecraft—work to be used in conjunction with the U.S.'s first successful satellite, Explorer 1. It was an exciting time at JPL: three months after Viterbi started the Soviet Union launched Sputnik and the space race was on.

As with many great inventions, the Viterbi algorithm came somewhat unexpectedly. After obtaining his PhD, Viterbi accepted the position of assistant professor at the University of California, Los Angeles in 1963. He was looking for a simpler way to teach students about extracting digital signals from noise. With only that in mind, he developed a proof for the superiority of one error-correcting tool (convolutional codes) over another (block codes) for a given amount of decoding complexity. A colleague pointed out that his method could be used to improve the performance of actual communication systems—assuming the complex hardware needed could be built. At the time, it required racks of electronics; by the mid-1980s, the Viterbi algorithm could be readily implemented on a microchip.

The Viterbi algorithm works with any sequence of symbols that follow what is called the "Markov model." This is any sequence in which the probability of the next state depends only on the present state. The game of baseball can be used as an example. The current state may be defined in terms of the runners on base and number of outs. There are only certain possible next states, and there are different probabilities associated with each. The same thing applies to data that has been run through a convolutional coder. The Viterbi algorithm is a computationally efficient way of identifying the most likely sequence. It gives a receiver trying to decode a weak signal a boost. It's important to mobile phones because mobile signals constantly fluctuate between weak and strong.

* * *

The analog cellular telephone market was growing, and the U.S. was firmly in the lead. Europe began looking at the opportunities for digital cellular. By 1987, laboratory tests confirmed that digital cellular offered significant advantages over analog cellular and was technically feasible. CEPT members agreed on the key technical parameters of GSM. Specifically, narrowband time division multiple access (TDMA) was selected as the GSM radio technology or "air interface."

An analog radio channel carries just one conversation at a time. A digital radio channel, however, can use timesharing to carry multiple conversations. For example, a digital radio channel running 48,000 bits per second (bps) may be divided into three alternating timeslots to handle three conversations; each conversation is allocated 16,000 bps. As long as each user receives the correct bits, the users are unaware that they are sharing the same channel. TDMA describes the protocol for accessing and sharing the channel. (In practice, there's more to it than simply dividing the bits into three groups; the channel also has to carry supervisory data for setting up and tearing down conversations.)

TDMA was a reasonable choice for GSM because computers and telephone networks had been using time division multiplexing for years. TDMA also gained popularity in satellite applications during the 1970s. The GSM specification called for 200-kHz channels supporting eight conversations at 13,000 bits per second per conversation. That was a moderately aggressive speech encoding rate[15] because the original telephone standard for digitally encoded speech was 64,000 bits per second. GSM promised about three times the capacity of analog cellular networks.

Though the GSM standard was developed by committees, a quality standard was achieved in an acceptable time frame thanks to committee leaders adept at cutting red tape. For example, CEPT meetings normally required simultaneous translation into English, German, and French. That not only slowed the sessions—it made it hard to arrange meetings on short notice. Noting the participants were willing to conduct meetings exclusively in English, the leaders simply ignored the simultaneous translation requirement. When someone suggested investigating the potential health hazards of mobile radio, the leaders pointed out that several independent

---

[15] GSM's aggressive voice encoding rate is based on linear predictive coding (LPC), a powerful tool for analyzing and simulating human speech. Next generation standards use codebook-excited linear predictive coding (CELP), enabling 8,000 bps voice encoding.

studies were inconclusive, and persuaded committee members to drop the potentially counter-productive topic.

The biggest challenge, however, was that many delegates lacked the formal authority to make decisions. If delegates waited for guidance from their national administrations, the standard could have been delayed by years. The committee leaders pushed delegates to make tentative decisions, knowing that the longer each decision stood without challenge the more it would harden like concrete.

Though GSM was developed by committees, there were individual heroes. For example, Stephen Temple of the UK Department of Trade and Industry suggested that operators sign a "Memorandum of Understanding" (MoU) underscoring their commitment to implement GSM by 1991. GSM turned the corner when fourteen operators in thirteen countries signed the MoU, assuring manufacturers there would be a market for GSM networks and phones. While anyone could produce a paper standard, GSM had firm business commitments.

There were technology innovators, too. Dr. Jan Uddenfeldt of L.M. Ericsson received the Edward Rhein Prize, one of Germany's highest scientific awards, for his contributions to the development of GSM technology. Uddenfeldt's team recognized that mobile TDMA required solving the "delay spread" problem. When a digital transmitter sends information, it produces a waveform (also known as a "symbol") containing one or more bits. The delay spread is the time period over which an individual symbol is received. It becomes spread out because in the mobile environment signals take different paths of different lengths—causing different delays.

Uddenfeldt's group found the delay spread was 10-15 microseconds— rather long considering that each symbol was only about four microseconds in duration. It meant that at any given moment the receiver is likely to see multiple symbols. Uddenfeldt led development of the GSM adaptive equalizer, a device that tests the channel and then adjusts the timing of received waveforms to reduce symbol overlap.[16]

By 1988, there were ten signed contracts for the construction of GSM networks. Three years later, trial networks were up and running. Though GSM was not yet in commercial operation, the industry was already beginning to think about the next step in wireless evolution (third-generation or "3G" wireless). Predictably, a committee was formed and another

---

[16] Uddenfeldt also contributed to the development of GSM handoff algorithms and the implementation of slow frequency hopping.

acronym produced; Europe decided to name its 3G project the universal mobile telecommunication system (UMTS).

A number of GSM "firsts" were achieved in 1992. The first GSM network launched commercial service. The first handheld GSM phones were introduced. And the first GSM international roaming agreement was signed. Given growing interest in GSM beyond Europe, the acronym was preserved but the words were changed from "groupe spécial mobile" to "global system for mobile communications."

GSM experienced its share of birthing pains. Because it required new networks built from scratch, there were huge coverage gaps; GSM phones worked in some locations but not others. Audio quality was sometimes poor—and acceptable at best. However, the biggest problems were shortages and high prices of mobile terminals. Some wondered if GSM stood for "God send mobiles."

All of the problems were gradually solved. One year after launch, GSM reached one million subscribers. Two years later, GSM boasted 10 million subscribers. After five years, GSM had 70 million subscribers in 100 countries. From that point on, GSM experienced explosive growth, reaching the 500 million subscriber mark in 2001. By 1998 Nokia had become the world's leading supplier of mobile handsets.

Why was GSM so successful? A popular theory is that by mandating a single technology standard Europe avoided market fragmentation and, consequently, boosted consumer confidence. But there are many standards that fail; for example, the relatively ad hoc Internet became far more successful than the more official and elaborate Open Systems Interconnection (OSI) standard. Likewise, there are many proprietary technologies that succeed despite competition such as the VHS videocassette recorder standard (by JVC) that triumphed over Sony's Betamax.

Other factors help explain GSM's success. GSM introduced desperately needed competition to Europe's mobile phone markets. GSM enabled continent-wide roaming and greater economy of scale. Because GSM was the first commercially available digital cellular technology, it conferred first-mover advantage on European manufacturers. Mandating GSM's use in Europe also helped—not by boosting consumer confidence in a specific technology but by ensuring a large captive market for European manufacturers.

The U.S. mobile phone industry, meanwhile, made the mistake of being too cautious. Though the U.S.'s analog standard performed poorly by today's standards—the service was plagued by dropped calls and noise—it worked from coast-to-coast and the number of subscribers continued to grow. Performance was slowly improving and operators feared that upgrading to a new technology might disrupt business. New spectrum would not become available until existing users were relocated, a process that usually takes years. The near-term plan was to replace analog technology with digital technology in the existing spectrum, but as slowly and carefully as possible.

In late 1988, the Cellular Telecommunications Industry Association (CTIA) published a series of digital cellular recommendations. One goal was to choose a digital technology that could deliver ten times the capacity of analog cellular. Another goal was to replace analog one channel at a time. Networks in the largest cities were getting crowded.

In early 1989, the Telecommunications Industry Association (TIA), a large organization involved in setting standards, selected a narrowband TDMA technology dubbed digital AMPS (D-AMPS).[17] D-AMPS promised a three-fold increase in capacity, though that assumed voice encoders (vocoders) running just 8,000 bps. However, engineers were optimistic that a half-rate vocoder (4,000 bps) with acceptable audio quality could be developed that would double capacity again, providing a cumulative six-fold increase over analog. It wasn't the ten-fold increase that had been sought, but it was a significant improvement.[18]

Around the same time a small company based in San Diego, California proposed a radically different digital cellular technology: code division multiple access (CDMA). It was using CDMA in satellite applications because it is fairly immune to interference from conventional radio signals. One of its engineers, Klein Gilhousen, realized that in theory CDMA could multiply the capacity of cellular telephone networks. Assuming specific technical challenges could be solved CDMA would allow every channel to be reused in every cell. (In Douglas Ring's original cellular scheme, a given frequency could only be used in one out of every seven cells.) On paper, that suggested CDMA would deliver up to a 40-fold capacity increase over analog cellular (assuming half-rate vocoders).

CDMA enables more aggressive frequency reuse by managing rather than preventing interference. But it requires tight control over the power output of every mobile transmitter on the network at all times. Even

---

[17] D-AMPS was also known as "U.S. TDMA" because it was a variant of the TDMA technology used by Europe's GSM standard, as well as "IS-54," the TIA document number.

[18] The mobile phone industry has all but abandoned half-rate vocoders; in fact, in 2007 the vast majority of mobile phones used 13,000 bps vocoders.

moderate power control errors can reduce network capacity. And that wasn't the only technical challenge. When the company first proposed CDMA, handset chips with the processing power and speed required did not yet exist. The company was betting that by the time manufacturers were ready to mass produce handsets such processors would be widely available.

It was a bold proposal. Here was a small company telling the U.S. cellular telephone industry that the D-AMPS technology it just selected was too little, too late. But there was also something compelling about CDMA. If it worked, it would leapfrog Europe's GSM technology.

Given the small company's engineering pedigree, it was a good bet. Its roots trace back to Linkabit, a company founded in 1968 by a trio of modern communications heroes: Irwin Jacobs, the former MIT professor and UCSD engineering professor for whom the UCSD School of Engineering is named; Andrew Viterbi, for whom the USC School of Engineering is named; and Leonard Kleinrock, the UCLA professor who pioneered packet switching and ARPANET, the predecessor to the Internet.[19] Jacobs and Viterbi left Linkabit after it was purchased by M/A-COM and founded their new company in 1985. They named it Qualcomm.

Rebuffed by the CTIA, Qualcomm took its CDMA proposal directly to mobile phone operators. William C.Y. Lee at PacTel Cellular was intrigued. PacTel operated a cellular network in Los Angeles and had one major reservation about D-AMPS: There was a real risk—given the subscriber growth rate—that by the time the upgrade was completed the company would face another capacity crisis.

Explaining how CDMA works is almost as difficult as implementing it. CDMA employs the "direct sequence" flavor of spread spectrum technology. With Hedy Lamarr's flavor of spread spectrum, frequency hopping, the signal hops to specific frequencies within a range of frequencies. With direct sequence spread spectrum (DS/SS), the signal is spread out continuously over the range of frequencies.

Both flavors support multiple, simultaneous conversations. It's easy to visualize how that's accomplished with frequency hopping. Different conversations are assigned different hopping sequences so they rarely land on the same frequency at the same time. An analogous technique can be used

---

[19] UCSD is the University of California at San Diego and UCLA is the University of California at Los Angeles; both are state-funded schools. USC is the University of Southern California and is privately-funded.

with direct sequence spread spectrum to support multiple users. Some additional background is required to understand that technique, however.

Robert Dixon's book *Spread Spectrum Systems*, published in 1976, helped popularize spread spectrum. It provided a solid technical overview of what had been a classified military technology. The first commercial applications using spread spectrum were developed for satellites in the 1980s. Equatorial Communications Systems attempted to build a satellite network for newswire services; Qualcomm developed a highly successful satellite communications service called OmniTRACS for managing long-haul truck fleets.

The main technical obstacle to the commercialization of spread spectrum was generating and synchronizing "pseudorandom" codes. For example, Hedy Lamarr envisioned a shipboard transmitter and matching torpedo-based receiver that appear to observers to hop randomly from frequency to frequency. The hopping sequence wasn't truly random, however; it was determined by identical player piano-style rolls at each end of the link. Similarly, Federal Telecommunication Laboratories used identical, circular pieces of film (also known as "noise wheels").

These mechanical code generators had three major drawbacks. They were bulky, unreliable, and produced codes that were too short for many applications. For example, if two frequency hopping stations are expected to communicate daily using piano-style rolls, then they must configure the piano rolls in an endless loop so they never stop. However, once a code is repeated it is no longer pseudorandom—it's a pattern.

Needed instead was an all-electronic source for pseudorandom codes. Solomon W. Golomb, a mathematician at the Jet Propulsion Laboratory in Pasadena, California pioneered the generation of pseudorandom sequences using digital circuits called "shift registers." He studied and characterized these sequences, enabling development of pseudorandom code generators that are small (fit within an integrated circuit), reliable (have no moving parts) and produce long codes. Golomb is now a professor at USC and was one of Viterbi's mentors; gamers may also know him as the inventor of Polyominoes, an early computer puzzle.

Now we are ready to examine direct sequence spread spectrum. Direct sequence spreads information over a range of frequencies by expanding the data. It's a simple concept: The more data that is transmitted in a given amount of time, the more bandwidth is consumed. The easiest way to accomplish this is to combine the user information with a pseudorandom bit sequence. As a result, each original bit of user data is represented by a sequence of special bits called "chips."

For example, a "1" bit sent by the user might become "1101001110" and a "0" bit sent by the user might become "1010110101." Notice that each user bit is now represented by ten binary chips. Notice also that in order to send the user data at 10,000 bits per second it is necessary to transmit 100,000 chips per second.

Here is where things get interesting. In the conventional digital realm, every bit of data is precious; a single bit error can result in a misplaced decimal point with disastrous consequences. In the direct sequence spread spectrum world, it's not necessary to read all of the chips correctly. The receiver merely needs to read the majority of chips associated with a user bit accurately in order to derive the correct user bit.

One advantage of a wideband communications system such as direct sequence spread spectrum is that its broad signals are less vulnerable to frequency-specific impairments than narrowband systems such as D-AMPS and GSM. For example, when a narrowband signal takes multiple paths to the receiver the copies may arrive at the receiver out-of-phase and cancel each other out before the adaptive equalizer can realign them. Wideband signals, in contrast, contain many frequencies so the copies will only very rarely cancel each other out. Instead, copies arriving at different moments may be isolated and recombined using a "rake receiver."

A direct sequence channel can support multiple simultaneous conversations by assigning each conversation a unique code. For example, imagine that we want five conversations to share the channel. By using codes that are sufficiently distinct, we can combine the chip streams from five different conversations to produce a composite chip stream that receivers using the five different codes can examine to recover the five conversations. It's this method of sharing a digital channel that was dubbed CDMA, for code division multiple access.

It's easier to visualize how CDMA works by assuming each user bit is encoded as 100 chips. To recover the correct user bits, each receiver must see 51 or more chips corresponding to the correct user bit. Notice the receiver will recover the correct user bit whether it reads 51 or 87 out of 100 chips corresponding to that user bit. By choosing five sufficiently distinct codes, five receivers can correctly recover the user bits for five different conversations.

A more popular but less exact way of explaining how CDMA works is the cocktail party analogy. Imagine you are in a large room and there are 50 different conversations taking place. How do you understand the person you are talking to over the general din? You do so by focusing on the sound of that person's voice.

However, if a person nearby is speaking 100 times louder than everyone else is, that person's voice will overwhelm the voice you are trying to hear. A similar problem occurs in a CDMA cellular network; how can the cell site hear a user near the outer edge of the cell if another user is right next to the cell site? Ordinarily, the signal from the nearby user will be much louder.

That's why CDMA requires dynamic power control. The cell site tells each mobile transmitter how much power to use. The nearby transmitter is instructed to turn its power down, and the far away transmitter is told to crank its power up. Unfortunately, the signals from a mobile device vary over a wide range—changing from moment to moment. How can the network hope to precisely control the transmit power of multiple mobile devices?

The solution turned out, as it often does, to be extraordinarily simple. The transmit power of each mobile can be carefully controlled by adding a 1,200 bps power control loop in which, for example, a 1 bit means "increase power by one increment" and a 0 bit means "decrease power by one increment." Using this low-speed power control loop, the base station can send one power command every millisecond to every mobile. A steady stream of power control bits keeps each mobile transmitter at precisely the right power level.

Once it had conceived a dynamic power control solution, Qualcomm set out to demonstrate CDMA in San Diego. The field test proved that CDMA works and could increase capacity. However, it also revealed that the projected forty-fold capacity gain over analog was unrealistic. Qualcomm revised its CDMA capacity claim to 10-20 times analog assuming use of 8,000 bps vocoders.

Qualcomm's CDMA concept evoked strong reactions: people either loved or hated the idea. About half of U.S. cellular operators in major cities were so impressed that they decided to wait for CDMA. South Korea embraced the technology, sensing an opportunity to develop, manufacture, and sell CDMA equipment worldwide. Others were extremely skeptical of Qualcomm's claims. Some commentators accused Qualcomm of fraud.

Some of the negative reaction was just sniping by competitors. But most of it was from engineers who had been taught the proper way to deal with interference is to prevent it by assigning different users to different frequencies or time slots. Here was Qualcomm suggesting they could maximize cellular radio capacity by putting different users on the same frequency and managing the interference. The idea contradicted standard radio engineering practice.

Qualcomm is a vivid example of the saying, "The pioneers are the guys with arrows in their backs." Some of the criticism of CDMA ventured beyond facts and reason and into the realm of conspiracy theories. One Stanford professor stated that CDMA was an attempt to "violate the laws of physics," that Qualcomm's lawyers prevented him from publishing papers in respected engineering journals debunking CDMA, and that the first commercial CDMA network was a fake. A British consultant compared the CDMA industry to a British woman who claimed to have given birth to seventeen rabbits. Even the *Wall Street Journal* ran an article suggesting industry support for CDMA was owed mainly to Irwin Jacobs' extraordinary salesmanship.

As CDMA networks acquired millions of users, Qualcomm's harshest critics quickly revised their stories. Some congratulated Qualcomm on transforming an ill-conceived technology into a success. Others denied they ever said CDMA wouldn't work. But they all still agreed on one thing: Qualcomm lied. It would have been hard to admit they had falsely accused Qualcomm, so they took a parting shot and announced that the topic had grown tiresome.

Commercializing CDMA was an uphill battle. Qualcomm had to develop the integrated circuits needed to build CDMA base stations and handsets, as no such ICs existed. The company also had to license other manufacturers to show that CDMA enjoyed widespread support and to ensure operators they could count on a choice of suppliers. Qualcomm passed these tests with flying colors, winning over Motorola and AT&T (later spun off as Lucent Technologies), and developing a CDMA standard.[20]

The fledgling CDMA industry received a big boost in 1993 when the FCC allocated 160 MHz in the 1900 MHz band for the new Personal Communications Service (PCS). Though the FCC did not mandate a specific technology, it did stipulate that PCS operators must use digital rather than analog technology. A number of PCS operators—most notably PrimeCo and Sprint—chose CDMA as their technology.

Unlike existing cellular telephone operators, the new PCS operators did not have to worry about migrating current subscribers from analog to digital. PCS operators were free to aggressively build out digital, exploit its

---

[20] Interim Standard 95 (IS-95).

advantages, and market it. With the establishment of PCS, the U.S. mobile phone market was transformed from a duopoly into a vibrant market with five or more competing operators in each major city.

PCS also provided the opportunity to try out a new method of allocating licenses: spectrum auctions. The first PCS auctions (A and B blocks) brought in about $15 per "pop" (the winning bid divided by the population in the service area). When the C block netted roughly $40 per pop, some observers questioned the bidders' sanity; many C block winners did not survive. However, given the growth in mobile phone market penetration over the next decade, we now know that $40 per pop was not an unreasonable valuation.

By the time CDMA service launched in Hong Kong, South Korea, and the United States, the GSM standard developed in Europe had acquired an insurmountable lead in the global market. However, European vendors and policy makers worried that CDMA might eclipse GSM in capacity and emerging data applications. After considering several third-generation (3G) options including more advanced versions of the TDMA technology upon which GSM was based, Europe's GSM industry selected wideband CDMA (WCDMA) as its 3G standard.

It was more than a little ironic. For years, many GSM proponents dismissed CDMA as promising more than it could deliver; by the late 1990s, they ridiculed the U.S. for falling so far behind. Just as it became clear that GSM had become the undisputed global standard, Europe announced that the next major step in the evolution of wireless technology required switching to CDMA. Apparently, the GSM industry saw the shift to CDMA was inevitable and decided it would be wiser to lead the migration than resist it.

Third-generation wireless technology is more than just the next highest rung on the performance ladder. When the mobile phone industry upgraded to digital cellular technology, it inspired visions of advanced products and multimedia applications. However, bringing that vision to life would require greater capacity and faster transmission speeds. Though the transition to 3G wireless started in the late 1990s, the percentage of mobile phone subscribers using 3G products and services did not become significant until 2007.

Qualcomm was elated that the GSM industry embraced CDMA. While the company would collect royalties and planned to develop its own family of WCDMA chips, it did not want to cede complete control of the CDMA market to others. Qualcomm developed its own 3G standard known as "evolution-data only" or EV-DO.

EV-DO had some key advantages. It was an upgrade to existing CDMA networks, so it didn't require building new networks. It required about one-third of the bandwidth of WCDMA, so it could be deployed by carriers with limited spectrum, such as those operating in the 450 MHz band. And it was a step ahead of WCDMA development; operators in the U.S. and Korea were first to offer 3G services. However, WCDMA has since taken the lead and will almost certainly become the dominant 3G technology.

Few consumers worry about competing air interface standards. Instead, they make their purchasing decisions based on products and prices. Consumers can always change service providers later (though the timing may be influenced by their service contract). The choice of air interface standards is more of an issue for operators, because it can limit the products available for their subscribers.

For example, operators have abandoned the original U.S. digital cellular standard (D-AMPS) in favor of GSM and CDMA. Most notably, Cingular Wireless switched to GSM—which also put the operator on the road to WCDMA. By late 2007, there were over 500 million CDMA subscribers (all varieties) worldwide and more than two billion GSM subscribers.

Nothing illustrates the mobile phone industry's phenomenal success better than the growth in annual handset shipments. An estimated one billion handsets (GSM and CDMA) were shipped in 2006.[21] That is significantly greater than the number of new subscribers because there is quite a sizable market for replacement handsets; it's not unusual for mobile handsets to be considered obsolete within two years.

* * *

The success of mobile phones is largely due to the development of the digital signal processor (DSP), a microprocessor optimized for signal processing. Put another way, the DSP is to the cell phone what the microprocessor is to the personal computer. The DSP enables affordable, battery-powered, multimedia handsets that can run all day.

The first single-chip DSP was introduced by Bell Labs in 1979. Texas Instruments entered the market in 1983 and is now the leading manufacturer. Qualcomm is also a leading supplier of DSPs for mobile phones. By 2007, DSPs featured clock rates up to 1 gigahertz and the ability to perform 8,000 million instructions per second.

---

[21] By comparison, the number of personal computers shipped in 2006 was about one-quarter of that figure.

Today, many handsets include a DSP running a real time operating system to handle traditional phone functions and a separate chip for user data applications. However, the trend appears to be towards a single chip with multiple processor cores running a high level operating system such as Linux, Windows Mobile or Symbian; such operating systems offer better tools for developers plus compatibility with desktop PCs and the Internet.

What this means is that the mobile handset is no longer just a phone. It has become a handheld computer that can run applications, access content, and interact with other computers and the Internet.

Digital wireless technology has also spread beyond mobile phones. Cordless phones, wireless local area networks (WLANs), satellites, and other digital wireless platforms are growing, too.

Digital wireless technologies have flourished in the market for unlicensed wireless devices. Up until 1981, opportunities for operating wireless transmitters without an FCC license were few and far between. The FCC finally acknowledged that new technologies and applications warranted more liberal rules. Hewlett-Packard and FCC staffer Michael Marcus were instrumental in establishing new rules in 1985 for unlicensed use of low-power and spread spectrum devices. Consumers could finally buy and use devices that contained radio transmitters without applying for special licenses, because those devices used technology less likely to create harmful interference.

Cordless phones, in particular, migrated from notoriously noisy analog technology to low-power digital radio and spread spectrum. Though initially expensive, digital cordless phones delivered greater range and privacy. Most analog cordless phone users probably never knew how easy it was for someone to eavesdrop on their telephone conversations.

Before Europe developed GSM, several countries experimented with public wireless services based on second-generation cordless telephone technology (CT2). However, CT2 ventures made three crucial mistakes. They assumed new technology would succeed simply because it possessed technical advantages. They failed to take into account competitive responses. And they proceeded despite a lack of solid market research. CT2 was initially tripped up by shiny, new, credit card-operated payphones (one of the original selling points of CT2 was that it offered an alternative to unreliable public call boxes, also known as telephone booths). If there was any remaining doubt, CT2 was finished off by GSM, which promised continuous coverage compared to CT2's limited coverage zones.

The wireless local area network (wireless LAN) industry also got off on the wrong foot. However, in this case perseverance paid off. Wireless LAN technology was originally developed as an alternative to cables. The theory was that corporate users would pay high prices for wireless LAN equipment to avoid the cost, delays, and inconvenience associated with installing new cables.

Wireless LANs gradually caught on in enterprise applications requiring mobility such as warehouse and retail store inventory tracking. Up until then, customers used portable bar code scanners with licensed narrowband FM radios. However, users had a difficult time coordinating frequencies with neighboring companies, and units could not be shifted from one facility to another because they were licensed for use in specific locations. Unlicensed wireless LANs using spread spectrum avoided these headaches, delivered higher throughput, and were less susceptible to giving and receiving interference.

As enterprise use of wireless LANs grew (led by two companies, Symbol Technologies and Telxon), and more highly integrated semiconductor solutions were developed, wireless LAN hardware prices gradually declined. Wireless LAN standards were developed under the auspices of the Institute of Electrical and Electronics Engineers (IEEE). The IEEE 802.11b standard, also known as "Wi-Fi," took off as the growing market for personal computers and Internet access in homes and small businesses created demand for a simple and inexpensive networking solution.

The price of wireless LAN cards dropped from more than $500 each to less than $50 each. Enhanced standards (including 802.11g and 802.11a) were developed for higher speeds and greater range. Locations such as coffee shops began setting up Wi-Fi "hotspots" offering free or low-cost Internet access.

The miniaturization of electronics also enabled laptop computers and handheld personal digital assistants (PDAs). This, in turn, led to a need to create ad hoc connections between various portable devices (e.g. cell phone-to-laptop computer) and between portable devices and desktop machines (e.g. PDA-to-printer). In other words, a personal area network (PAN). That called for an inexpensive, small, and low-power wireless solution that would work over short distances.

A short-range wireless solution was proposed for such applications. The Bluetooth concept was developed by Ericsson in 1994 and quickly garnered the support of IBM, Intel, Nokia, Sony Ericsson, and Toshiba. Bluetooth was originally defined to run at speeds up to 721 kbps over short distances. Later versions boosted range and speed.

The name "Bluetooth" was inspired by the tenth century Danish king known as Harold Bluetooth. King Bluetooth united warring factions in Scandinavia; Bluetooth's inventors saw the technology uniting devices through short-range communications.

It took longer to cost-reduce Bluetooth than expected and some industry participants gave up on it, but it is now incorporated in a large number of devices. The most popular application is linking wireless headsets to cell phones. Bluetooth can also be used to link cell phones to laptop computers for access to cellular data services.

Radio and TV broadcasting are also migrating to digital wireless technology. Satellite-based digital radio services (introduced by Sirius Satellite Radio and XM Satellite Radio) primarily target the automobile market with subscription-based services. FM and AM broadcasters are adding HD (hybrid digital) Radio developed by Ibiquity Corp. to their existing stations and frequency allocations. Though HD Radio service is free, it faces competition from satellite radio, Internet radio and devices that can store hours of music and other audio programming such as Apple's iPOD.

The development and market rollout of high definition television (HDTV) is likely to have greater impact. HDTV delivers a qualitatively better viewing experience. It also drives the convergence of home entertainment, personal computers, and the Internet.

U.S. broadcasters petitioned the FCC for HDTV spectrum in 1987. The FCC responded by establishing an industry advisory committee to select an HDTV standard. Four proposals were studied. Realizing it could not choose one over the other three, the FCC asked the groups to join forces, creating what became known as the Grand Alliance. The Grand Alliance developed the Advanced Television Systems Committee (ATSC) standard, approved in December of 1996. HDTV is being rolled out in existing TV spectrum, and part of the UHF television band is being reallocated for mobile services.

Realizing it could not insist on a forced march to HDTV—that might disenfranchise stations and consumers who can't afford the upgrade—the FCC decided to aim a bit lower. The FCC mandated that as of March 1, 2007 all new TVs must have digital tuners, and that by February 17, 2009 all full-power TV stations must cease broadcasting on analog channels. That bypasses the challenges and costs associated with producing and displaying high definition content, because it's possible to digitally broadcast and receive standard definition content. However, consumers who were content to watch mildly snowy analog TV using rabbit ear antennas may suddenly find they can't reliably receive the new digital TV pictures. The public's reaction and the FCC's response should be interesting.

As Martin Cooper has said, a big difference between landline phones and mobile phones is that mobile phones would be associated with people rather than places. The trouble is that people go many places, and sometimes they're not sure where those places are. The Global Positioning System—a satellite network that enables mobile users to determine their precise locations—was developed by the U.S. Department of Defense for military applications but has been extended to civilian uses. Dr. Ivan A. Getting and Dr. Bradford W. Parkinson are credited with developing GPS. The Navy and Air Force began experimenting with radio-locating using the Transit satellite system in 1964. NAVSTAR was developed in the early 1970s and evolved into today's GPS. Modern GPS satellites were launched starting in 1989. The GPS achieved full operational status in 1995 with a constellation of 24 satellites.

The GPS system transmits the exact location of each satellite along with precision timing signals. Receivers (on the ground, at sea, or in the air—GPS is a three dimensional system) determine their exact location by measuring the time it takes the signals to reach them. However, that requires extremely accurate clocks. Roger Easton proposed equipping the satellites with cesium atomic clocks.

What about the mobile receivers? Equipping them with atomic clocks was out of the question. Hideyoshi Nakamura of Aerospace Corporation developed a brilliant solution that enabled receivers with imprecise clocks to make precise measurements. He realized that determining the user's exact location required solving four unknowns: the user's distance from each of three satellites plus the receiver's clock error. If just three satellites are used, the user gets a location reading that looks good but is thrown off by the receiver's clock error.

However, clock error is a constant, so there should be a simple way to eliminate it. And there is. By taking a fourth satellite reading, the receiver obtains two erroneous location fixes. The receiver can then calculate the clock error by determining the value at which the two readings merge into a single (correct) location.

The FCC mandated that U.S. mobile phone operators must provide precision location information for calls to E911 enhanced emergency services. Though in theory mobile phone networks should be able to pinpoint the locations of mobile users, the integration of GPS receivers in mobile phones has proved the preferred solution. The combination of an integrated GPS receiver and a network connection in a mobile phone—also known as assisted GPS—often provides more accurate, reliable, and fast locating than a dedicated, handheld GPS receiver.

Two other satellite-based digital wireless services were developed in the late 20th century with high expectations. Both were initially major disappointments, but they have managed to hang on. Mobile satellite services were intended to extend voice and data services to the world's oceans, rural areas, and underdeveloped countries. However, the spread of terrestrial cellular service exceeded expectations, giving satellite operators Iridium and Globalstar more competition than existed when they began the lengthy process of planning and developing their satellite networks.

Iridium and Globalstar use fleets of satellites in low earth orbit. The beauty of this approach is that the satellites are close enough to the ground (less than 1,000 miles) that they can be reached via handheld devices, and a fleet of several dozen satellites can cover most of the planet. (In contrast, a geosynchronous satellite is deployed in an orbit 22,000 miles above the earth.) Iridium uses TDMA technology and was developed by Motorola; Globalstar uses CDMA technology and was developed by Qualcomm. Both were spun off as separate businesses; Iridium is privately held and Globalstar is publicly traded. By late 2007, Iridium claimed it had approximately 225,000 subscribers worldwide. Around the same time, Globalstar reported just over 285,000 subscribers.

Iridium and Globalstar may have found their niche—serving maritime, aviation, and remote site applications.

Another low earth orbit satellite project was conceived to provide nothing less than a global broadband Internet. It was a grand scheme, but it never got off the ground. With investment from Craig McCaw, Bill Gates and Saudi prince Alwaleed bin Talal, Teledesic was designed to support millions of simultaneous users equipped with fixed (non-mobile) terminals. Announced in 1994, the original design called for 840 satellites orbiting the earth at an altitude of 700 km for an estimated cost of $9.55 billion.

McCaw envisioned Teledesic as an engine for social change. The network would upgrade the entire earth's telecommunications infrastructure in one fell swoop. Users could download data at speeds up to 720 Mbits/s. Teledesic would enable knowledge workers to live anywhere, and would enable businesses in the most remote or underdeveloped areas to access advanced network services.

Gradually, it was concluded that Teledesic was too ambitious. The plan was modified in 1997 to reduce its cost and complexity. However, the failure of the Iridium and Globalstar projects to meet their business objectives cast a dark shadow over Teledesic. The project was officially halted on October 1, 2002.

* * *

The astounding success of GSM and the ultimate triumph of CDMA raise important questions about the sources of future innovation and the role of standards. Has technology matured to the point that further progress can only be achieved through large-scale collaboration or is there still a place for "skunk works" and even the occasional lone inventor? How important are standards—and how real is the threat of market fragmentation?

There's a tendency to think that as technology advances its development moves further beyond the reach of individuals and small businesses. But that's not true. During the 1960s, only big corporations developed computers. By the 1980s, people were developing computers and other microprocessor-based products in their garages and on their kitchen tables. The technology became *more* accessible.

There's also a tendency to idealize the standards-setting process. In most cases, someone develops a better technology and the industry decides to create a standard around it. It rarely happens the other way around. Most companies are not willing to wait years for a committee to develop a standard. Instead, they develop their own solution—something they can sell to customers sooner rather than later—and promise to support the standard when it's ready.

Market fragmentation is not caused by proprietary technology. If that were so, new technologies would rarely if ever succeed before a standard has been developed. Instead, market fragmentation simply reflects the fact that a consensus solution—whether formal or de facto—has not yet emerged. Nor is market fragmentation always a bad thing: sometimes it is simply the market's way of saying one size does not fit all. The mobile phone market is fragmented in several respects (handset operating system, air interface, and so on)—and very robust.

The wireless market will continue to attract large corporations because it is a very large market. But there will always be room for ideas "just crazy enough to work."

Chapter Thirteen
Wireless: the Next Generation

Wireless entrepreneurs have long dreamed of using wireless to replace wires. However, the dream has been thwarted by a persistent performance gap. When wireless LANs were introduced in the early 1990s, most could not deliver one-tenth the throughput of inexpensive Ethernet LANs running 10 Mbps over twisted pair cables. As wireless LANs slowly climbed to 10 Mbps, wired LANs raced ahead to even faster speeds: Fast Ethernet (100 Mbps), Gigabit Ethernet, and 10 Gigabit Ethernet.

When Greg Raleigh returned to Stanford University to earn his PhD in Electrical Engineering, he wasn't thinking about how to replace wire with wireless. He did, however, choose to write his thesis on one of the hottest topics in wireless research: smart antennas. Smart antennas consist of antennas with multiple elements and the electronic circuitry to leverage those elements. In other words, dumb aluminum plus computer chips.

At first, entrepreneurs were attracted to the idea of using smart antennas to focus radio signals like laser beams, locking onto and tracking mobile users. Unfortunately, in most cases the modest performance gains did not justify the cost.

Raleigh was unimpressed with prevailing smart antenna theory, so his first goal was to create a more generic—and consequently more powerful—radio channel model for developing and analyzing smart antennas. A good radio channel model predicts what the signals from the transmitter will look like when they reach the receiver. Using reflection geometry, in which radio signals are treated like light rays and wave fronts bouncing off objects, Raleigh found he could derive the answer simply by computing the sum of all paths.

With his new channel model in hand, he soon found himself confronted with a startling conclusion: the theoretical capacity of a wireless channel is greatest in the presence of multipath propagation.

Every wireless engineer knows that multipath propagation is the source of a very troublesome impairment, multipath fading. The idea is drilled into their heads—and with good reason. If Raleigh's model was correct, however, it meant that engineers had been so busy mitigating the ill effects of natural multipath propagation that they never noticed multipath could be artificially created and exploited.

Raleigh realized that with the proper signal processing algorithms and multiple antennas at both ends of a wireless link, he could harness multipath propagation to dramatically increase the speed and range of wireless LANs. Physically, his solution looks like just another smart antenna implementation. Functionally, it is worlds apart. Smart antennas typically enhance the performance of a single data stream in the presence of natural multipath. Raleigh's solution sends multiple unique data streams via separate paths to multiply spectral efficiency. Raleigh appropriated the term MIMO (pronounced *mai-moh*) to distinguish his solution from run-of-the-mill smart antennas.

Raleigh was not the only person to develop the theory leading to MIMO (multiple input/multiple output). Other contributors include Jack Winters (co-founder and CTO of Eigent Technologies), Arogyaswami Paulraj (professor of electrical engineering at Stanford University), Thomas Kailath (co-founder of Numerical Technologies), Gerard J. Foschini (researcher at Bell Labs), David Tse (associate professor of electrical engineering at the University of California at Berkeley), and Sergio Verdu (professor of electrical engineering at Princeton University). But it was Raleigh who championed the idea of integrating MIMO with consumer-grade wireless LANs to achieve huge performance gains—and he developed the chipsets to bring that vision to life.

A little more background is needed to understand how MIMO works and why it resembles magic. When Guglielmo Marconi discovered that radio waves could travel around hills and over the horizon, he was thrilled because that meant that wireless was not limited to line-of-sight applications. But engineers soon discovered that the news was not all good. If radio waves can bend and bounce, then they can take multiple paths from the transmitter to the receiver. Some of the paths waste power. Others add delay. By the time a signal reaches the receiver it may barely resemble the signal hurled into free space by the transmitter.

Over the past century, multipath propagation has been a leading source of disruption in wireless communication systems. It literally causes a radio signal to interfere with itself. In the extreme case, two multipath signals arrive at the receiver equal in strength but 180 degrees out-of-phase, and cancel each other out. The receiver sees nothing.

Engineers discovered various ways to mitigate the harmful effects of multipath propagation. One strategy is to pick out the strongest multipath signal and ignore all of the others. Another strategy is to realign the multipath components and then recombine them. Smart antennas—with their ability to concentrate the transmit signal energy on the best path and collect the strongest multipath components at the receiver—were the optimum solution.

In the 1990s, smart antennas attracted the best companies and the best minds, like Raleigh. He first described how to exploit multipath propagation in a paper co-authored by John M. Cioffi and presented at the 1996 GLOBECOM conference: "Spatio-Temporal Coding for Wireless Communications." However, the components needed to build consumer-grade MIMO products were not yet available.

In the interim, Raleigh and V.K. Jones started Clarity Wireless to develop broadband wireless products around a technology called vector orthogonal frequency division multiplexing (V-OFDM). OFDM is another flavor of spread spectrum and is increasingly favored by engineers. Unlike frequency hopping (which hops from narrowband channel to narrowband channel), and direct sequence (which spreads the signal out over a continuous range), OFDM uses many discrete channels at the same time.

Raleigh and Jones built a prototype V-OFDM system running 100 Mbps in 20 MHz of spectrum, and demonstrated that it could operate error-free for two weeks over a distance of six miles using just one watt of power. They proved the technical merit of V-OFDM, but ran into a chicken-and-egg business dilemma. Clarity Wireless was created to provide broadband wireless services. In order to sell broadband wireless services you need coverage; in order to achieve coverage you need customers. Luckily, a much bigger company was interested in the technology; in 1998, Raleigh and Jones sold Clarity Wireless to Cisco Systems. An industry association[22] was established with Cisco's backing to promote OFDM-based broadband wireless technology.

In 2001, Raleigh and Jones created another startup, Airgo Networks. The goal this time was to commercialize MIMO technology and the business plan was to develop MIMO-based chipsets for wireless LAN products. Wireless LANs were the perfect target application; there are many reflections at high frequencies indoors, guaranteeing strong multipath signals. Since existing coverage is not an issue for wireless LANs, there is no chicken-and-egg problem.

Airgo Networks demonstrated that MIMO increases wireless LAN coverage, speed and capacity—all at the same time. That is no small feat.

---

[22] The Broadband Wireless Internet Forum.

There are many ways to boost one of the three parameters, but it's almost always at the expense of the other two. By multiplying spectral efficiency, MIMO-based wireless LANs increase all three parameters over existing, non-MIMO wireless LANs.

In Raleigh's 1998 PhD dissertation ("On Multivariate Communication Theory and Data Rate Multiplying Techniques for Multipath Channels"), he showed that MIMO is least computing-intensive when used in conjunction with OFDM. Consequently, Airgo Networks created its "True MIMO" technology around MIMO-OFDM.

Airgo's MIMO-OFDM, like Qualcomm's CDMA, is a complex and computing intensive technology. At first glance, it doesn't seem like a good candidate for consumer-grade products. But like Qualcomm's founders, Raleigh and Jones understood that if they could embed their MIMO-OFDM solution in silicon chips, then it could be mass produced at a low, per unit cost.

MIMO's impact on the wireless LAN market was almost immediate. Despite the popularity of wireless LANs, products often lacked the range and throughput needed in homes and small businesses. MIMO fixed that. Given the success of personal video recorders (PVRs) and the introduction of high definition television (HDTV), it was time for the wireless LAN industry to start targeting entertainment applications. MIMO was far and away the most promising technology for achieving the speeds that would be needed—in the hundreds of megabits per second range.

Finally, wireless LAN technology was poised to replace wires. MIMO-based wireless LANs allowed consumers to set up home networks without running cables under carpets and drilling holes through walls and floors. They enabled small businesses to set up networks without paying to have cables installed in rented facilities. Longer term, they will facilitate the convergence of PCs, home entertainment, and the Internet.

There was just one problem. The rest of the wireless LAN industry had been slow to embrace MIMO. Consequently, Airgo Networks developed chipsets supporting its proprietary MIMO-OFDM technology that were backwards compatible with existing wireless LAN standards. Raleigh believed his chipsets would demonstrate the benefits of MIMO, find a market niche or two, and position Airgo Networks to lead development of a MIMO-based wireless LAN standard. But political battles erupted in the IEEE 802.11n committee established to define a next-generation wireless LAN standard.

It was a familiar scenario. Airgo Networks, a startup, not only demonstrated the merit of MIMO, it was gaining market share. The incumbent wireless LAN chipset suppliers—large companies such as Broadcom and Intel—knew that MIMO was the best way forward, but they didn't want to risk losing market share. The incumbent chipset providers tried to bypass the standards-setting process by developing their own "standard" in private, hoping the 802.11n committee would accept it as a fait accompli. The specification failed to pass because it ignored key 802.11n constituencies, but it bought time for its backers by delaying the standard. The 802.11n committee was established in January 2004; four years later, the standard still hadn't been completed.

*   *   *

Engineers disagree about the likely impact of MIMO in the mobile environment. Skeptics say that multipath signals are often too weak; differences in path length are often too great; and at times multipath signals are negligible (such as when the mobile device has line-of-sight access to the cellular tower). However, most experts believe that while the gains in the outdoor mobile environment won't be as dramatic as in the indoor wireless LAN setting, it's still worth doing. Mobile vendors are almost unanimous in the belief that MIMO and OFDM will be key technologies going forward.

Third-generation wireless technology (WCDMA and EV-DO) is likely to continue rolling out until at least 2012. Meanwhile, the industry has developed and begun to deploy enhancements to 3G technology, which some people call "3.5G" technology. And the industry is already working on the next generation, sometimes referred to as fourth-generation (4G) wireless. (Others are more cautious, preferring to call it "pre-fourth-generation" wireless or "3.9G.")

3.5G enhancements have been developed for both WCDMA and EV-DO. The main enhancement to WCDMA is called HSDPA (high speed downlink packet access) and delivers downlink throughputs from 1.8 Mbps to 14.4 Mbps. The main improvements to EV-DO are Rev A (featuring downlink speeds up to 3.1 Mbps) and Rev B (offering downlink speeds up to 14.7 Mbps using multiple EV-DO channels).

The third-generation wireless technology currently being deployed delivers performance comparable to cable modem and DSL services. The wireless services are generally more expensive, though there are "all you can eat" flat-rate plans for as little as $40 per month.

What will tomorrow's mobile technology offer? The 3.9G/4G standards—which probably won't be deployed in earnest before 2015—promise speeds in the tens of megabits per second with peak rates exceeding 100 Mbps.

Some people question whether there is a need for such speed. Faster throughputs will make it easier to distribute and exchange content—even as content becomes richer. Experience has taught us that users and developers have no trouble filling fatter pipes.

However, there is more to wireless performance than peak downstream data rates. The performance experienced by individual mobile users depends on multiple factors including downlink speed (the most often cited figure), uplink speed, latency (delays encountered in the "core" network), and the number of users sharing the same channel at the same time.

Major enhancements to cellular radio and core networks take years to plan and implement. Incumbent operators require a migration path that preserves as much of their capital investment as possible and allows them to move forward cautiously. This creates opportunities for new entrants not encumbered by legacy systems and existing customers. New entrants have every incentive to deploy new technology as quickly as possible.

That is precisely what is happening in the mobile phone industry. New applications such as video and mobile TV are emerging that exceed the capabilities of existing second generation cellular networks. Operators are upgrading to third generation standards, but it isn't clear whether 3G will have sufficient speed and capacity to handle the demand for multimedia content.

If mobile multimedia remains a premium service that people use sparingly, then 3G networks should have sufficient capacity. However, if mobile multimedia is priced so that most subscribers use it every day, then peak demand could exceed network capacity—particularly when there is major breaking news.

Consequently, the cellular industry is pursuing two development paths: mobile TV (using separate broadcast networks to deliver the most popular content to mobile users) and 3.9/4G technologies. Meanwhile, several companies led by chipmaker Intel Corp. are developing and deploying a data-centric wireless technology alternative known as WiMAX.[23]

No doubt we are heading towards a future in which multimedia is a standard feature of mobile communications. For example, an Israeli company

---

[23] Worldwide Interoperability for Microwave Access.

called Vringo has developed video ringtones—short video clips that can be sent to the called party when placing a call between compatible handsets. And an application developed to demonstrate WiMAX lets fans attending NASCAR races watch live video feeds from inside the racecars, in the service pits, and at various locations around the track.

*   *   *

Mobile TV may be the ultimate expression of next-generation mobile service. Not many people are likely to stare at two-inch screens for hours at a time, but they probably will watch sports highlights, breaking news, and short "mobisodes" produced specifically for mobile viewers. What is not yet known is whether mobile TV demand justifies construction of separate mobile TV broadcast networks.

Mobile TV broadcast networks assume that most users will want the most popular content. Therefore, it makes more sense to broadcast the content on a dedicated channel than to establish private connections to each user. Though there are several competing mobile TV standards,[24] they have several commonalities. They all use a "time slicing" technology in which data for multiple TV channels is sent in bursts over a single high-speed channel. They also use high-power transmitters with overlapping coverage to ensure good coverage.

Mobile TV has been implemented in the U.S. in the 700 MHz band (being reclaimed from UHF-TV) using Qualcomm's MediaFLO (FLO stands for "forward link only") technology. MediaFLO claims to support 19 real-time video channels and 65 recorded video channels. Both Verizon Wireless and AT&T Mobility are using the technology. Verizon has introduced mobile TV service at prices starting at $13 per month.

Unfortunately, the emerging 4G standards have even less memorable names than their archaic 3G and 2G cousins. The GSM camp's 4G technology is called LTE (long term evolution).[25] The Qualcomm CDMA camp's 4G technology is called ultra mobile broadband (UMB).[26] Both standards presume that mobile operators will upgrade their core networks (which link their cell sites to each other, the public telephone network, and

---

[24] Mobile TV standards include digital video broadcasting – handheld (DVB-H), digital multimedia broadcasting (DMB), and Qualcomm's MediaFLO.

[25] Ironically, LTE is being developed by the Third Generation Partnership Project (3GPP).

[26] UMB is being developed by the Third Generation Partnership Project 2 (3GPP2).

the Internet) from the traditional circuit-switched telephone model to an all-IP (Internet protocol) approach.

Though there are two competing 4G standards, they will likely be very similar, making use of many of the same tools and techniques. There are probably more opportunities for differentiation in terms of time-to-market and cost. The industry tends to be very optimistic about how soon new technologies will become commercially available and widely used. Though there is talk about 4G being introduced in 2010, deployment in earnest is unlikely to begin before 2015. If nothing else, operators will want to let 3G (and 3.5G) play out before they invest in another major upgrade.

WiMAX, a competing solution, was inspired by the success of Wi-Fi wireless LAN technology. WiMAX proponents point out that cellular telephone networks are big, complex and difficult to change; the cellular infrastructure market is dominated by a few giant corporations; and cellular operators' top priority remains telephone service. They also believe WiMAX will prove easier to deploy; that it will benefit customers by being open to more manufacturers; and that it will more closely resemble the Internet. In other words, WiMAX proponents believe that mobile phone operators have created expectations of ubiquitous mobile multimedia that they can't satisfy, while WiMAX operators will be free to focus on high-speed data applications and make aggressive use of advanced wireless technologies such as MIMO and OFDM.

WiMAX faces challenges of its own, however. WiMAX operators will generally be relegated to higher frequencies (2-10 GHz) where range and building penetration are harder to achieve. Most of the radio and core network enhancements defined for WiMAX are also planned for mobile phone systems. And as Clarity Wireless discovered, it's difficult for new operators with little coverage to compete against established carriers with vast coverage, huge financial resources, and hordes of subscribers.

WiMAX proponents are right about one thing: Mobile data will enjoy tremendous growth over the next decade. Though mobile data accounted for a fraction of operators' service revenues in 2007, it is a growing fraction. Sales of smart phones are increasing. Strong sales of digital cameras, iPODs, and laptop computers also bode well for mobile data services.

* * *

The need to provide ubiquitous and robust in-building coverage and the desire to access the most cost-effective network available are driving network convergence. If users are going to rely exclusively on their mobile phones, then indoor coverage should be as comprehensive and reliable as outdoor coverage. If multimedia is going to be a routine part of mobile communications, then they need both comprehensive coverage and robust signals.

In theory, network convergence will allow users to access the same services from any network. In practice, the focus is on interoperability between mobile phone, Wi-Fi, and landline telephone networks. For example, convergence solutions allow a business user talking on a desk phone to leave the office and (at the push of a button) continue the conversation on a mobile phone. Another potential scenario is transferring a call from a mobile phone network (consuming billable airtime) to a free Wi-Fi network in the home.

Network convergence could be a bigger part of next-generation wireless than first meets the eye. Wi-Fi networks already support speeds in excess of 10 megabits per second and 802.11n promises throughputs in excess of 100 megabits per second. Wireless LANs could become part of the mobile network infrastructure—pressed into service wherever there is demand for optimum indoor coverage and/or maximum speed.

However, the integration of Wi-Fi and mobile phones poses a couple of challenges. Wi-Fi was not conceived as a power-efficient technology, but new power management protocols should correct that. Mobile operators' reluctance to support Wi-Fi integration could be a bigger problem. It's not necessarily in operators' best interests to sell handsets that can make free calls over Wi-Fi networks. However, operators understand that good in-building coverage is essential to getting users to rely exclusively on their mobile phones, and Wi-Fi may be part of the solution.

There is an alternative solution for indoor coverage—particularly in homes and small businesses—that is attracting tremendous interest. Users can buy and install miniature cell sites called "femtocells" in their homes and offices. Instead of letting users make free calls in unlicensed Wi-Fi spectrum, femtocells increase the mobile operator's traffic capacity and keep subscribers in the operator's licensed spectrum.

Driving down the cost of femtocells is the biggest challenge. Most femtocell designs are too expensive for consumers. Sprint has introduced a femtocell (the AIRAVE made by Samsung) on a trial basis in two cities. The cost issue is addressed by charging a fixed price for the unit ($49.99) and a recurring monthly fee ($15 for one person, $30 for a family) for unlimited use. The unit connects to Sprint's network through any existing broadband Internet service.

There are a few remaining technical challenges. Mobile speeds could eclipse cable and DSL speeds with the roll-out of 3.5G services. Therefore, users may be surprised to find that performance slows when connected to a nearby femtocell. For example, a user accustomed to communicating at 5 Mbps outdoors using HSDPA technology may be limited to 500,000 bps indoors, because that's the speed of the connection between the femtocell and the Internet.

Handoffs are another issue. It would be a problem if a home-based femtocell connected to every user who happens to pass by. However, femtocells can be programmed to only accept connections from authorized phones. Plus, the first products may not support handoffs of any kind; they will simply provide coverage to make and receive calls from within the home or small business.

The long-term vision is that millions of femtocells will be deployed, ensuring ubiquitous in-building coverage and enabling operators to offload much of their electric power and backhaul expense to subscribers. As a growing percentage of traffic is handled by subscriber-owned femtocells, operators can free up capacity on their own networks for premium services.

*   *   *

In addition to Bluetooth, there are two new short-range wireless technologies that look particularly promising: near field communications (NFC) and ultra wideband (UWB). NFC supports wireless communications at very short distances (up to roughly ten inches) and is intended for secure transactions. Transmission rates are in the low hundreds of kilobits per second range. The NFC-equipped handset is waved past or tapped against a point of sale terminal, a vending machine, or a poster equipped with a tiny NFC chip. NFC can be used to pay tolls or download URLs for further information.

Ultra wideband (UWB), in contrast, uses narrow pulses or other ultra-wideband (greater than 500 MHz) transmission schemes to send data at high speeds without causing interference to other devices and services. Speeds well above 500 megabits per second are possible. Ironically, narrow pulse UWB signals bear a striking resemblance to Marconi's spark-gap signals; we have come full circle.

While UWB can be used for specialized applications such as radar, it offers a high-speed mode for mobile handsets that can be used in place of or in combination[27] with Bluetooth. UWB is being embraced for transferring multimedia content between handsets and PCs; using handsets to drive larger video displays; personal area social networking between handsets; and handset-to-kiosk communications. WiMedia is an ultra wideband-based standard. It has been selected by both the Bluetooth Special Interest Group (SIG) and the USB Implementers Forum as the foundational technology for their high-speed wireless solutions.

Do handsets need a short-range wireless link running hundreds of megabits per second? Transmission rate is not the only consideration. UWB can be used to enable quick content transfers. For example, assume a user wants to download several albums of music from a PC to a handset or PDA before heading out the door. It will take several minutes at Bluetooth speeds, but mere seconds at UWB data rates.

*   *   *

The evolution of mobile handsets and other portable electronic devices is equally impressive. Creators of the 1960s television series *Star Trek* guessed that centuries of technological development would yield clamshell devices that look suspiciously like today's mobile phones. But don't be fooled: *Star Trek* communicators used subspace (faster than light) transmission to communicate at great distances with zero latency. In *Star Trek: the Next Generation*, handheld communicators were replaced with badge communicators featuring a built-in, universal language translator.

(From our present vantage point, subspace transmission seems physically impossible. However, in the future a means of modulating gravity waves might be discovered. A universal translator seems equally improbable, requiring some way of very quickly deriving meaning from patterns of sound.)

What did 250 years of technology evolution yield? Strip away subspace transmission and the universal translator, and you are left with a phone that even today's entry-level users in developing countries would look down on.

Today's mobile phones range from ultra low cost units supporting voice and text messaging to mid-range multimedia phones with built-in digital cameras and color displays to smart phones designed to interoperate with desktop PCs, the Web, and corporate intranets.

[27] NFC can be used to automate the Bluetooth connection setup process.

All indicators suggest mobile phones will become more intelligent, more multimedia, and more interconnected with other devices, networks, and services. The excitement surrounding Apple's iPhone says that the combination of a mobile phone and MP3 player is a sure winner. Consumers also express strong interest in mobile phones with GPS navigation. It may be unclear whether hordes of subscribers will pay an extra \$15 for new mobile TV services, but it's a safe bet that some form of mobile video will succeed.

Video displays for mobile phones are evolving along multiple paths. The main challenges are achieving an acceptable viewing experience while minimizing power consumption and cost. Three development paths look most promising: displays that use ambient light, projection displays, and retinal projection displays.

Displays that use ambient light could dramatically reduce power consumption. A technology called interferometric modulation (IMOD) uses simultaneous reflections off a membrane and a thin-film structure to produce interference and, consequently, generate the desired colors. One advantage of an IMOD display is that its brightness is naturally calibrated to the ambient light. Another advantage is that it supports "always on" operation for use on the outside of a "clamshell" phone to indicate the time and to present user-specific alerts. Two-color IMOD displays developed by Qualcomm are coming to market; full-color versions require further development.

Displays that use ambient light may solve the power consumption problem, but they don't qualitatively change the small screen viewing experience. Texas Instruments has developed a "pico-projector" that can be integrated in a cell phone to project a larger image on any flat surface. The pico-projector uses millions of microscopic mirrors to project images. However, the technology has two major drawbacks: it consumes more power than conventional displays and can only be used in dim lighting.

A technology called virtual retinal display produces a large-screen viewing experience by projecting the image directly on the viewer's retina. However, this technology works best as a wearable display and is used mainly in military applications.

Another challenge for mobile devices is making it easier for users to enter data. Telephone keypads are fine for entering numbers, but entering text is cumbersome. The simplest solution is the multi-tap method. For example, to type the letter "c" the "2" key (associated with "abc") is tapped three times in rapid succession. This method can be quite fatiguing, particularly if every word is spelled out. Experienced texting users make heavy use of abbreviations.

There are predictive typing programs such as Nuance's T9 that enable quick text entry. The user taps the number keys just once per letter; the software "predicts" the intended word based on factors such as frequency of occurrence and context. This approach has its drawbacks, though. The user must spell out every word. Sometimes the software will predict the wrong word and the user must pause to examine alternative selections. Surprisingly, entering words with one tap per number key can also be fatiguing.

Some handsets feature voice recognition capability, though this is most reliable when used for specific functions such as dialing numbers and accessing address book entries. Solutions have also been developed that use the handset's built-in digital camera to capture and decode a bar code.

Another technology has been developed to help users quickly find and use handset functions. For example, if the user enters the word "camera" a menu of camera tasks appears enabling the user to scroll down and select the desired function. Studies suggest that minimizing the number of key clicks required to complete a task is key to achieving positive user experiences.

Will mobile devices with built-in cameras and media players have enough memory to handle multimedia content? It wasn't that long ago that the capacity and cost of portable memory was a significant limiting factor. The evolution of flash memory has more than kept pace with application requirements, though. For example, flash memory vendor SanDisk offers small cards with four gigabytes of memory that can be inserted in mobile phones. The firm claims its near-term technology roadmap will yield affordable, 32 gigabyte cards within a few years—enough capacity for more than a dozen full-length movies on a single card.

Unfortunately, battery technology has not kept pace; chemistry is evolving much more slowly than electronics. Most recent improvements in battery life have been achieved through greater semiconductor integration and better power management. Lithium-ion batteries are widely used in consumer electronics devices such as mobile phones due to their high energy-to-weight ratio. Though fuel cells promise up to a 20x improvement over lithium-ion batteries, they require complex "micro-plumbing" and are years away from general use.

Several companies focus on designing and manufacturing advanced handset antennas. The trend is to use stub or internal antennas enabling more stylish handsets. Multiple internal antennas can be used for diversity (better reception), beamforming (more efficient transmission), and MIMO (higher speeds). Antennas can also be configured to minimize the amount of radiation absorbed by the user's body. Though studies regarding potential health hazards have been inconclusive, handsets are held in proximity to the brain, and many countries impose safety limits.

Because mobile phones are also computers, battles are being waged for dominance of the operating system, user interface, applications architecture, and end-user application markets. It is inevitable that a growing fraction of mobile phones will use a high-level operating system such as Windows Mobile or mobile Linux. Handset user interfaces will include the intelligence to help users find and use features. Mobile applications will be tightly integrated with the Web and the user's desktop PC.

The mobile applications market is wide open. With more than 2.5 billion mobile users, a growing percentage equipped with handsets that can download applications and content over the air, the opportunities for content and application developers are immense. The combination of a simple game or ringtone plus a little viral marketing (itself a mobile application) will create many instant millionaires.

Chapter Fourteen

Lessons in Creativity and Technology Development

Lesson #1: Creative people identify and exploit weaknesses in prevailing ideas and perspectives

You can't be creative by following the crowd. That doesn't lead to novel solutions. Nor can you be creative just by flaunting conventional wisdom. Any crank can do that. Creative people see possibilities that others overlook.

The Elizabethan philosopher Francis Bacon identified four common sources of intellectual blindness: idols of the tribe, idols of the den, idols of the marketplace, and idols of the theater. The idols of the tribe are false or misleading ideas accepted by the community. The idols of the den are false or misleading ideas accepted by the individual. The idols of the marketplace are false or misleading ideas resulting from the misuse of language. And the idols of the theater are false or misleading ideas resulting from the abuse of authority.

Bacon's point was that powerful influences cause people to believe things that are either not true or not entirely true. Or as Edwin H. Armstrong was fond of saying, "It ain't ignorance that causes all the trouble in this world. It's the things people know that ain't so."

Creative people critically examine accepted beliefs. First they learn as much as they can about the subject. Then they look for false assumptions and incomplete explanations. Soon, opportunities begin to present themselves.

The opportunities are infinite. It would be impossible to invent a more challenging, endless, and fascinating puzzle than the world around us. Nature's fabric is manifold, subtle, and often counter-intuitive. There may never be one theory that explains everything, just as there has never been a single way of doing science.

Competing theories fuel progress. And it's not surprising, because there has never been a consensus about what makes a good theory. The French physicist and philosopher Henri Poincaré insisted that fundamental scientific principles are based on agreement. Pierre Duhem pointed out that for any set of observations there are many satisfactory explanations. Karl Popper argued that the more opportunities for refutation a theory presents, the better the theory. Thomas Kuhn suggested that science evolves through sudden paradigm shifts. History's verdict is clear: scientists must be free to pursue any idea—as long as it doesn't contradict facts or reason.

Volta invented the battery by bringing a different perspective to Galvani's research. Faraday discovered electric and magnetic fields because he was not blinded by Newtonian physics. Armstrong invented FM radio by rejecting the assumption that FM had to be based on a narrowband solution.

Creative people often succeed by finding and exploiting errors or limitations in current thinking. Sometimes that means challenging what Thomas Kuhn called "normal science." In other cases, it simply means looking at the world through a different lens.

Lesson #2: Creative people borrow ideas from other fields

Creativity often results from the juxtaposition of seemingly unrelated ideas. Analogies from one field may be used to find solutions to problems in another. Or ideas from different fields may be combined to form new ideas.

James Clerk Maxwell used a mechanical model to develop his dynamical theory of the electromagnetic field. At first he wondered if his mechanical model was an accurate representation of nature's hidden machinery. Eventually he concluded that his model only represented logical connections. The important thing was that it worked.

The mathematics so essential to the physical sciences may also be viewed as an analogy. Like Maxwell's mechanical model, mathematics represents logical connections. In fact, French physicist and philosopher of science Pierre Duhem concluded that Maxwell simply traded his mechanical model for a model consisting of mathematical symbols.

Some creativity researchers are confused by the widespread trafficking in ideas; they erroneously conclude that creativity is predominantly collaborative. Creative people frequently work with others, exchanging facts and insights, but discovering and inventing are rarely shared acts. For example, imagine that two individuals contributed ideas that led to a major invention. Then imagine that one of those individuals died more than a century before the other was born. Certainly they were not co-inventors.

Galvani had laboratory assistants but he alone combined ideas from biology and physics to develop his "animal electricity" theory. Faraday worked for and was influenced by Davy but went on to conduct original research. Morse found partners to help him bring his telegraph to market. Bell hired Watson as his research assistant. There are many more examples. Creative people share ideas and work with others, but group-think rarely engenders creative leaps.

Lesson #3: The creativity of scientists, inventors and entrepreneurs requires patience and persistence

Though new technology is often carefully planned, it rarely succeeds according to plan. Sometimes the market isn't quite ready. In other cases the features, packaging, timing, and cost are not quite right. Many of these issues can only be resolved through direct market interaction.

Most new technologies require a market gestation period. Samuel Morse waited six years to build his first demonstration telegraph line. Wireless was mainly used in niche applications (maritime communications) for the first 25 years.

Frequency modulation (FM), television, spread spectrum-based wireless LANs, cellular radio, and Bluetooth all required gestation periods. Often, new technologies succeed in military or industrial applications first. These customers are willing to pay high prices for new technologies that give them a competitive edge. Over time, new applications are discovered, designs are cost-reduced, and the market expands. This leads to a virtuous cycle in which lower costs drive higher volumes and vice-versa.

Creative people are patient and persistent not only because they believe in their own ideas, but because they believe that it is only a matter of time before others will, too.

Lesson #4: The true inventors are the people who do the most to create, promote, and distribute a new technology

Who deserves credit for a major invention? The history of technology is riddled with claims, counter-claims, and often long drawn-out legal disputes. The public is at a loss to know who to believe—particularly when even judges and scholars can't agree.

It is not enough to stumble on an idea. An inventor understands the value of an invention and conveys that understanding to others.

The discovery of insulin provides an instructive example. Canadian Frederick Banting is credited with discovering insulin in 1922. However, the French physiologist Marcel Eugène Emile Gley studied pancreatic extracts 17 years earlier. Gley even described his finding in a sealed envelope deposited with the Société de Bologie and opened after Banting's discovery was announced. The world, however, continued to recognize Banting as insulin's discoverer.

During an international symposium on diabetes, Gley protested. Oscar Minkowski, who discovered the relationship between the pancreas and diabetes, responded: "I know just how you feel. I could also have kicked myself for not having discovered insulin, when I realize how close I came to it."

Patents were created to encourage inventions. No one wants to invent something and then watch someone else copy the idea and make a fortune. Unfortunately, the patent process is imperfect and as the stakes grow higher people discover more ways to abuse it. Some companies put more effort into obtaining patents than developing products. Others try to patent every solution, no matter how trivial. Patent holders attempt to enforce their patents for purposes not originally intended.

History has generally been a good judge of priority. It favors the claimants who had the greatest impact. The question is not who was first to make a claim, but who was first to make a difference.

Lesson #5: The best technology is not always the most successful

One of the toughest lessons for technologists to accept is that the highest performance technology is not necessarily the winner. What the market wants is the right product, with the right features and packaging, at the right cost. It's all about value. In many cases, a technology that is just good enough wins.

That's not to say the market prefers poor performance. For any high-tech product there is a performance level that will satisfy the vast majority of customers. But other factors go into the purchasing decision. If additional performance requires trade-offs in any of those areas, it may not be worth it.

Lesson #6: The best standards come from proprietary technologies

Good business managers know that it is better to own 10% of a large market than 100% of a tiny market. That is why most technology companies try to position their solution as a "standard."

The benefits of industry-wide standards are exaggerated. Allegedly, industry-wide standards ensure that products from different vendors will interoperate; that manufacturers will enjoy the greatest economy of scale; and that consumers can buy products secure in the knowledge that they will not become obsolete.

It's not that simple. Consider railroad track standards. The assumption is that it would be most convenient and cost-effective if railroads in neighboring countries adhered to the same standard. This avoids the need for transferring passengers and cargo to different trains at the border.

However, there are other facts to consider. Even with standardized tracks, not all trains travel all routes. Therefore, changing trains between some if not most endpoints is inevitable. The same benefit—not having to change trains at the border—can be achieved by constructing a single line between hubs in both countries. That is probably more efficient than replacing all of the tracks in one or both countries. There are also very effective partial solutions such as rails that support multiple gauge cars and flatcars that accommodate different-size freight containers.

Industry-wide standards, much like socialism, are based on the false assumption that a centrally planned system is more efficient than a self-organizing system.

Take another look at telecommunications standards. The lack of a single standard does not preclude products from one vendor talking with those from another. Vendors often cooperate through licensing, strategic alliances, and consortia. Most successful telecom standards started as proprietary or ad hoc solutions that were later transformed into formal standards.

The media complained for years that Europe was ahead of the U.S. in wireless. They were right for the wrong reasons. Europe's lead was invariably attributed to the adoption of a single mobile phone standard. The media completely overlooked the fact that by licensing multiple GSM operators in each country—usually competing with a single incumbent analog operator—Europe's mobile phone market became more competitive than the U.S. market with its analog "duopoly."

Critics predicted that because the U.S. permitted multiple standards, users would be forced to carry multiple devices to communicate while traveling. That never happened. The critics failed to anticipate the development of affordable devices supporting multiple standards. The critics also failed to anticipate operator consolidation into nationwide networks.

Another familiar complaint is that the absence of a single standard inhibits market development. Supposedly, customers hesitate to buy because they fear they will choose the wrong technology and watch their investment go down the drain. This ignores two important facts. Some individuals habitually buy the latest gadget knowing they will discard it as soon as something better comes along. And many organizations buy new technology on the basis that it will "pay for itself."

Industry-wide standards are usually the product of negotiation and compromise. Proprietary solutions are often the result of innovation.

Lesson #7: Creative ideas threaten the status quo

Scientists, inventors, and entrepreneurs with innovative but not-yet-proven ideas are often accused of being incompetent, dishonest or crazy. Once they prove their ideas are correct, they find themselves assaulted by people suddenly claiming priority. First they say it will never work—then they say they invented it.

When Samuel Morse began promoting his telegraph he was told there was no need for it. When he became famous, legal challenges were mounted against both his priority and the scope of his patent. When Qualcomm proposed its CDMA technology for cellular telephone networks, the company's founders were accused of dishonesty and fraud. Now other companies claim they co-invented CDMA.

Creativity is at once a rewarding and hazardous endeavor. If you want to leave your mark on this world like Morse, Bell, Marconi and Armstrong, you need to be incredibly driven, obsessed with an idea that others have either rejected or don't yet appreciate, and prepared to hunker down by yourself for as long as it takes to develop and promote your idea—and you have to do it at precisely the right moment in history.

Lesson #8: Creativity is recognizing opportunities and knowing when and how to act on them

Researchers studying human innovation define creativity as the ability to engender products or processes that are novel and appropriate.[28] In other words, the result must be not only original but useful or meaningful to others.

One popular theory asserts that there are two kinds of creativity. Great inventions and works of art are the result of Creativity with a big "C." The solutions to everyday problems are the result of creativity with a small "c." The implication is that everyone can be taught to be creative. Unfortunately, that theory only serves to confuse mundane work with profound achievement.

We don't know whether creativity is genetic. While no rational investigator would attribute creativity to mysterious forces, we do know that creative acts are rare and repeatedly creative individuals are even rarer.

Like it or not, creative people are different. They tend to be contrarians and workaholics. Most have an unusually strong sense of purpose. There are no secret formulas that enable ordinary people to be creative. However, there may be ways that certain types of individuals can increase their odds of being creative.

We don't know where creativity comes from. Creative people often report that breakthroughs appear suddenly or unexpectedly. Sometimes it happens after a long and frustrating search. Sometimes it comes from an unexpected direction.

Creative people make their own luck. Heinrich Hertz discovered electromagnetic waves and the photoelectric effect in the same series of experiments. He was convinced there are opportunities for achieving something great, and he was not afraid to embrace ambitious goals and hold himself to high standards.

Opportunities exist for those who have the courage and vision to act. Perhaps what really sets creative people apart from the rest of us is they do not ask or wait for permission.

---

[28] The definition of creativity is discussed by Prof. R. Keith Sawyer in <u>Explaining Creativity: the Science of Human Innovation</u>, Oxford University Press, 2006.

GLOSSARY

Glossary

ACTION-AT-A-DISTANCE: Isaac Newton's theory of universal gravitation assumed that gravity acts instantaneously and directly on distant objects. The same assumption was wrongly applied by Newton's followers to electric and magnetic forces.

ADVANCED MOBILE PHONE SYSTEM (AMPS): The first generation, analog cellular telephone standard developed in the U.S. and used in several other countries.

AIR INTERFACE: The method used to send and receive information over a radio channel. The air interface includes characteristics such as frequency allocation, modulation type, encoding scheme, and communications protocol.

ALTERNATING CURRENT (AC): Current with regularly changing polarity. Electric power is usually generated and distributed as AC. Audio and radio signals are naturally AC.

AMATEUR ("HAM") RADIO: The hobby of setting up and using radio communications equipment for pleasure and as a public service (but not business).

AMPÈRE'S CIRCUITAL LAW: An equation relating the current in a closed loop to the magnetic field produced by the current.

AMPLITUDE MODULATION (AM): A method of adding information to a radio carrier by varying its strength over time. For example, speech can be added by varying the radio signal's amplitude in accordance to the speech waveform's amplitude.

ANALOG RADIO: The use of continuously variable radio signals to represent continuously variable content such as voice.

ANODE: The (usually) positive electrode in a battery, vacuum tube, or other device.

ARC TRANSMITTER: An arc lamp modified to oscillate at radio frequencies to produce continuous waves.

AUDION: The name Lee de Forest gave to the vacuum tube triode that he invented.

BACKHAUL: A communications link used in radio networks to connect cell sites (a.k.a. "base stations") to a central switch or core network.

BASE STATION: A part of a radio network housing a transmitter and receiver and connected to an antenna.

BLUETOOTH: A short-range radio technology used, for example, to connect mobile phones to headsets.

CAPACITANCE: The ability of a material or a device to store electric charges and resist changes in voltage.

CARRIER: An unmodulated radio signal, or the plain continuous wave component of a radio signal. The word "carrier" may also refer to a telecommunications network operator.

CATHODE: The (usually) negative electrode in a battery, vacuum tube, or other device. In a vacuum tube the cathode is heated by a filament to emit electrons.

CELL SITE: The part of a cellular telephone network housing a transmitter and receiver and connected to an antenna.

CODE DIVISION MULTIPLE ACCESS (CDMA): A scheme permitting multiple users to access and share the same radio channel at the same time using different digital codes. CDMA works in conjunction with direct sequence spread spectrum.

COHERER: The first device used to detect electromagnetic waves. A coherer was a tube filled with metal filings with electrodes at either end. The coherer's resistance dropped sharply whenever a radio wave passed by it.

COMMUNICATIONS THEORY: The study of the amount of information that may be reliably exchanged over a communications channel. Also known as information theory, it covers topics including source coding, compression, and noise.

COMPETITIVE LOCAL EXCHANGE CARRIER (CLEC): In the U.S., a local telephone company permitted to compete with the dominant local phone company. CLECs were enabled by the Telecommunications Act of 1996.

CONDUCTOR: Any material that presents relatively little resistance to the flow of electricity—such as copper, silver, aluminum, and tin.

CONDUIT: A pipe usually made of plastic or metal for protecting and routing electrical wires.

CONTINUOUS WAVES: The pure sine waves produced by a radio frequency oscillator as distinguished from the damped waves produced by a spark gap transmitter. Continuous waves facilitate operation on discrete frequencies and the use of modulation to add information content.

CORDLESS PHONE: A telephone using a short-range wireless technology to connect to a nearby base unit (usually connected to a standard phone line) for portable operation in a home or office.

CTIA: "CTIA" originally stood for "Cellular Telecommunications Industry Association." The group now calls itself "CTIA – the Wireless Association." CTIA is a U.S. cellular telephone industry association for operators, manufacturers, and others.

CURRENT: The flow of positive or negative charges in an electrical network or circuit.

DAMPED WAVES: The waves produced by spark gap transmitters—waves that steadily decrease in amplitude to zero.

DETECTOR (RADIO): A primitive detector, such as the coherer, merely indicates the presence of radio waves. Later detectors also extracted information from modulated radio waves.

DIAMAGNETISM: A term coined by Michael Faraday to indicate the response of any material to an applied magnetic field. The effect was central to demonstrating the relationship between magnetism and light.

DIELECTRIC: Dielectric is actually a concept rather than a thing. It is the effect of an electric field on a medium, and applies to vacuums as well as all forms of matter. Capacitors are based on the dielectric effect and typically consist of two conductors separated by an insulating material or air.

DIGITAL AMPS (D-AMPS): D-AMPS was the first digital cellular "air interface" standard in the U.S.

DIGITAL SIGNAL PROCESSOR (DSP): A microprocessor specially-designed to process communication signals.

DIODE: An electronic device with two electrodes that permits the flow of electricity in one direction and resists flow in the opposite direction. Diodes are used to convert alternating current to direct current and to detect and demodulate radio signals.

DIRECT SEQUENCE: Direct sequence is a form of spread spectrum used by cordless telephones, wireless LANs, and third-generation mobile phones. It combines a pseudorandom code with the information to be transmitted to create a signal occupying much greater bandwidth.

DISPLACEMENT CURRENT: The current that is created in a dielectric or vacuum by a changing electric field. In a dielectric material, it denotes the relative motion of electric charges. Maxwell assumed that all space contains a medium ("ether") through which light is propagated, and that this medium served as the dielectric in a vacuum.

DUOPOLY: The original FCC licensing plan for cellular telephone operators permitted two operators in each city. Because the operators tended to divide the market by a tacit understanding, the arrangement was perceived as similar to a monopoly.

DUPLEX TELEGRAPH: The duplex telegraph was a technical solution for sending and receiving simultaneously over a single telegraph line.

DYNAMIC POWER CONTROL: The biggest challenge for CDMA cellular networks is that signals from all mobiles on the same channel must arrive at the base station with equal strength. This is accomplished with a simple feedback loop that tells each mobile transmitter when to increase or decrease its transmit power.

DYNAMO: A device that uses mechanical motion and electromagnetic induction to generate electricity. The opposite transpires in an electric motor.

EDISON EFFECT: Thomas Edison discovered (or rediscovered) the thermionic emission of charged particles from a filament in an evacuated glass bulb. Later, this effect was used to develop vacuum tube diodes and triodes.

ELECTRIC CHARGE: An electric charge is a property of subatomic particles such as electrons and protons. It is the "stuff" of electricity. The flow of electricity is sometimes described as the movement of electrons, which by convention possess a negative charge, through a conductor.

ELECTRICAL CIRCUIT: The interconnection of electrical components to form a closed loop.

ELECTRIC FIELD: The space surrounding an electric charge such as an atom with a net positive or negative charge. An electric field is also produced by a time-varying magnetic field.

ELECTRICAL IMPULSE: A transient electric current caused, for example, when a switch is first thrown into the "on" position (i.e. before the current reaches its steady state).

ELECTRICAL LOAD: Any electrical circuit or device to which power is transferred by another electrical circuit or device.

ELECTROCHEMISTRY: The branch of chemistry that studies the relationship between electricity and chemical reactions.

ELECTRODE: An electrical conductor used to make contact with a non-conductor in (for example) a battery or a vacuum tube.

ELECTROLYSIS: The use of electricity to separate elements from compounds or compounds from mixtures.

ELECTROMAGNETIC SPECTRUM: The range of frequencies (or wavelengths) for electromagnetic radiation.

ELECTROMAGNETIC WAVE: A self-perpetuating wave (such as light or radio) consisting of alternating electric and magnetic fields that propagates through free space.

ELECTROMAGNETISM: The effects, or the field of study, related to the convertibility of electric and magnetic fields.

ELECTROPHORUS: A device invented by Alessandro Volta that imparts opposite electric charges to a dielectric and a metal shield through a process of contact and separation.

ELECTROSCOPE: A device for detecting and measuring electric charges.

ELECTROSTATIC: An effect produced by a stationary electric charge on nearby objects.

EMPIRICAL RESEARCH: Scientific research based on observation of natural occurrences or experiments.

EQUALIZATION: A system for adjusting a transmitter and receiver to the communications channel. In wireless, an adaptive equalizer adds delays to the strongest multipath signals to restore phase alignment.

ETHER: Sometimes called the "luminiferous ether" to distinguish it from the chemical compound of the same name, ether was supposedly the medium permeating all space and through which light propagates. However, scientists have been unable to find any evidence of the ether's existence.

FARADAY'S LAW OF INDUCTION: The scientific law that relates the change in magnetic flux (the amount of magnetism) to the voltage induced in a wire loop.

FEEDBACK: A process in which part of an output signal is fed back into the input for greater amplification or control.

FEMTOCELL: A small cellular telephone base station that may be purchased and installed by an enterprise or home owner to enable better network coverage—particularly indoors.

FLIP-FLOP: An electronic circuit that has two stable states and can serve as a memory device for a single binary data bit. Flip-flops may be interconnected output-to-input to create shift registers.

FORCE FIELD: In contrast to gravity, the forces due to electric charges and magnetism act over short distances and are propagated at finite velocity, producing complex force fields that interact independently with local objects.

FREE SPACE: The medium (whether a vacuum or air) through which electromagnetic waves propagate.

FREQUENCY: The number of sinusoidal waves (sound, radio frequency, etc.) per unit time—typically denoted as cycles per second, or Hertz.

FREQUENCY HOPPING: A form of spread spectrum transmission in which a narrowband radio signal hops continuously from one channel to another over a range of frequencies.

FREQUENCY MODULATION (FM): A method of adding information to a radio carrier by varying its frequency over time. For example, speech can be added by varying the radio signal's frequency in accordance to the speech waveform's amplitude. FM is relatively immune to many types of natural and man-made noise.

FREQUENCY REUSE: A key benefit of cellular radio is that it enables frequencies to be reused throughout a city or other local area.

FULL-DUPLEX: A communications link permitting each party to speak (send) and listen (receive) simultaneously. For example, this may be accomplished by using two parallel communications links—one for transmitting and one for receiving (with their roles reversed at the other end of the link).

GALVANOMETER: An instrument for detecting and measuring electrical current.

GAUSS'S LAW: The law that relates the flux produced to the electric charge that produces it.

GLOBAL POSITIONING SYSTEM (GPS): A satellite network enabling mobile receivers to calculate their precise locations by measuring the propagation time for signals from multiple satellites.

GLOBAL SYSTEM FOR MOBILE COMMUNICATIONS (GSM): Europe's continent-wide second generation cellular telephone standard based on digital radio technology. Today, GSM is the dominant mobile phone standard worldwide.

GROUND (ELECTRICAL): The earth acts as a giant receptacle for electric charges. Therefore, it can be used for safety purposes; as a reference for measuring voltage; and as a component in a radio antenna system.

HALF-DUPLEX: A communications link that allows one party to speak (send) at a time. Half-duplex operation requires a special communications protocol for changing from receive to transmit and vice-versa.

HANDOFF: In a cellular radio system calls are handed off to an adjacent cell as the user moves into that cell. In analog and TDMA cellular systems, handoffs require changing frequencies. CDMA systems use "soft" handoffs.

HD RADIO: A digital broadcast radio system being launched in the U.S.

HETERODYNE: The creation of a new radio frequency by mixing two frequencies together. The heterodyne principle was first used to produce a clear musical tone from Morse code transmissions.

HIGH DEFINITION TELEVISION (HDTV): A digital broadcast television system that provides higher resolution images and other digital features.

HIGH FREQUENCY ALTERNATOR: One of the first devices used by wireless pioneers to produce continuous waves was simply a high-speed, alternating current power generator.

HIGH LEVEL OPERATING SYSTEM (HLOS): An operating system designed to support a wide range of applications and third-party developers. Examples include Windows Mobile, Symbian, and mobile versions of Linux and UNIX.

INCUMBENT LOCAL EXCHANGE CARRIER (ILEC): In the U.S., the dominant local phone company. ILECs are often remnants of the old Bell System.

INDUCTANCE: A basic electrical circuit characteristic, often represented by a coil of wire that resists changes in current.

INDUCTION: The ability of a changing magnetic field to produce a current in a nearby coil or wire. At one time induction was considered a promising technology for wireless communications.

INDUCTOR: A device that exhibits inductance and is often used in transformers, tuned circuits, and antennas.

INSULATOR: Any material that resists the flow of electricity. Particularly good insulators include glass and porcelain.

INTEGRATED CIRCUIT (IC): A semiconductor device that embeds multiple discrete components—sometimes millions in the same tiny package. ICs include memory chips, microprocessors, and digital signal processors (DSPs).

INTERFERENCE (WAVE): The combining of two or more waves— usually at the same frequency but not necessarily the same phase. Interference may be either constructive or destructive. Interference between light waves causes a distinctive pattern of light and dark bands. Interference between radio waves causes fading.

INTERMEDIATE FREQUENCY (IF): Early radios required the user to tune the amplifier and didn't work well on some frequencies. The superheterodyne was an improvement; it uses an amplifier tuned to a fixed frequency plus a "mixer" to shift the received signal to the IF.

ION: An atom or molecule with a net electric charge due to an excess or deficit of electrons.

IP (INTERNET PROTOCOL): The communications protocol used on the Internet that sends user data in sequential packets.

JAMMING: Intentionally interfering with a radio transmitter to prevent the intended receivers from accessing the message content.

LEYDEN JAR: A primitive capacitor composed of a glass jar with inner and outer electrodes. The Leyden jar enabled natural philosophers and the public to use electricity for a variety of purposes.

LINES OF FORCE: Literally, a curve representing electric or magnetic forces in a specific location. The fact that such lines are typically curves confirms that electric and magnetic forces are projected at finite velocity; an instantaneous force would always follow a straight line.

LOAD (ELECTRICAL): An electrical device or circuit that receives power from a source circuit. The efficient transfer of power from the source to the load is a key performance characteristic.

LOCATION BASED SERVICE (LBS): Services employing location information provided by a handset with GPS locating capability or cellular network providing user location information.

LONG TERM EVOLUTION (LTE): A project to develop a fourth generation technology in the GSM family of digital cellular solutions. LTE is intended to support downloads at 100 Mb/s and uploads at 50 Mb/s.

LOW EARTH ORBIT SATELLITE (LEOS): Satellites in low orbits circling the earth and deployed in fleets to provide uninterrupted service. The Global Positioning System is an example of a LEOS system.

MAGNETIC FIELD: The force field around a magnet.

MAGNETIC POLE: One of the opposite ends of a magnet.

MOBILE TV: A broadcast or unicast system specifically designed to deliver television-style content to mobile phones and other portable devices.

MODULATION: The process of adding information, such as a speaker's voice, to a radio signal. The two most common forms of modulation are amplitude modulation (AM) and frequency modulation (FM).

MORSE CODE: A code devised by Samuel F.B. Morse to transmit alphanumeric characters via telegraph. The Morse code consists of different combinations of dots and dashes to represent individual characters. The most common letters in the alphabet are represented by the fewest symbols. For example, the letter "e" is represented by a single dot.

MULTIPATH PROPAGATION: Radio signals often take multiple paths from the transmitter to the receiver due to reflections. These signals may interfere with each other due to phase and amplitude differences. Multipath propagation is particularly evident in the mobile environment.

MULTIPLE INPUT-MULTIPLE OUTPUT (MIMO): A method of using multiple antennas at both ends of a radio link to transmit multiple streams of data simultaneously.

MULTIPLE TELEGRAPH: An archaic term for conducting multiple telegraph conversations over the same wires at the same time. (Today, this might be called multiplexed telegraph.) The multiple telegraph is what Alexander Graham Bell set out to develop when he invented the telephone.

NARROWBAND: This term is used both in reference to conventional radio channels and particularly narrow radio channels. A conventional radio channel is considered "narrowband" in contrast to wideband channels such as those used in spread spectrum transmission. Narrowband channels also result from channel splitting to conserve bandwidth.

NATURAL PHILOSOPHER: Prior to the rise of modern science, scholars who studied the natural world were often called "natural philosophers." In part, this was because many considered ancient philosophers such as Aristotle to be the highest authorities.

NEAR FIELD COMMUNICATIONS (NFC): A very short-range wireless technology for secure transactions based on tapping or swiping the target "reader."

NEGATIVE CHARGE: One of two mutually attractive electric charges. Electrons are considered negative charges and, therefore, electricity is sometimes envisioned as the movement of negative charges.

NORDIC MOBILE TELEPHONE (NMT): An analog cellular telephone standard developed in Scandinavia and used in several European countries.

OHM: A basic measure of electrical resistance to direct current electricity. The ohm is also used to measure the alternating current equivalent, impedance.

ORTHOGONAL FREQUENCY DIVISION MULTIPLEXING (OFDM): A type of spread spectrum transmission that uses multiple discrete RF carriers distributed over a wideband channel. OFDM offers advantages over other schemes; equalization is simpler and OFDM is a particularly good match for use with MIMO technology. OFDM is used or planned for use in WiMAX, 802.11n wireless LAN, and 3.9/4 G mobile phone technologies.

OSCILLATOR: An electronic circuit that produces a repetitive signal—usually a pure sine wave or a square wave. Vacuum tube-based oscillators were a major breakthrough for wireless communications, producing clean signals at low cost. Oscillators are used in transmitters to produce the RF carrier and receivers for use in mixers (enabling superheterodyne circuits) and beat frequency oscillators (BFOs) for producing audible tones from Morse code signals.

PAGING: A wireless service very popular in some countries before mobile phones came into widespread use. Paging networks are typically one-way and are used to alert or inform mobile users.

PAN (PERSONAL AREA NETWORK): A wireless network that permits communications with people and devices in the user's immediate vicinity. For example, a PAN enables a user to synchronize data in a handset or PDA to a desktop PC. Another classic PAN application (conceptually) is exchanging electronic business cards between cell phones or PDAs.

PARALLEL CIRCUIT: A circuit connecting elements in parallel; the voltage across each element is the same and the current through each element is proportional to that element's resistance.

PARTICLE THEORY: One theory popular among investigators trying to understand the nature of light was that it is a wave phenomenon; another theory was light is a particle phenomenon. The particle theory explains the photoelectric effect; when certain materials are struck by photons of light, electrons are knocked free from atoms.

PATENT CAVEAT: A patent caveat—no longer offered in the U.S.—was a notification of intent to file a patent application. The patent caveat allowed the inventor to announce a claim in order to prevent others from filing for the same claim while the patent application was being prepared.

PERSONAL COMMUNICATIONS SERVICE (PCS): A wireless service in the 1900 MHz band created by the FCC and Industry Canada in 1994. PCS provided new spectrum for mobile phone services based on digital radio technology. It also enabled new networks using the GSM standard in North America.

PERSONAL DIGITAL ASSISTANT (PDA): A handheld device for entering, storing and displaying personal and business information. The first PDA was the Apple Newton, a device touted for its ability to decode ordinary handwriting and learn the user's preferences. The PDA market came into its own with the development by Palm Computing of the Graffiti handwriting recognition system using a special, easy-to-learn character set.

PERMANENT MAGNET: A permanent magnet is distinguished from an electromagnet in that the permanent magnet always acts as a magnet while the electromagnet only acts as a magnet when there is current flowing in its wire winding.

POSITIVE CHARGE: One of two mutually attractive electric charges. Protons are considered positive charges.

PROTOCOL (COMMUNICATIONS): A set of rules defining procedures for accessing a communications channel, making transmissions, listening, and ending a communications session.

PSEUDORANDOM CODE: A sequence of bits that appears to be random, i.e., does not seem to follow any discernible pattern. Spread spectrum transmission requires combining the user information with a pseudorandom code to "spread" the signal and provide enhanced security.

PUSH-TO-TALK (PTT): A protocol that enables conversations directly between two or more users on a single radio channel. When there are just two participants in the conversation, the user who is speaking may indicate the current transmission is finished by saying "over." If there are three or more participants, one person (usually a dispatcher) takes charge; the other users wait for that person's permission to speak.

RADIO COMMON CARRIER (RCC): After the Bell system began operating the Mobile Telephone Service (MTS), the FCC created a category for competing, independent wireless operators. RCCs primarily offered paging and trunked two-way mobile radio for business users.

REACTANCE: The component in a circuit or device's impedance attributable to inductance and/or capacitance and offering resistance to the flow of alternating current.

REGENERATIVE RECEIVER: A receiver based on the regenerative amplifier—a device that maximizes amplification by feeding some of its output back into its input. While a non-regenerative vacuum tube amplifier might amplify a signal by a factor of ten, a regenerative vacuum tube amplifier can amplify the signal by a factor of 10,000.

RELAY (ELECTROMAGNETIC): A device used to activate a separate circuit. Samuel Morse used relays to regenerate telegraph signals to achieve greater distances. Each time the sending telegraph key was depressed, it actuated a remote relay that switched on the next leg of the link, which was powered by its own battery.

RESISTOR: An electrical component that resists the flow of direct current and is used for purposes such as achieving specific voltage drops.

RESONATE: In radio, a circuit or electrical component tuned to a specific frequency is optimally matched to signals at that frequency and is said to "resonate." For example, an antenna resonant at a specific frequency will receive or radiate with maximum efficiency at that frequency.

SELF INDUCTION: When current flows through a coil, it creates a magnetic field. When the current is switched off, the magnetic field collapses, inducing an opposite current in the coil.

SEMICONDUCTOR: A material with electrical properties somewhere between those of conductors and insulators. The use of pure semiconductor materials such as silicon and germanium in combination with carefully controlled impurities enables the production of transistors.

SERIES CIRCUIT: A circuit in which the elements are connected in series. The same amount of current flows through each element in the series; the voltage drop across each element is proportional to its resistance.

SHIFT REGISTER: A group of registers connected in series such that data is shifted from one to the next to perform various operations. For example, special shift registers can be used to generate pseudorandom codes.

SIGNAL-TO-NOISE RATIO (SNR): The ratio of signal strength to noise strength at the receiver. Higher signal-to-noise ratios are better.

SMART ANTENNA: An antenna with multiple elements and special electronics for purposes such as steering signals and/or combating multipath fading.

SMART PHONE: A combination mobile phone and PDA, or any mobile phone capable of running user applications such as browsing the Internet.

SPARK TRANSMITTER: An early type of radio transmitter that produced a signal by generating a spark.

SPECIALIZED MOBILE RADIO (SMR): A radio service created by the FCC for third-party operators of trunked, two-way radio systems. SMR operators typically provide dispatch and team communications for utilities, field service operations, public safety agencies, and transportation providers (such as limousine services).

SPECTRAL EFFICIENCY: The number of bits of data per unit frequency (Hertz) for a radio link. The spectral efficiency of a radio network, in contrast, is measured in bits per Hertz per unit area.

SPECTRUM ALLOCATION: A part of the radio spectrum allocated by government for specific uses. For example, the 2400 MHz band has been allocated for use by microwave ovens and unlicensed wireless LANs.

SPREAD SPECTRUM: A radio transmission technology that spreads the user information over an extended frequency range. The advantages of spread spectrum include enhanced security, greater immunity to multipath fading, and the ability to share the same spectrum with other users.

STAR TOPOLOGY: A network configuration in which users or other network elements communicate directly with central nodes.

STATIC ELECTRICITY: A type of electricity often created by rubbing together two different materials—resulting in a transfer of electrons so that one material assumes a net positive charge and other a net negative charge. Static electricity may be discharged suddenly to produce a spark.

STATISTICAL LAW: While conventional physical laws are obeyed in each and every instance, statistical laws define overall behavior. For example, the ability to send messages over an imperfect communications channel may be described statistically.

SUPERHETERODYNE: A receiver that mixes incoming signals with a local oscillator to produce a new signal at the amplifier's fixed frequency. The superheterodyne receiver was a major advance over early designs because it required fewer controls and performed consistently well over a range of frequencies.

SYNTONY: Early term for "tuning."

TELEGRAPH: A device for sending text messages using wires, electrical signals, and electromagnets. The telegraph created a social revolution, greatly increasing the speed at which news and other information spread from place to place.

TELEPHONE EXCHANGE: Instead of running phone lines directly between users wishing to speak with each other, all of the users are connected to a central location with equipment for establishing ad hoc connections. At first, this was done manually using patch cords and patch panels. Later, automatic switches were introduced so that users could simply dial the desired destination number.

THEORY: A scientific explanation for related phenomena based on a system of facts and laws. Scientists and philosophers do not agree on what makes a good theory—though most believe the ability to make accurate predictions is a key factor. A theory may be widely accepted but it never has the certainty of empirical facts or laws. In a sense, theories are tentative explanations, and over time any theory may be superseded by another.

TIME DIVISION MJLTIPLE ACCESS (TDMA): A digital radio technology that achieves increased capacity by dividing digitized radio channels into separate time slots for separate conversations or sessions. For example, digital AMPS (D-AMPS) allowed three users to share the same channel.

TRANSFORMER: A common electrical device that uses induction to convert electricity at one voltage to another voltage. Transformers may also be used to transfer signals between physically isolated circuits.

TRANSISTOR: A device that uses semiconductor materials to perform the same or similar functions as vacuum tube triodes. Transistors enabled electronic devices that are smaller; require less power; are more reliable; and are more affordable.

TRIODE: A vacuum tube device that uses three elements to amplify signals and produce oscillations. The triode was created by inserting a current-controlling grid between the cathode and anode.

TRUNKED RADIO: An automated radio system that enables a number of users to share a smaller number of channels on a first-come, first-served basis. A trunked radio system may operate like a telephone exchange; the users connect to a base station that automatically finds and assigns an available channel.

TUNING: Tuning most often refers to setting a transmitter and/or receiver to a specific frequency. It may also refer to modifying a device or circuit to work optimally on a specific frequency or frequencies.

ULTRA MOBILE BROADBAND (UMB): A project to create a fourth generation standard in the family of standards based on Qualcomm's CDMA technology. UMB is essentially an alternative to long term evolution (LTE).

ULTRA WIDEBAND (UWB): An emerging technology that uses extraordinarily wideband signals to send data at high data rates over shared spectrum. Some UWB schemes produce signals that resemble those produced by early spark transmitters.

VACUUM TUBE: A vacuum tube diode consists of a cathode and an anode in an evacuated glass tube and was first used as a radio detector. A grid was inserted between the cathode and anode to create a triode capable of amplifying signals and generating oscillations.

VALVE: An early term for a diode vacuum tube. Such devices were called "valves" because they conduct electricity in one direction much as a water valve only permits water flow in one direction.

VOICE ENCODER (VOCODER): A circuit used to convert voice or other audio into a digital bit stream. A key goal of vocoder design is transmitting intelligible voice at the lowest possible bit rate.

VOLTAGE: A measure of electromotive force. According to Ohm's Law, the voltage applied across a specific resistance determines the amount of current that will flow through that resistance.

WAVE THEORY: One theory popular among investigators trying to understand the nature of light was that it is a particle phenomenon; another theory was that light is a wave phenomenon. The wave theory explains effects such as reflection, refraction, and interference.

WAVELENGTH: The length, usually measured in metric units, of a single complete cycle of a radio wave. Wavelength is inversely proportional to frequency.

WIDEBAND RADIO: A radio technology that uses a relatively wide channel. For example, spread spectrum and wideband TDMA are wideband technologies.

WIMAX: A standard developed to compete with mobile phone systems and championed by Intel. Proponents emphasize WiMAX's use of OFDM and MIMO technology; its option for using the same channel for transmit and receive (requiring less spectrum but adding transmission delays); and its use of IP-based infrastructure. WiMAX operators emphasize data devices and applications.

WIRELESS LAN: A wireless network intended for use within a home, a larger building, or a campus of buildings. Wireless LANs use unlicensed spread spectrum technology.

Bibliography

Additional resources for this book may be found at:
http://www.telescopebooks.com

Agar, Jon *Constant Touch: A Global History of the Mobile Phone* (2003) Icon Books

Aitken, Hugh G.J. *The Continuous Wave: Technology and American Radio, 1900-1932* (1985) Princeton University Press

Aitken, Hugh G.J. *Syntony and Spark: the Origins of Radio* (1985) Princeton University Press

Armstrong, Edwin Howard and other contributors *The Legacies of Edwin Howard Armstrong* (1990) The Radio Club of America

Bacon, Francis *Novum Organum* (1952) Encyclopedia Britannica

Bell Laboratories "High-Capacity Mobile Telephone System Technical Report," December, 1971

Belrose, John S. "Reginald Aubrey Fessenden and the Birth of Wireless Telephony," *IEEE Antennas and Propagation Magazine*, Vol. 44, No. 2, April 2002, pp. 38-47.

Bilby, Kenneth *The General: David Sarnoff* (1986) Harper & Row

Boorstin, Daniel J. *The Creators: A History of Heroes of the Imagination* (1993) Vintage Books

Boorstin, Daniel J. *The Discoverers: A History of Man's Search to Know His World and Himself* (1985) Vintage Books

Brodsky, Ira *A Manager's Guide to Wireless Networking* (1997) Van Nostrand Reinhold

Brodsky, Ira *Wireless: the Revolution in Personal Telecommunications* (1995) Artech House

Bruce, Robert V. *Bell: Alexander Graham Bell and the Conquest of Solitude* (1990) Cornell University Press

Buchwald, Jed Z. *The Creation of Scientific Effects: Heinrich Hertz and Electric Waves* (1994) the University of Chicago Press

Calhoun, George *Digital Cellular Radio* (1988) Artech House

Campbell, Lewis; Garnett, William *The Life of James Clerk Maxwell* (1882) Macmillan and Co.

Cardwell, Donald *The Norton History of Technology* (1995) W. W. Norton & Company

Carter III, *Samuel Cyrus Field: Man of Two Worlds* (1968) G.P. Putnam's Sons

Cheney, Margaret *Tesla: Man Out of Time* (1981) Barnes & Noble

Clark, Ronald W. *Benjamin Franklin: a Biography* (2004) Castle Books

Conway, Flo; Siegelman, Jim *Norbert Weiner: Dark Hero of the Information Age* (2006) Basic Books

Cox, Donald C. "Universal Digital Portable Radio Communications," *Proceedings of the IEEE*, April, 1987

Cropper, William H. *Great Physicists: the Life and Times of Leading Physicists from Galileo to Hawking* (2001) Oxford University Press

Dahl, Per F. *Flash of the Cathode Rays: A History of JJ Thomson's Electron* (1997) IOP Publishing

Derry, T.K.; Williams, Trevor I. *A Short History of Technology: From the Earliest Times to A.D. 1900* (1993) Dover Publications

Dixon, Robert C. *Spread Spectrum Systems* (1994) John Wiley & Sons

Doubleday, Russell *Stories of Inventors: the Adventures of Inventors and Engineers* (1904) Project Gutenberg eBook

Dreher, Carl *Sarnoff: An American Success* (1977) Quadrangle/New York Times Book Company

Duhem, Pierre *The Aim and Structure of Physical Theory* (1974) Atheneum

Dunsheath, Percy *A History of Electrical Engineering* (1962) Faber and Faber

Fahie, J. J. *A History of Wireless Telegraphy* (1901) Dodd, Mead, and Co.

Faraday, Michael *Experimental Researches in Electricity* (1952) Encyclopedia Britannica, Great Books of the Western World

Farley, Thomas "Mobile and Cellular Telephone History,"
http://www.privateline.com/PCS/history.htm

Finger, Stanley *Minds behind the Brain: a History of the Pioneers and their Discoveries* (2000) Oxford University Press

Frank, Philipp *Philosophy of Science: The Link between Science and Philosophy* (1957) Prentice-Hall

Gilder, George *Microcosm: The Quantum Revolution in Economics and Technology* (1989) Touchstone

Gilder, George *Telecosm: The World after Bandwidth Abundance* (2000) Touchstone

Gilbert, William *On the Loadstone and Magnetic Bodies* (1952) Encyclopedia Britannica, Great Books of the Western World

Hamilton, James *A Life of Discovery: Michael Faraday, Giant of the Scientific Revolution* (2002) Random House

Hertz, Heinrich *Electric Waves* (1893) Macmillan and Co.

Hijiya, James A. *Lee De Forest and the Fatherhood of Radio* (1992) Associated University Presses

Hillebrand, Friedhelm (editor) *GSM and UMTS: the Creation of Global Mobile Communications* (2002) John Wiley & Sons

Hong, Sungook *Wireless: from Marconi's Black Box to the Audion* (2001) MIT Press

Hunt, Bruce J. *The Maxwellians* (1991) Cornell University Press

Ito, Mizuko; Okabe, Daisuke; Matsuda, Misa *Personal, Portable, Pedestrian: Mobile Phones in Japanese Life* (2005) MIT Press

Kirby, Richard S.; Withington, Sidney; Darling, Arthur B.; Kilgour, Frederick G. *Engineering in History* (1990) Dover Publications

Knight, David *Humphry Davy: Science & Power* (1992) Blackwell Publishers

Kobb, Bennett Z. *Spectrum Guide* (1995) New Signals Press

Kuhn, Thomas S. *The Structure of Scientific Revolutions* (1970) University of Chicago Press

Lewis, Tom S.W. *Empire of the Air* (1991) Edward Burlingame Books

Lindholm, Christian; Keinonen, Turkka; Kiljander, Harri *Mobile Usability: How Nokia Changed the Face of the Mobile Phone* (2003) McGraw-Hill

Lodge, Oliver *Past Years: An Autobiography* (1932) Charles Scribner's Sons

Mahon, Basil *The Man Who Changed Everything* (2004) John Wiley & Sons

Masini, Giancarlo *Marconi* (1995) Marsilio Publishers

Maxwell, James Clerk "On Physical Lines of Force," (1861) The London, Edinburgh, and Dublin Philosophical Magazine and Journal of Science

Maxwell, James Clerk *The Dynamical Theory of the Electromagnetic Field* (1982) Wipf and Stock Publishers

May, Charles Paul *James Clerk Maxwell and Electromagnetism* (1962) Franklin Watts

Meyer, Herbert W. *A History of Electricity and Magnetism* (1971) MIT

Miller, Arthur I. *Insights of Genius* (1996) Springer-Verlag

Millikan, Frank Rives "Joseph Henry and the Telephone," Smithsonian Institutional History Project

Mock, Dave *The Qualcomm Equation* 2005 AMACOM

Moyer, Albert E. *Joseph Henry: the Rise of an American Scientist* (1997) Smithsonian Institution Press

Murray, James B. Jr. *Wireless Nation* (2002) Perseus Publishing

Nahin, Paul J. *Oliver Heaviside: the Life, Work, and Times of an Electrical Genius of the Victorian Age* (1988) Johns Hopkins University Press

Nahin, Paul J. *The Science of Radio* (1996) American Institute of Physics

Northam, Phil *How Smartphones Work* (2006) Symbian Press

Pera, Marcello *The Ambiguous Frog* (1992) Princeton University Press

Poincaré, Henri *The Value of Science* (2001) Modern Library

Popper, Karl *The Logic of Scientific Discovery* (2002) Routledge Classics

Raby, Ormond *Radio's First Voice: the Story of Reginald Fessenden* (1970) Macmillan of Canada

Regal, Brian *Radio: The Life Story of a Technology* 2005 Greenwood Press

Ring, Douglas H., "Mobile Telephony - Wide Area Coverage," Bell Laboratories Technical Memorandum, December 11, 1947

Rowlands, Peter *Oliver Lodge and the Liverpool Physical Society* (1990) Liverpool University Press

Sarkar, Tapan K.; various contributors *History of Wireless* (2006) John Wiley & Sons

Sawyer, R. Keith *Explaining Creativity: the Science of Human Innovation* (2006) Oxford University Press

Seitz, Frederick "The Cosmic Inventor: Reginald Aubrey Fessenden (1866-1932)," (1999) *Transactions of the American Philosophical Society*

Sexton, Michael *Marconi: The Irish Connection* (2005) Four Courts Press

Shannon, Claude; Weaver, Warren *The Mathematical Theory of Communication* (1998) University of Illinois Press

Siegel, Daniel M. *Innovation in Maxwell's Electromagnetic Theory* (1991) Cambridge University Press

Silverman, Kenneth *Lightning Man: the Accursed Life of Samuel F.B. Morse* (2004) De Capo Press

Simon, Marvin K.; Omura, Jim K.; Scholtz, Robert A.; Levitt, Barry K. *Spread Spectrum Communications, Volume 1* (1985) Computer Science Press

Standage, Tom *The Victorian Internet* (1998) Walker Publishing Company

Stashower, Daniel *The Boy Genius & The Mogul* (2002) Broadway Books

Tuttlebee, Wally H.W. *Cordless Telecommunications in Europe* (1990) Springer-Verlag

Tyndall, John *Faraday as a Discoverer* (1873) D. Appleton and Co.

Weightman, Gavin *Signor Marconi's Magic Box* (2003) Da Capo Press

Wiener, Norbert *Cybernetics: of Control and Communication in the Animal and Machine* (1961) MIT Press

Williams, L. Pearce *The Origins of Field Theory* (1980) University Press of America

Additional sources:

LM Ericsson Website, corporate history

Motorola Website, corporate history

Nokia Website, corporate history

Interviews with Martin Cooper, Donald C. Cox, Greg Raleigh, Jan Uddenfeldt and Andrew Viterbi

http://www.sparkmuseum.com/

Acknowledgements

Thanks to my wife, Maureen, for encouraging my first foray into history of technology. My editors, Karen Heyman and Joan Engebretson, deserve credit for making the book interesting and readable. I am indebted to Andrew Viterbi, Martin Cooper, and Jan Uddenfeldt for reviewing the manuscript and contributing valuable ideas. Thanks to Donald C. Cox for his insights and articles, Ed Eckert for articles from the Bell Labs archives, as well as Greg Raleigh, Bruce Hunt, and Jed Buchwald for sharing their knowledge. And special thanks to John D. Jenkins at the SparkMuseum for information on spark equipment and images of early radios; Triune Communications for artistic design; and David Strom for his assistance.

Index

NOTES

NOTES

NOTES

NOTES

NOTES